MW00560517

THE ELEMENTS OF AIRCRAFT PRELIMINARY DESIGN

ROGER D. SCHAUFELE
Department of Aerospace Engineering
California State University, Long Beach

ARIES PUBLICATIONS, Santa Ana, California 92705

Published by Aries Publications, Santa Ana, California 92705

First published 2000

Copyright © 2000 by Roger D. Schaufele

ISBN No. 0-9701986-0-4

Library of Congress Catalog Card Number 00-091000

Typesetting by Victoria Graphics, Orange, CA
Cover design and artwork by Dillon Design

Printed in the USA by Kni, Inc., Anaheim, CA

To Barbara

Acknowledgments

I am indebted to many friends and colleagues who have encouraged me during the preparation of this book. I owe particular thanks to Professor Tuncer Cebeci of California State University Long Beach, for giving me the opportunity to teach a course in aircraft preliminary design, which became the inspiration for the book. I am also deeply indebted to Professor Richard Shevell of Stanford University, for providing me with much background material as well as wise counsel in developing the manuscript from the course notes. In addition, I am extremely grateful to a number of aircraft manufacturers, especially the Douglas Aircraft Company, McDonnell Douglas Corporation, and their successor, the Boeing Company, for allowing the use of data and information on many of the aircraft that I worked on during my career as a design engineer at Douglas. I am grateful to Laju Tejwani, who typed and retyped the original draft, and to Victoria Mason who typed the final draft, as well as Professors Hamid Hefazi, Eric Kendall and Dr. Eric Besnard for their helpful suggestions. I also wish to thank Ann Ebeling, for her valuable proofreading skills in checking the final draft. And finally, my thanks to the students who made so many suggestions for improving the clarity of the text and figures.

Preface

This book has been developed from a set of lecture notes and handouts for a one-semester 3 credit hour course entitled "Aircraft Performance and Design". The basic purpose of the course, and of this book, is to teach students the concepts and procedures associated with the aircraft preliminary design process, and through the examples and homework assignments, allow each student to do a preliminary design of an aircraft for a set of requirements selected by the student.

The material is organized in a manner to allow the design to evolve from the initial mission requirements, using methods and procedures based on those in use in the aircraft industry, but in many cases simplified to eliminate detailed refinements, while maintaining the fundamental parameters which shape the design. It should be noted that aircraft preliminary design is an "open-ended" process; there is not one single unique solution to a set of mission requirements. A variety of choices may be made in establishing an aircraft preliminary design. The book describes where these choices need to be made, and how to evaluate the impact of those choices on the final resulting design.

The methods and procedures presented in this book make generous use of available data from actual aircraft designs. These data are included to add realism to the presentation, but in no case should they be considered as definitive information on a particular aircraft. All authoritative data on a particular aircraft model must come from the manufacturer, not from the information in this book.

Many of the methods presented in the text are amenable to conversion to electronic personal computer programs, and indeed many of the students who have taken the course using this material have adapted existing programs or written new ones to perform the required calculations. Future editions of the book will incorporate appropriate computer based methods.

The minimum prerequisites for the material in the course are the usual college engineering curricula at least through the junior year, although courses in applied aerodynamics, aircraft propulsion, and aircraft structures and materials are extremely useful.

The material is presented in English units, utilized almost exclusively in the U.S. aircraft industry.

About the Author

Roger D. Schaufele retired from Douglas Aircraft Company, McDonnell Douglas Corporation in 1989, as Vice President/ General Manager, Commercial Advanced Products. Schaufele joined Douglas in 1949 as an Aerodynamicist on the Douglas X-3 Research Aircraft. Later assignments included Project Aerodynamicist on the DC-8, DC-9, & DC-10 jetliners. In 1971 he was appointed Director, Technologies for Douglas and in 1976 he was appointed Director, Engineering Design, and in 1981 was made Vice President, Engineering, where he participated in the development of the MD-11, C-17, and T-45 aircraft. In 1987, he was appointed Vice President/General Manager, Commercial Advanced Products, where he oversaw the launch of the MD-90. After retirement, he served as a corporate consultant to McDonnell Douglas on the MD-12 program. He holds a Masters degree in Aeronautics from the California Institute of Technology (1952) and a Bachelors degree in Aeronautical Engineering from Rensselaer Polytechnic Institute (1949). He also served two years in the U.S. Navy as an Aviation Engineering Officer at the Bureau of Aeronautics, Washington, D.C. He is a Fellow of the American Institute of Aeronautics and Astronautics and the Society of Automotive Engineers and has written numerous technical papers and articles dealing with aircraft design and technology development. He also served on the Board of Directors of the Society of Automotive Engineers, and several committees for the National Academy of Engineering, NASA, and the U.S. Congress. He is currently a consultant to the NASA Aerospace Safety Advisory Panel and Professor of Aircraft Design in the Aerospace Engineering Department, California State University, Long Beach.

Table of Contents

1

REVIEW OF BASIC CONCEPTS

THE AIRPLANE IN MOTION

In the airplane preliminary design process achieving the performance objectives of altitude, speed, range, payload, and takeoff and landing distance requires analysis of the airplane in motion. It is therefore convenient to adopt some symbols and conventions related to airplane motion. A set of mutually perpendicular axes are defined within the

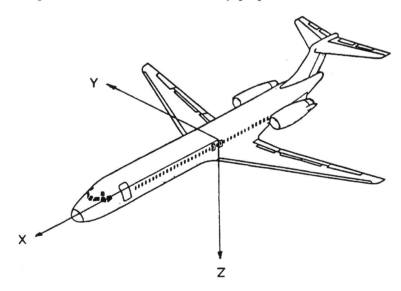

Fig. 1-1 The Airplane Axis System

1

airplane as shown in Fig. 1-1 with their origin at the airplane center of gravity or c.g. This is a right hand axis system with the positive X and Z axes in the plane of symmetry and with the X axis out the nose of the airplane pointing along the flight path. The Z axis is perpendicular to the X axis, positive downward, and the positive Y axis is out the right hand wing perpendicular to the plane of symmetry.

For the material presented in this book, the airplane is considered to be a rigid body with six degrees of freedom, three linear velocity components along these axes, and three angular velocity components around these axes. The angular motion around the Y axis is called pitch; the angular motion about the X axis is called roll; and the angular motion about the Z axis is called yaw. Nearly all of the airplane motions encountered in aircraft preliminary design and performance are in the plane of symmetry. The other three components of the airplane's motion lie outside the plane of symmetry. The symmetric degrees of freedom are referred to as the longitudinal motion, and the asymmetric degrees of freedom are referred to as the lateral-directional motion. In the plane of symmetry, Fig. 1-2, the inclination of the flight path to the horizontal is the flight path angle, γ, and the angle between the flight path and the airplane reference line is the angle of attack, α. The angle between the airplane reference line and the horizontal is the airplane's pitch angle, θ. When the flight path does not lie in the plane of symmetry, Fig. 1-3, the angle between the flight path and the airplane's center line is the yaw angle, ψ. For straight flight in this situation, the yaw angle is equal in magnitude but opposite in sign to the sideslip angle, β. In roll about the flight path, the angle between the Y axis and the horizontal is the roll or bank angle, ϕ.

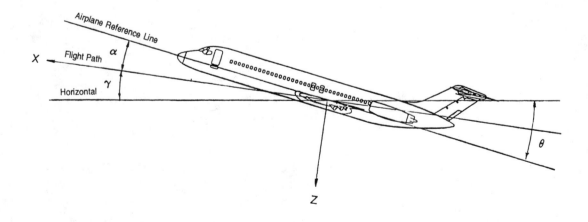

Fig. 1-2 Aircraft Axis Notation in the Plane of Symmetry

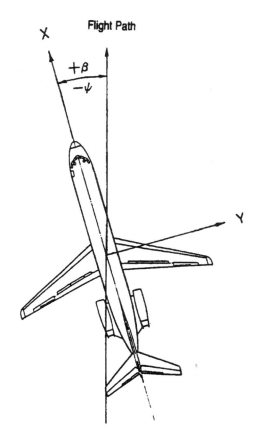

Fig. 1-3
Aircraft Axis Notation for Asymmetric Flight

AERODYNAMIC FORCES AND MOMENTS

The aerodynamic forces acting on an aircraft consist of two types: pressure forces which act normal to the aircraft surface, and viscous or shear forces which act tangentially to the aircraft surface. The pressure forces are due to the air pressure acting on the aircraft surface, and by definition can only act normal to the surface. The viscous or shear forces do not depend on air pressure, only on the viscosity or stickiness of the air. Viscosity is a property of air that gives rise to the shear stresses developed between adjacent parallel layers of air very close to the airplane surface. The region close to the airplane where the shear stresses are developed is called the boundary layer.

The physical parameters that govern the aerodynamic forces and moments acting on an aircraft have been developed through a method called dimensional analysis. This procedure is treated in detail in many textbooks on aerodynamics, and will only be summarized here. Dimensional analysis considers the dimensions or units of the physical quantities involved in the development of aerodynamic forces and moments, and divides them into two groups, fundamental and derived. The fundamental units are mass, length, and time, and all physical quantities have dimensions that are derived from a combination of these three fundamental units. Equations that express physical relationships must have dimensional homogeneity, that is, each term in the equation must have the same units in order for the equation to have physical significance. The broad physical relationships are postulated by logic, reason, or perhaps some experimental evidence, and then the specific relationships are derived by dimensional analysis. For aerodynamic forces and moments acting on an aircraft in the plane of symmetry the broad physical relationships are postulated as

$$F_{AERO}, M_{AERO} = f \text{ (shape, size, attitude, velocity, fluid properties)}$$

The specific relationship for aerodynamic forces, derived from dimensional analysis is

$$F_{AERO} = K\rho \, V^2 L^2 f\left(\alpha, \ \frac{\rho VL}{\mu} \ \frac{V}{a} \right) \qquad (1\text{-}1)$$

where

  K is a constant of proportionality or dimensionless coefficient

  V is the velocity of the aircraft

  L is an arbitrary characteristic length

  ρ is the air density

  α is the attitude of the airplane with respect to the flight path

  μ is the coefficient of viscosity for air*

  $\frac{\rho VL}{\mu}$ is a dimensionless quantity called Reynolds number, R

  a is the speed of sound in air

  V/a is a dimensionless quantity called Mach number, M

The aerodynamic forces and moments acting on the airplane in the plane of symmetry are shown in Fig. 1-4. The resultant of the aerodynamic forces is resolved into the lift component acting perpendicular to the flight path, or velocity vector, and the drag component acting parallel to the velocity vector. The lift and drag components are defined as acting at the airplane center of gravity, while all of the moments acting on the airplane are

---

*It is usually more convenient to work with a quantity called the kinematic viscosity, v, defined as μ/ρ. Reynold's number is then R VL/v.

lumped into one couple acting around the airplane center of gravity. The equations for lift and drag of the airplane may be written as

$$\text{Lift} \;=\; C_L \;\frac{\rho V^2 S}{2} \qquad\qquad (1\text{-}2)$$

$$\text{Drag} \;=\; C_D \;\frac{\rho V^2 S}{2} \qquad\qquad (1\text{-}3)$$

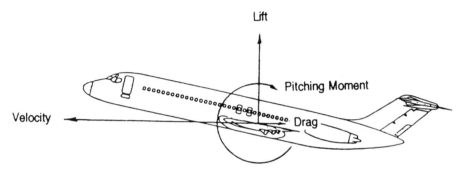

Fig. 1-4 Aerodynamic Forces and Moments in the Plane of Symmetry

where C_L and C_D are the lift and drag coefficients, respectively, and the area term in the equation (1-1) is arbitrarily taken as the wing area, S. To make the equation for the aerodynamic moment about the center of gravity dimensionally correct, the length of the wing mean chord, c, the mean distance from the leading edge to the trailing edge of the wing, is arbitrarily selected. The moment in the plane of symmetry is called the pitching moment, and the equation is written as

$$\text{Moment} = M_{cg} = Cm \;\frac{\rho V^2 S c}{2} \qquad\qquad (1\text{-}4)$$

where Cm is defined as the pitching moment coefficient. As noted in equation (1-1), while the primary relationship between the physical quantities involved in the development of aerodynamic forces and moments is expressed in terms of the dimensionless coefficients, these coefficients are functions of both Reynolds number and Mach number. The aerodynamic forces and moments acting on the airplane in asymmetric flight are shown in Fig. 1-5. The side force acts normal to the airplane center line, while the aerodynamic moments acting around the Z-axis through the c.g. are lumped together and called the yawing moment. In addition, the aerodynamic moments acting around the X-axis are lumped together and are called the rolling moment.

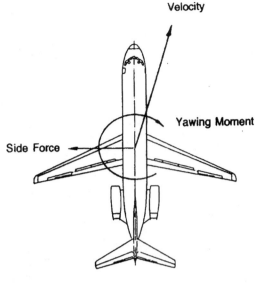

Fig. 1-5
Aerodynamic Forces and
Moments in Asymmetric Flight

The equations for side force, yawing moment, and rolling moment are

$$\text{Side force} \quad = \quad C_y \frac{\rho}{2} V^2 S \qquad (1\text{-}5)$$

$$\text{Yawing moment} \quad = \quad C_n \frac{\rho}{2} V^2 S\, b \qquad (1\text{-}6)$$

$$\text{Rolling moment} \quad = \quad C_l \frac{\rho}{2} V^2 S\, b \qquad (1\text{-}7)$$

where C_y, C_n, and C_l are the side force, yawing moment, and rolling moment coefficients, and b is the airplane wing span, selected as more appropriate than the wing mean cord for use with the asymmetric moment coefficients.

In summary, then, these three defined aerodynamic forces acting along the airplane axes, and three aerodynamic moments acting around the airplane axes.

Axis	Force Along	Moment Around
X	Drag	Rolling Moment
Y	Side Force	Pitching Moment
Z	Lift	Yawing Moment

RELATIVE WIND

Up to now, the aerodynamic forces acting on the airplane have been defined in terms of the airplane velocity vector. It should be noted that the aerodynamic forces and moments depend only on the relative velocity between the airplane and the air that it is flying through. The same aerodynamic forces are generated if the airplane moves through the air with a velocity, V, or if the airplane is held fixed in space, as in a wind tunnel, and the air moves past the airplane, with a velocity, V, equal and opposite to the actual velocity, as shown in Fig. 1-6.

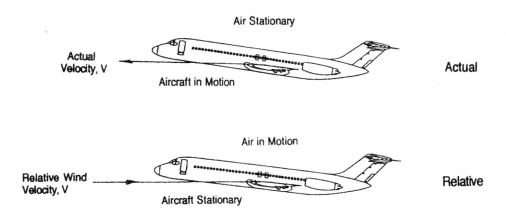

Figure 1-6   Relative Velocity and Relative Wind

FLIGHT SPEED TERMINOLOGY

One of the key parameters of a specific airplane design is the maximum level flight speed. For a variety of reasons, both technical and economic, various types of airplanes are designed to operate at flight speeds most appropriate to their design mission. For example, propeller driven personal utility airplanes are usually designed with maximum speeds of 250 knots or less, while commercial jet transports are designed with maximum speeds of about 500 knots or a Mach number of 0.88. Military fighter and attack aircraft have maximum speeds of around 1400 knots, or a Mach number of 2.5, while a specialized rocket powered research airplane, the X-15, was designed for a maximum speed of 3600 knots, or a Mach number of 6.0. Over such a wide range of flight speeds, the characteristics of the airflow around the airplane change dramatically. These changes, associated with the compressible nature of air, are directly related to the flight Mach number defined in equation (1-1) as the flight speed divided by the speed of sound in the ambient air in the atmosphere. This situation has given rise to some general terms to describe airplane flight speeds in terms of Mach number as illustrated in Fig. 1-7. Also shown are the types of airplanes having maximum level flight speeds within the various flight speed regimes. By far the largest number of aircraft in operation today, and indeed the greatest number of new designs will be the types with maximum speeds in the subsonic and transonic speed regimes, and the material in this book will focus on these types.

STANDARD ATMOSPHERE

Before starting any of the preliminary design and performance calculations outlined later in the book, it is appropriate to establish a standard set of characteristics for the earth's atmosphere in which aircraft operate. The U.S. Standard Atmosphere is a widely used set whose essential characteristics, that is, the temperature, pressure, density, and viscosity as a function of altitude have been derived using:

$$p \ = \ \rho RT \qquad \text{equation of state for a gas} \qquad (1\text{-}8)$$

$$dp \ = \ \rho g\, dh \qquad \text{hydrostatic equation} \qquad (1\text{-}9)$$

where

p = pressure in lb/sq. ft.
ρ = density in slugs/cu ft
T = absolute temperature in degrees Rankine
R = gas constant (1718 ft-lb/slug °R) for air
g = gravitational constant (32. 17 ft/sec^2)
h = height above sea level in ft

With these equations, only a defined variation of T with altitude is required to establish the standard atmosphere. The defined variation, based on experimental data, is shown in Fig. 1-8. It should be noted that once the temperature variation with altitude was defined, the characteristics of the standard atmosphere can be calculated directly. The

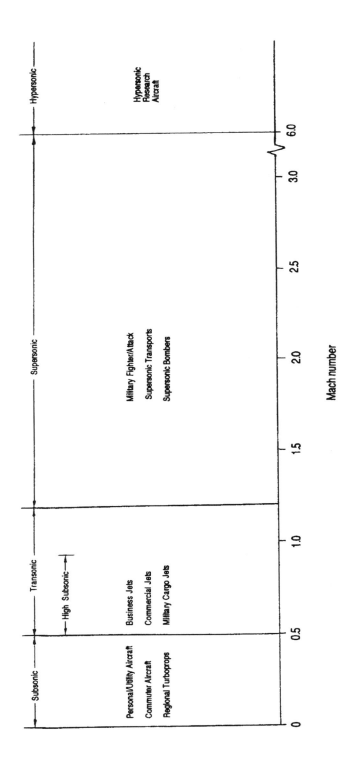

Figure 1-7 Flight Speed Terminology

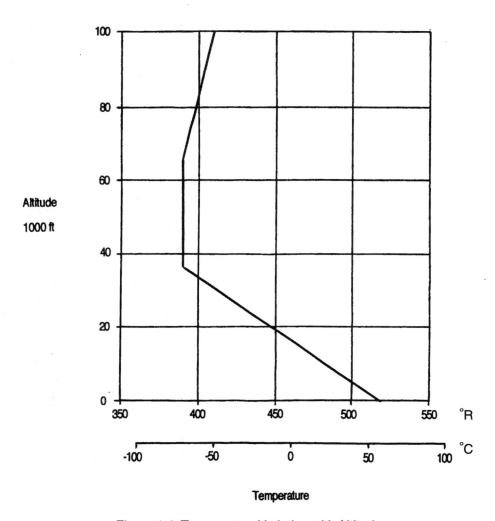

Figure 1-8 Temperature Variation with Altitude

characteristics of the U.S. Standard Atmosphere are tabulated in Fig. 1-9. From sea level to 36,089 ft, the temperature decreases linearly with altitude. This region is called the troposphere. Above 36,089 ft, the temperature is constant up to 65,617 ft, in the region called the stratosphere. Above 65,617 ft the temperature increases linearly beyond 100,000 ft, the upper level of interest for current or foreseeable aircraft.

Although the concept of geometric altitude, the altitude above sea level as determined

Altitude	Temperature		Pressure	Density	Density Ratio	Kinematic Viscosity	q / M²	Sonic Velocity	
ft	°F	°R	psf	slugs/cu ft	σ	sq ft/sec	lb/sq ft	ft/sec	knots
0	59.0	518.7	2116.2	.0023769	1.0000	.0001572	1481.0	1116.4	661.5
1000	55.4	515.1	2040.9	.0023081	.9710	.0001610	1429.0	1112.6	659.2
2000	51.9	511.6	1967.7	.0022409	.9427	.0001650	1377.0	1108.7	656.9
3000	48.3	508.0	1896.7	.0021752	.9151	.0001691	1328.0	1104.9	654.6
4000	44.7	504.4	1827.7	.0021110	.8881	.0001732	1279.0	1101.0	652.3
5000	41.2	500.9	1760.9	.0020482	.8616	.0001776	1233.0	1097.1	650.0
6000	37.6	497.3	1696.0	.0019869	.8358	.0001820	1187.0	1093.2	647.7
7000	34.0	493.7	1633.1	.0019270	.8106	.0001866	1143.0	1089.3	645.4
8000	30.5	490.2	1572.1	.0018685	.7860	.0001914	1100.0	1085.3	643.0
9000	26.9	486.6	1512.9	.0018113	.7619	.0001963	1059.0	1081.4	640.7
10,000	23.3	483.0	1455.6	.0017556	.7385	.0002013	1019.0	1077.4	638.3
11,000	19.8	479.5	1400.0	.0017011	.7155	.0002066	979.8	1073.4	636.0
12,000	16.2	475.9	1346.2	.0016480	.6932	.0002120	942.1	1069.4	633.4
13,000	12.6	472.4	1294.1	.0015961	.6713	.0002175	905.6	1065.4	631.4
14,000	9.1	468.8	1243.6	.0015455	.6500	.0002233	870.2	1061.4	628.8
15,000	5.5	465.2	1194.8	.0014962	.6292	.0002293	836.0	1057.4	626.4
16,000	1.9	461.7	1147.5	.0014480	.6089	.0002354	802.9	1053.3	624.0
17,000	-1.6	458.1	1101.7	.0014011	.5892	.0002418	770.8	1049.2	621.6
18,000	-5.2	454.6	1057.5	.0013553	.5699	.0002484	739.8	1045.1	619.2
19,000	-8.8	451.0	1014.7	.0013107	.5511	.0002553	709.8	1041.0	616.7
20,000	-12.3	447.4	973.3	.0012673	.5328	.0002623	680.8	1036.9	614.3
21,000	-15.9	443.9	933.3	.0012249	.5150	.0002697	652.7	1032.8	611.9
22,000	-19.5	440.3	894.6	.0011836	.4976	.0002772	625.6	1028.6	609.4
23,000	-23.0	436.8	857.2	.0011435	.4806	.0002851	599.4	1024.5	606.9
24,000	-26.6	433.2	821.2	.0011043	.4642	.0002932	574.1	1020.3	604.4
25,000	-30.2	429.6	786.3	.0010663	.4481	.0003017	549.7	1016.1	601.9
26,000	-33.7	426.1	752.7	.0010292	.4325	.0003104	526.2	1011.9	599.4
27,000	-37.3	422.5	720.3	.0009931	.4173	.0003195	503.4	1007.7	596.9
28,000	-40.9	419.0	689.0	.0009580	.4025	.0003289	481.5	1003.4	594.4
29,000	-44.3	415.4	658.8	.0009239	.3881	.0003387	460.3	999.1	591.9
30,000	-48.0	411.9	629.7	.0008907	.3741	.0003488	439.9	994.8	589.3
31,000	-51.6	408.3	601.6	.0008584	.3605	.0003594	420.3	990.5	586.8
32,000	-55.1	404.8	574.6	.0008270	.3473	.0003703	401.3	986.2	584.2
33,000	-58.7	401.2	548.5	.0007966	.3345	.0003817	383.1	981.9	581.6
34,000	-62.3	397.6	523.5	.0007670	.3220	.0003935	365.5	977.5	579.0
35,000	-65.8	394.1	499.3	.0007382	.3099	.0004058	348.6	973.1	576.4
36,000	-69.4	390.5	476.1	.0007103	.2981	.0004185	332.3	968.8	573.8
37,000	-69.7	390.0	453.9	.0006780	.2843	.0004379	330.9	968.1	573.6
38,000	-69.7	390.0	432.6	.0006463	.2710	.0004594	316.7	968.1	573.6
39,000	-69.7	390.0	412.4	.0006161	.2583	.0004820	301.8	968.1	573.6
40,000	-69.7	390.0	393.1	.0005873	.2462	.0005056	287.7	968.1	573.6
41,000	-69.7	390.0	374.6	.0005598	.2346	.0005304	274.2	968.1	573.6
42,000	-69.7	390.0	357.2	.0005336	.2236	.0005564	261.3	968.1	573.6
43,000	-69.7	390.0	340.5	.0005087	.2131	.0005837	249.0	968.1	573.6
44,000	-69.7	390.0	324.6	.0004849	.2031	.0006123	237.4	968.1	573.6
45,000	-69.7	390.0	309.4	.0004623	.1936	.0006423	226.2	968.1	573.6
46,000	-69.7	390.0	295.0	.0004407	.1845	.0006738	215.6	968.1	573.6
47,000	-69.7	390.0	281.2	.0004201	.1758	.0007068	205.5	968.1	573.6
48,000	-69.7	390.0	268.1	.0004004	.1676	.0007415	195.8	968.1	573.6
49,000	-69.7	390.0	255.5	.0003818	.1597	.0007778	186.7	968.1	573.6
50,000	-69.7	390.0	243.6	.0003639	.1522	.0008159	177.9	968.1	573.6
51,000	-69.7	390.0	232.2	.0003469	.1451	.0008559	169.5	968.1	573.6
52,000	-69.7	390.0	221.4	.0003307	.1383	.0008978	161.6	968.1	573.6
53,000	-69.7	390.0	211.0	.0003153	.1318	.0009418	154.0	968.1	573.6
54,000	-69.7	390.0	201.2	.0003006	.1256	.0009879	146.8	968.1	573.6
55,000	-69.7	390.0	191.8	.0002865	.1197	.0010360	139.9	968.1	573.6
56,000	-69.7	390.0	182.8	.0002731	.1141	.0010871	133.3	968.1	573.6
57,000	-69.7	390.0	174.3	.0002604	.1087	.0011403	127.1	968.1	573.6
58,000	-69.7	390.0	166.2	.0002482	.1036	.0011961	121.1	968.1	573.6
59,000	-69.7	390.0	158.4	.0002366	.0988	.0012547	115.4	968.1	573.6
60,000	-69.7	390.0	151.0	.0002256	.0941	.0013161	110.0	968.1	573.6
61,000	-69.7	390.0	144.0	.0002151	.0897	.0013805	104.8	968.1	573.6
62,000	-69.7	390.0	137.3	.0002050	.0855	.0014481	99.9	968.1	573.6
63,000	-69.7	390.0	130.9	.0001955	.0815	.0015189	95.2	968.1	573.6
64,000	-69.7	390.0	124.8	.0001834	.0777	.0015932	90.8	968.1	573.6
65,000	-69.7	390.0	118.9	.0001777	.0740	.0016712	86.5	968.1	573.6
70,000	-67.3	392.4	92.7	.0001376	.0579	.0021219	82.4	971.0	575.3
75,000	-64.6	395.1	73.0	.0001077	.0453	.0026938	64.9	974.4	577.3

Figure 1-9 Characteristics of the U.S. Standard Atmosphere

11

by a tape measure is most familiar, of prime importance for aircraft preliminary design and performance calculations is pressure altitude, the geometric altitude on a standard day for which the pressure is equal to the ambient atmospheric pressure. Aircraft altimeters are pressure gages calibrated to read pressure altitude. Also important is the density altitude, the geometric altitude on a standard day for which the density is equal to the ambient air density. Pressure altitude, density altitude, and temperature are related through the equation of state, $p = \rho RT$.

It should be noted that another standard atmosphere has been defined by the International Civil Aviation Organization (ICAO). The ICAO Standard Atmosphere and the U.S. Standard Atmosphere are identical up to 65,617 ft. Beyond 65,617 ft, the ICAO Standard Atmosphere maintains a constant temperature up to 82,800 ft, while the U.S. Standard Atmosphere reflects an increasing temperature with a constant gradient to beyond 100,000 ft. We will use the U.S. Standard Atmosphere throughout this book.

DYNAMIC PRESSURE

In the discussion of aerodynamic forces and moments, the expressions for all of them show a dependency on the quantity $\frac{\rho V^2}{2}$. This quantity which appears throughout aerodynamic theory, is equal to the kinetic energy of a unit volume of air, and is defined as the dynamic pressure, q.

$$q = \frac{\rho V^2}{2} \tag{1-10}$$

Another form of the equation for dynamic pressure which is especially useful in aircraft preliminary design performance calculation is

$$q = \frac{\gamma p M^2}{2} \tag{1-11}$$

where

γ is the ratio of specific heats for air equal to 1.4

p is the ambient pressure

M is the flight Mach number

AIRSPEED TERMINOLOGY

One of the more confusing concepts in aircraft preliminary design and performance studies is that of airspeed. Since the very early days airplanes have been equipped with airspeed indicators, which are operated by the pressure difference between two pressures sensed by devices mounted on the airplane. One pressure used in airspeed measurement is the impact or total pressure, usually sensed by a pitot or total head tube, Fig. 1-10a, which has an open hole at the front end to capture the total pressure. The other pressure used is the static pressure, that is, the ambient pressure at the operating altitude of the airplane, usually sensed by small flush holes located on a static tube, Fig. 1-10b. On many airplanes, the pitot tube and the static tube are integrated into one device called the pitot-static tube, Fig. 1-10c. On larger aircraft the static pressure is sensed by flush holes in the fuselage called static ports, Fig. 1-10d, which are located in an area where the static pressure is equal to the ambient static pressure. Airspeed indicators are calibrated to read

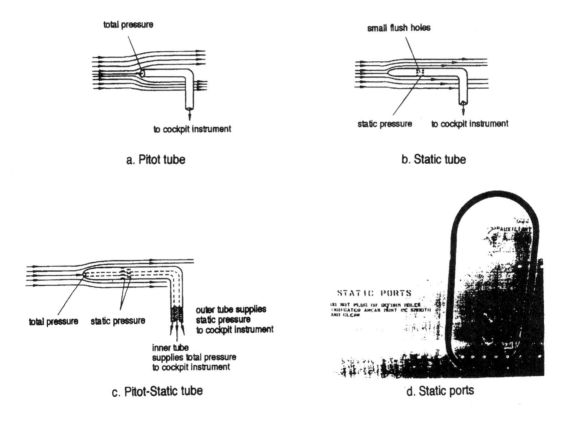

Figure 1-10   Aircraft Airspeed Sensors

airspeed as a function of the difference between total and static pressure. In order to develop some meaningful definitions of airspeed over a range of aircraft operational altitudes, some specific terminology has been adopted as follows.

13

IAS Indicated airspeed

This is the airspeed registered on the cockpit instrument, but it is not corrected for any instrument calibration errors.

CAS Calibrated airspeed

This is the indicated airspeed reading corrected for static source position errors. Usually, it is not possible to locate a pitot-static tube or a static port in a place that senses the exact ambient static pressure, so corrections for this so-called position error are made. Calibrated airspeed refers to the fact that airspeed indicators are calibrated in airspeed units, usually knots, through the difference between total and static pressure at Sea Level Standard Day conditions by the equation

$$V_{CAL} = \sqrt{\frac{2(P_{total} - P_{static})}{\rho_{sea\ level}}} \tag{1-12}$$

EAS Equivalent airspeed

This is the calibrated airspeed adjusted for what are termed compressibility effects. Equivalent airspeed is a very important parameter in aircraft preliminary design and performance calculations. Equivalent airspeed is defined as

$$V_{EAS} = \sqrt{\frac{\rho_{ambient}}{\rho_{sea\ level}}}\ V_{TRUE} \tag{1-13}$$

The idea behind equivalent airspeed is that for any flight condition, that is any combination of true airspeed and ambient density, and therefore dynamic pressure, there is an equivalent airspeed at sea level standard day conditions that produces the same dynamic pressure. In equation form

$$q = \frac{\rho_{ambient}}{2}\ V^2_{TRUE} = \frac{\rho_{sea\ level}}{2}\ V^2_{EAS} \tag{1-14}$$

A chart showing the relationship between V_{EAS} and V_{TRUE} for the U.S. Standard Atmosphere is shown in Fig. 1-11. Equivalent airspeeds are reasonably close to the indicated airspeeds shown by the cockpit instrument. The difference is the compressibility correction to CAS in order to obtain EAS. The compressibility increment, ΔV_c, is a function of both Mach number and altitude as shown in Fig. 1-12. This correction arises as follows. For a compressible fluid such as air,

$$(P_{total} - P_{static}) = \frac{\gamma}{2}\ pM^2 \left\{ 1 + \frac{M^2}{4} + \frac{M^4}{40} + \frac{M^6}{1600} + ... \right\} \tag{1-15}$$

14

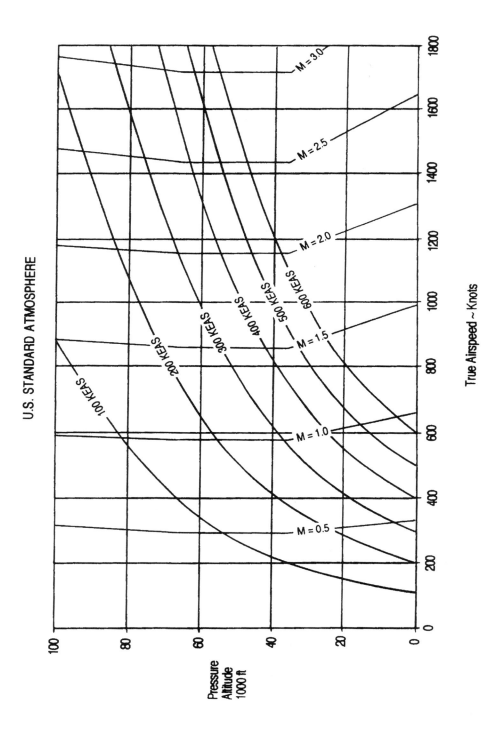

Figure 1-11 Relationship Between V_{EAS}, V_{TRUE} and Mach Number

15

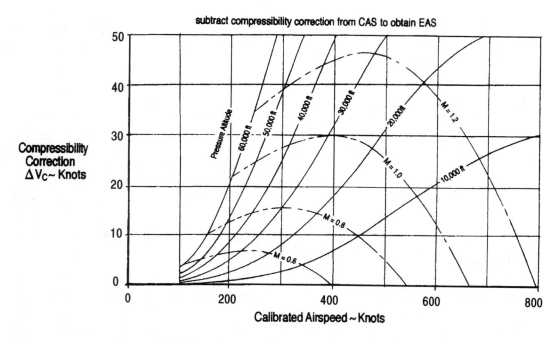

Figure 1-12 Airspeed Indicator Compressibility Correction

The airspeed correction sequence is shown schematically in Fig. 1-13.

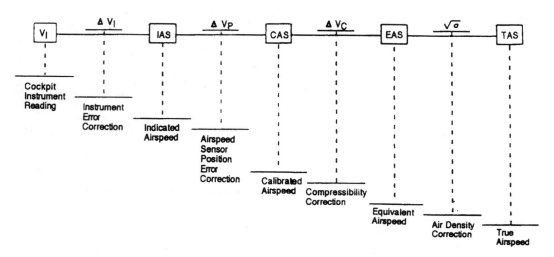

Figure 1-13 Airspeed Correction Sequence

Since CAS is directly related to $(P_{total} - P_{static})$, and EAS is directly related to the dynamic pressure, q, the correction is the Mach number series in the brackets of Equation 1-14.

TAS <u>True Airspeed</u>
  The true airspeed is the actual airspeed of the airplane at ambient conditions in the atmosphere and may be obtained by converting or correcting equivalent airspeed as follows.

$$V_{TRUE} = V_{EAS} \sqrt{\frac{\rho_{sea\ level}}{\rho_{ambient}}} \qquad (1\text{-}16)$$

FLIGHT PERFORMANCE EQUATIONS

Earlier in Part 1, it was noted that achieving the design performance objectives of maximum speed, range, payload, and takeoff and landing distance requires the analysis of the airplane in motion. An airplane axis system was defined, Fig. 1-1, pertinent airplane axis notation was defined, Fig. 1-2 and Fig. 1-3, and the aerodynamic force acting on the airplane were described in Fig. 1-4 and 1-5. In order to examine the major characteristics of the airplane's performance, equations involving the summation of forces and moments in the plane of symmetry have been developed, so that Newton's laws of motion may be utilized. For unaccelerated symmetric flight along a straight path, the summation of forces and moments for static equilibrium as shown in Fig. 1-14, may be written as

$$\Sigma F_X = T \cos \alpha - D - W \sin \gamma = 0 \qquad (1\text{-}17)$$

$$\Sigma F_Z = W \cos \gamma - L - T \sin \alpha = 0 \qquad (1\text{-}18)$$

$$\Sigma M_{cg} = 0 \qquad (1\text{-}19)$$

If the assumption is made that the angle of attack is always a relatively small angle, then $\cos \alpha = 1$ and $\sin \alpha = 0$. With this assumption, the equations reduce to

$$T - D = W \sin \gamma \qquad (1\text{-}20)$$

$$L = W \cos \gamma \qquad (1\text{-}21)$$

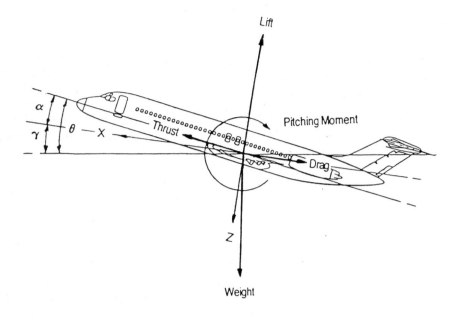

Figure 1-14 Forces and Moments Acting in the Plane of Symmetry

The climb gradient, γ, the gain in altitude for a given distance covered in the horizontal direction, with the attack angle assumption of $\sin \gamma = \gamma$ becomes:

$$\text{climb gradient} = \gamma = \frac{T - D}{W} \qquad (1\text{-}22)$$

and the climb velocity, or rate of climb is

$$R/C = \frac{(T - D)}{W} V \qquad (1\text{-}23)$$

If equation (1-20) is expressed in terms of lift coefficient, then

$$C_L = \frac{W}{S\,q} \cos \gamma \qquad (1\text{-}24)$$

or with small angle assumption, $\cos \gamma = 1$

$$C_L = \frac{W}{S\,q} \qquad (1\text{-}25)$$

AIRPLANE LIFT CURVE

Now in the discussion of aerodynamic forces and moments, it was noted that the lift coefficient is primarily a function of angle of attack, α. The variation of lift coefficient with angle of attack is a very important aerodynamic characteristic of an airplane, and is described in a plot such as Fig. 1-15, called the airplane lift curve. It was also noted that the airplane lift coefficient is also dependent on Mach number and Reynolds number, which will be discussed later, but for now, we will focus on the lift curve for a specific Mach number and Reynolds number corresponding to full scale airplane operation. As seen from Fig. 1-15, the lift curve has a zero value at some, usually negative, angle of attack, a linear region with a well defined slope, $dC_L/d\alpha$, and a departure from the linear slope as the maximum lift coefficient, $C_{L\,max}$, is approached. The characteristics of the lift curve, the zero lift angle, the slope, $dC_L/d\alpha$, and the $C_{L\,max}$, depend on certain geometric characteristics of the airplane and its components, as we shall see later.

The airplane lift curve has a special relationship to airplane operation in steady, unaccelerated flight. As we have seen for these steady conditions, Equation (1-25), the variation of the lift coefficient required to balance the weight at various steady flight speeds

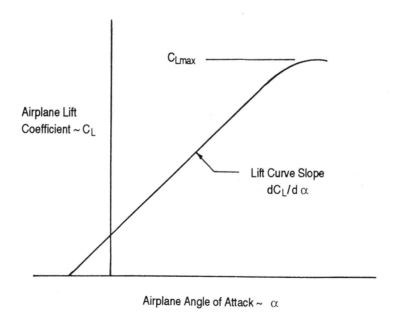

Figure 1-15 Airplane Lift Curve

19

is as shown in Fig. 1-16. The lowest steady flight speed is called the stalling speed, V_{Stall}, and it corresponds to operation of the airplane at its maximum lift coefficient, $C_{L\,max}$. At high flight speeds, and hence dynamic pressures, the lift coefficients required to balance the weight are reduced in accordance with Equation (1-25) as $1/q$ or $1/V^2$. Therefore, the airplane's speed along shallow, unaccelerated flight paths is primarily a function of lift coefficient, or angle of attack. In order to control the airplane's speed, the pilot must be able to control the equilibrium lift coefficient or angle of attack.

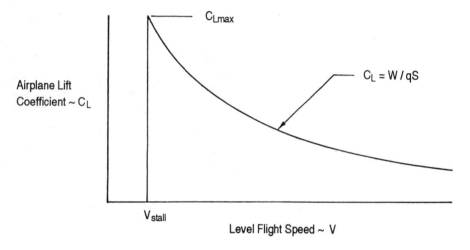

Figure 1-16   Variation of Lift Coefficient with Speed~Unaccelerated Level Flight

Going back to Equation (1-23), it can be seen that whether the airplane climbs or descends at a given speed depends on the difference between the thrust and drag at this speed. If thrust just equals drag, (T = D), then the rate of climb will be zero and the airplane will be in level flight. Since the thrust is basically a function of the cockpit throttle setting, under steady unaccelerated flight conditions, the airplane speed is determined by the value of the equilibrium lift coefficient, and the rate of climb or descent is regulated primarily through the throttle. For very large angles of climb or descent, this simple picture does not correspond to actuality, but for the preliminary design and performance methods used in this book, it is a valid concept.

AIRPLANE DRAG CURVE

Another aerodynamic characteristic of the airplane which is important in range and climb performance is the drag curve or drag polar, a plot of airplane drag coefficient vs airplane lift coefficient. As noted in Equation (1-1), the drag varies with angle of attack, but since in the normal operating range of angle of attack, C_L varies linearly with α, it has been found more convenient to describe the drag coefficient as a function of lift coefficient instead of angle of attack. The airplane drag curve, shown schematically in Fig. 1-17, has value of C_D at zero C_L, called the zero lift or parasite drag coefficient, C_{D_p}. At higher C_L's, the drag coefficient has a parabolic variation with C_L, due to the induced drag or drag due to lift coefficient, C_{D_i}, which varies as the square of the lift coefficient. As is the case with the lift curve, the drag curve varies in shape with both Mach number and Reynolds number, but for now we will focus on the drag curve that is representative of full scale airplane operation at subsonic speeds.

An important parameter in the cruise performance of the airplane, as well as certain aspects of climb performance, is the lift-to-drag ratio, (L/D). The lift-to-drag ratio may be visualized from the drag polar as shown in Fig. 1-18. At any point on the drag curve, the (L/D) is defined by the ratio of (C_L/C_D) at that point, and also by the slope of a line from the origin to the point in question.

If the (L/D) values are determined at various points along the airplane drag curve, a plot of airplane (L/D) vs lift coefficient, C_L, can be constructed. The (L/D) is zero at C_L = 0, reaches a maximum value, $(L/D)_{max}$ at some C_L, and then decreases at higher C_L's. Both the value of $(L/D)_{max}$ and the C_L at which $(L/D)_{max}$ occurs, $C_{L_{L/D_{max}}}$ are important aerodynamic characteristics of the airplane, as we shall see later.

MACH NUMBER EFFECTS ON LIFT AND DRAG CURVES

As noted in the section on flight speed terminology, the characteristics of the airflow around the airplane change dramatically as the flight Mach number is increased, due to the compressible nature of air. These changes in the airflow have a significant effect on the airplane lift and drag curves in the various Mach number ranges. For airplanes that operate entirely within the subsonic speed range as defined in Fig. 1-7, there are no significant effects of compressibility of the air on the airplane lift and drag curves, and a single lift curve as shown in Fig. 1-15, and a single drag curve as shown in Fig. 1-17 describe the lift and drag characteristics of the airplane. For airplanes that operate at high subsonic speeds in the transonic speed region, the airplane lift and drag curves will vary as the flight Mach number is increased due to the compressible nature of the air, so that there is a family of lift curves, and a family of drag curves, one for each flight Mach number of interest. The family of lift curves are characterized by an increase in the slope of the lift curve $dC_L/d\alpha$, and a decrease in the maximum lift coefficient, $C_{L_{max}}$, as the Mach

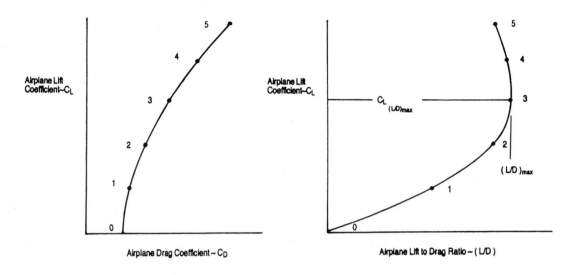

Figure 1-17 Airplane Drag Curve   Figure 1-18 Airplane (L/D) Curve

number is increased in the high subsonic region, as shown schematically in Fig. 1-19. The Mach number effects may be summarized by plotting the significant parameters as a function of Mach number. For example, the effect of Mach number on increasing the lift curve slope is shown in Fig. 1-20, while the effect of Mach number on decreasing the maximum lift coefficient, $C_{L_{max}}$, is shown in Fig. 1-21. The family of drag curves are characterized by increases in the parasite drag coefficient, C_{D_p} , and significant increases in the drag coefficient at higher C_L's as the Mach number is increased, as shown in Fig. 1-22. For the drag curves, the Mach number effects are usually shown in the form of C_D vs. Mach number of various values of lift coefficient, as shown in Fig. 1-23.

The explanation of these Mach number effects on the lift and drag curves has been derived from the theory of compressible flow, and confirmed by experimental data obtained in wind tunnels and from flight tests. It can be shown that for an airplane at a given angle of attack, the lift coefficient will increase as the Mach number inceases, because the suctions on the wing upper surface, and the pressures on the wing lower surface tend to grow with Mach number, roughly by the factor $1/\sqrt{1-M^2}$ in the high subsonic speed range, which results in the increase in the lift curve slope as shown in Figs. 1-19 and 1-20. Also, as the Mach number increases,at some flight Mach number, the local velocities on the wing near the leading edge, at high angles of attack near maximum lift coefficient, become supersonic, which leads to local shock waves and separation, limit-

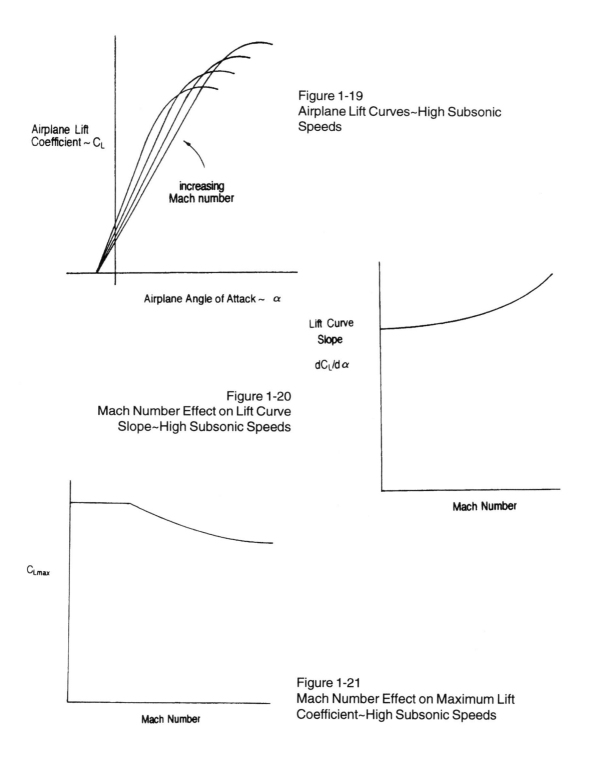

Airplane Lift Coefficient ~ C_L

increasing Mach number

Airplane Angle of Attack ~ α

Figure 1-19
Airplane Lift Curves~High Subsonic Speeds

Lift Curve Slope

$dC_L/d\alpha$

Mach Number

Figure 1-20
Mach Number Effect on Lift Curve Slope~High Subsonic Speeds

C_{Lmax}

Mach Number

Figure 1-21
Mach Number Effect on Maximum Lift Coefficient~High Subsonic Speeds

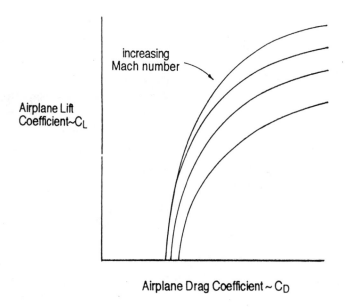

Figure 1-22   Airplane Drag Curves~High Subsonic Speeds

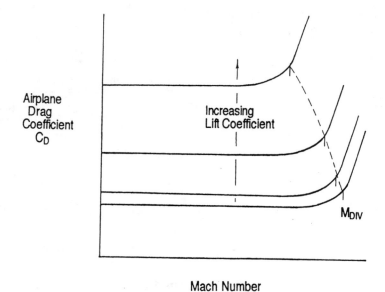

Figure 1-23 Mach Number Effect on Drag Curves~High Subsonic Speeds

ing the attainable maximum lift coefficient as shown in Fig. 1-21.

As for the drag cuves, the Mach number effects are due to the development of local supesonic flow around the wing, which eventually produces normal shock waves, and finally separated flow. Because of the energy loss in the shock wave, and the added pressure drag due to the separated flow, there are significant increases in the drag coefficient at a given lift coefficient as the flight Mach number is increased as shown in Fig. 1-22. The development of these conditions for a wing airfoil section typical of those used on many current jet trnasports and business jets is shown in Fig. 1-24. These are some important concepts and definitions associated with the sketches of Fig. 1-24. At the condition shown in the second sketch, the condition of lift coefficient and flight Mach number where the maximum local velocity on the wing surface is equal to the sonic velocity, is called the critical Mach number. At a higher flight Mach number, where the conditions are shown in the third sketch, with a local region of supersonic flow terminated by a normal shock wave, and the very beginning of flow separation behind the normal shock, the drag associated with the normal shock and the beginning of flow separation begins to rise abruptly. This condition is called the drag divergence Mach number M_{DIV}, for that particular lift coefficient. At higher flight Mach numbers, sketches four and five, the supersonic zones are longer, the normal shocks are stronger, and the drag continues to rise very abruptly. Although the wing is the primary source of local supersonic flow, shock waves and the associated drag increase, all parts of the airplane, i.e. the fuselage, tail surfaces, and engine nacelles will eventually experience these conditions at flight Mach numbers beyond 0.94.

For airplanes that are designed to operate at supersonic speeds, the lift and drag curves also vary with flight Mach number. The slopes of the curves are similar to those of the subsonic speed designs, but the significant parameters show a different trend at supersonic speeds. The pressure on the wing upper and lower surface tend to reduce as the Mach number is increased roughly by the factor $1/\sqrt{M^2-1}$, so that the lift curve slope, which increases at high subsonic speeds, decreases beyond Mach 1.0 as shown in Fig. 1-25. The maximum lift capability supersonically is usually described in terms of a maximum useable lift coefficient, which results from detached shock waves and unsteady flow, plus very high drag at high angles of attack supersonically. The drag curves at supersonic speeds are basically parabolic in shape, but with very high values of parasite drag coefficient, because of the added element of supersonic wave drag, as shown in Fig. 1-26, and very high drag levels at operating lift coefficients due to the wave drag element that increases with lift coefficient. The presence of wave drag at supersonic speeds has a significant impact on the maximum lift-to-drag ratio $(L/D)_{max}$ referred to in Fig. 1-18. Because of this added drag element, the $(L/D)_{max}$ values at supersonic speeds are usually less than half of the values at

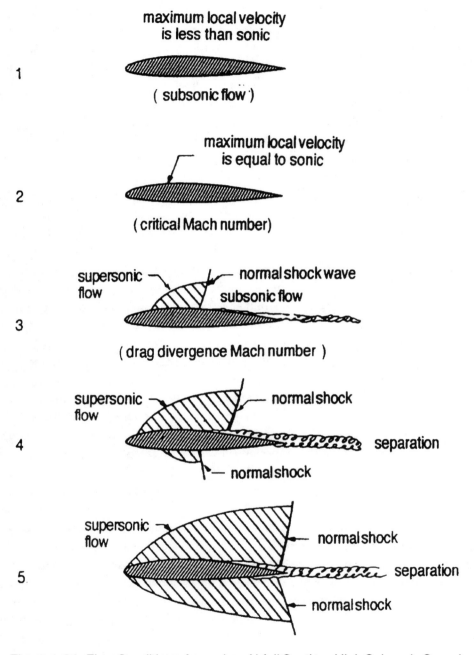

Figure 1-24 Flow Conditions Around an Airfoil Section~High Subsonic Speeds

subsonic speeds, for any specific configuration. For example, for large commercial transports, the $(L/D)_{max}$ values at subsonic speeds are slightly below 20, while the best supersonic transport designs are around 10 or less, as shown in Fig. 1-27. This makes efficient supersonic flight very difficult compared to subsonic operation.

PRELIMINARY DESIGN METHODS

The major characteristics of airplane performance along steady, unaccelerated flight paths can be determined in the preliminary design stage from the solution of equations (1-20) and (1-21). The specific performance characteristics, such as maximum speed, range, rate of climb and takeoff and landing distance, are all predicted from estimates of the aerodynamic lift and drag, the aircraft weight in various loading conditions, and the thrust forces produced by the propulsion system for the various flight conditions involved.

The development of aircraft preliminary designs involves the use of a number of methods that lead to a set of preliminary physical characteristics for an airplane capable of meeting the design objectives. These methods are usually based on valid physical principles and fundamental theoretical concepts, augmented by empirical trend data in areas where the physical principles are extremely complex, or where the theory is not able to handle the real situations that occur in actual flight. For example, the technical literature contains numerous works on aerodynamic theory, which use elegant mathematics to calculate solutions for many situations related to airplane design. Unfortunately, in order to obtain specific results from the theory, certain simplifying assumptions must be made, which often limit the usefulness of the results. In the early fundamental aerodynamic theory of flow around airfoils, finite span wings, and bodies such a fuselage and nacelles, it was assumed that air was incompressible and had no viscosity, which excluded the effects of Mach number and the real effect of skin friction drag. Furthermore, fundamental aerodynamic theory is not generally applicable where separated flow is involved, which is a key element in the determination of airplane maximum lift coefficient. Later aerodynamic theory treated airfoils, wings, and bodies at supersonic speeds, again with the assumption that air has no viscosity. Aerodynamic theory at transonic speed, which involves compressible subsonic flow, combined with areas of local supersonic flow with shock waves, is extremely complex, and solutions to design problems usually requires the use of large, electronic computers. Quite often, data from systematic wind tunnel tests of various aircraft components, or even complete airplane scale models, over a range of Mach numbers and Reynolds numbers, are used to guide the development of preliminary design methods. However, methods that are based on actual flight test data, obtained from the "big wind tunnel in the sky" often provide the most accurate results.

27

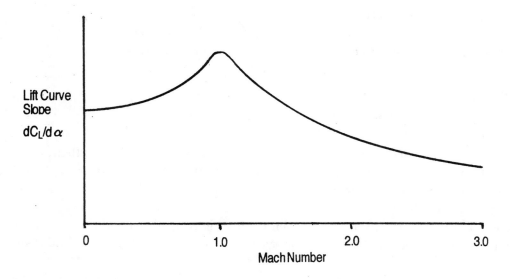

Figure 1-25   Mach Number Effects on Lift curve Slope

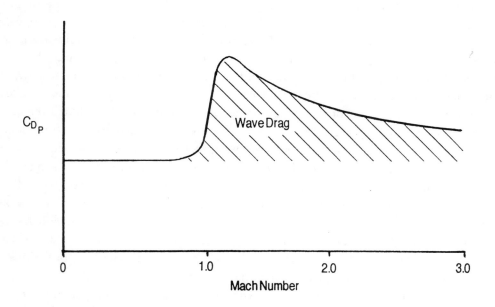

Figure 1-26   Mach Number Effects on Parasite Drag Coefficient

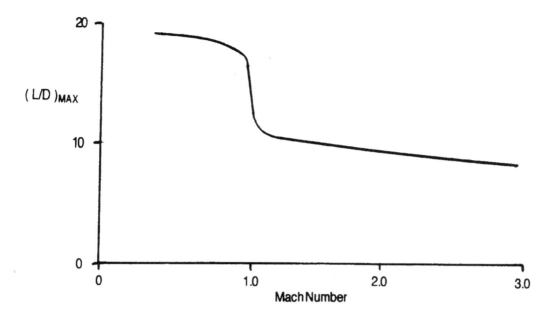

Figure 1-27   Mach Number Effects on Maximum Lift-to-Drag Ratio

The preliminary design group of every aircraft company has their own set of methods, usually developed over many years of continuous refinement, and while different in detail, these methods are quite similar in their basic formulation. The methods presented in the subsequent parts of this book are similar to those used throughout the aircraft industry, although some of the more simple methods have been developed by the author to reduce tedious calculations, while at the same time maintaining reasonable accuracy and proper relationship with the key parameters involved.

REFERENCES

1.1   Millikan, Clark B., Aerodynamics of the Airplane, Wiley, New York, 1941

1.2   Kuethe, Arnold M. and Schetzer, Jay D., Foundations of Aerodynamics, Wiley, New York, 1950.

1.3   Shevell, Richard S., Fundamentals of Flight, Prentice Hall, Englewood Cliffs, NJ, 1989

1.4   Liepmann, Hans W., and Puckett, Allen E., Aerodynamics of a Compressible Fluid, Wiley, New York, 1947

1.5   Anonymous, Aeronautical Vestpocket Handbook, 21st edition, Pratt & Whitney Division, United Technologies, East Hartford, CT, 1990

2

THE AIRCRAFT PRODUCT
DEVELOPMENT PROCESS

PRODUCT DEVELOPMENT SEQUENCE

Although preliminary design is a key element in the overall aircraft product development process, it is well to review the entire process before focusing on the specific elements of aircraft preliminary design. A chart showing the general sequence of activities in the product development process is shown in Fig 2-1. The major activities are generally representative of both military and commercial product development programs, although time scale and some of the details of the various phases may differ. Commercial product development programs usually take about 48 months from the authority to proceed (ATP) to initial delivery, and are in general shorter than military product development programs, since they avoid the yearly congressional review of the defense budget, and the usual priority and funding problems, which tend to stretch out the military development programs longer than necessary.

Another aspect of recent military programs that tends to lengthen the development time is the design, construction, and flight test of full scale prototype aircraft from the two top contenders for the production contract, a process that can add two to three years to the product development process.

Prerequisites for any product development are ongoing technology research and development (R&D) and marketing activities. Technology R&D in important disciplines such as aerodynamics, structures, materials, propulsion, and avionics systems is conducted by all aircraft manufacturers. The knowledge gained in this R&D activity is utilized by the design engineers in the various disciplines to decide on the "technology readiness" of new technology for incorporation in a new aircraft design.

"Technology readiness" means that a new level of technology in any of the major disciplines is well enough understood and documented by analysis and experimental

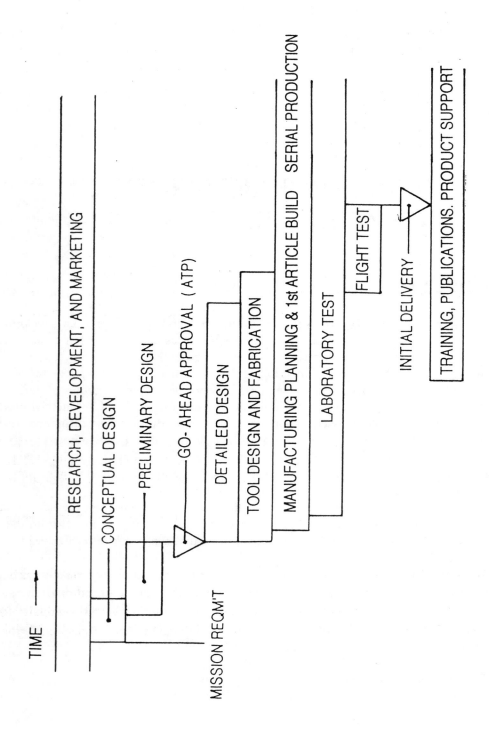

Figure 2-1 The Aircraft Development Process

32

tests such that it may be incorporated into a new design with an acceptable level of risk to the program. Some examples of technology readiness decisions that have been made in recent aircraft product development programs have been associated with the use of

- Fully digital fly-by-wire flight control systems
- All composite materials for the wing structural "box"
- Advanced unducted fan propulsion

It should be noted that the risk-reward tradeoffs are not necessarily the same for military and commercial aircraft. Military performance requirements usually demand the incorporation of the most advanced technology whereas commercial aircraft requirements place major emphasis on economics as well as performance, which tends to minimize the incorporation of advanced technology that may have associated economic risks.

The market research aspects of ongoing marketing activities are especially important in the aircraft product development process. Military aircraft manufacturers maintain continuous contacts with the military requirements organizations of the Air Force and Navy in order to keep current on future military aircraft mission requirements. Similarly, commercial aircraft manufacturers maintain a continuous dialog with airline planning departments in order to keep abreast of future airline equipment needs.

The manufacturers often assist their prospective customers with paper studies of future aircraft needs, including specific aircraft types. An example of the type of analysis that commercial transport manufacturers may make for prospective airline customers is shown schematically in Fig. 2-2. This type of analysis usually involves two steps, the first being a general analysis and forecast of the scope of future operations, and the second being a more detailed analysis of specific aircraft types when operated on important routes for the particular airline.

Another aspect of ongoing market research is the determination of what the competition is planning to do in the way of new product development. For military programs, it is an extremely difficult task because of the tight security usually placed on the preliminary design activity. In the commercial area, the manufacturers usually make public their preliminary design activities, through releases to the aviation press, and through numerous briefings to potential customers. Eventually, these interactions between the aircraft manufacturers and the potential customers lead to the development of a mission specification for a new airplane.

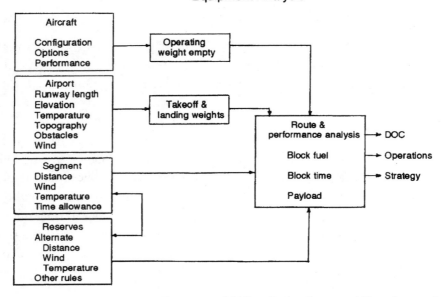

Operational Analysis

Market analysis
- Community
- Industry
- Airline
- Traffic
- Growth
- Share

Strategy analysis
- Competition
- Objectives
- Operational strategy
- Equipment
- Service quality
- Frequency

Operations analysis
- Alternative systems
  - Itineraries
  - Equipment
  - Frequency
  - Load factors
- Capacity required
- Fleet definition

Equipment analysis
- Airplanes
- Environment
- Routes
- Rules
- Performance
- Block time
- Payload & fuel

Economics analysis
- Operating costs
  - DOC
  - IOC
- Revenue
- Investment

Financial analysis
- Profit & loss
- Sources & uses of funds
- Balance sheet
- Financial ratios
- Rate of return

Equipment Analysis

Aircraft
- Configuration
- Options
- Performance

Airport
- Runway length
- Elevation
- Temperature
- Topography
- Obstacles
- Wind

Segment
- Distance
- Wind
- Temperature
- Time allowance

Reserves
- Alternate
  - Distance
  - Wind
  - Temperature
- Other rules

Operating weight empty

Takeoff & landing weights

Route & performance analysis
- Block fuel
- Block time
- Payload

→ DOC
→ Operations
→ Strategy

Figure 2-2 Analysis and Forecast of Airline Operations and Requirements

Adapted with permission from Reference 2.2

34

MISSION SPECIFICATION AND MISSION PROFILE

The mission specification is a concise statement of the basic performance objectives and other related criteria that must be met by the new design. The mission specification usually contains the following information

- purpose or use for which the aircraft being designed
- design payload
- required range or radius with design payload
- normal cruise speed/maximum speed
- normal cruise altitude
- takeoff distance, usually at maximum takeoff weight
- landing distance
- direct operating cost
- airport noise levels
- other requirements deemed important

Mission specifications can have their origins from a number of sources. For military aircraft programs, a mission specification is usually issued by the military service that intends to procure the final production aircraft. As noted earlier, the development of the mission specification often involves studies conducted by both the military services and the contractors to insure a realistic set of values for the mission parameters. The first military mission specification issued on December 23, 1907 is shown in Fig. 2-3, which resulted in the procurement of a specially designed biplane by the U.S. Army Signal Corps from the Wright Brothers. The mission specification has the main elements as noted above, including some very significant "other" requirements deemed important by the U.S. Army.

In earlier times, mission requirements often came from individual customers. An example of the development of a very simple mission specification, done through an exchange of telegrams, for Lindbergh's New York-Paris airplane of 1927 is shown in Fig. 2-4. Here the range requirement was paramount, the customer specified the Wright J-5 "Whirlwind" engine, the payload was minimal, only the pilot plus a few emergency supplies and some sandwiches, but cost and schedule were also very critical. As is well known and documented, the Ryan Company responded with a design that met all the requirements handily.

Sometimes mission specifications come from an airline, where internal studies of future operations lead to a concept for a new airliner. Such was the case of the American Airlines mission specification for a large, twin-engine, medium range transport, as shown in Fig. 2-5, originally issued in March 1966. As a result of numerous studies

SIGNAL CORPS SPECIFICATION No. 486
Advertisement and Specification for a Heavier-Than-Air Machine
GENERAL REQUIREMENTS

The general dimensions of the flying machine will be determined by the manufacturer, subject to the following conditions:

1. Bidders must submit with their proposals the following:
   a. Drawings to scale showing the general dimensions and shape of the flying machine which they propose to build under this specification.
   b. Statement of the speed for which it is designed.
   c. Statement of the total area of the supporting planes.
   d. Statement of the total weight.
   e. Description of the engine which will be used for motive power.
   f. The material of which the frame, planes, and propellers will be constructed. Plans received will not be shown to other bidders.
2. It is desirable that the flying machine be designed so that it may be quickly and easily assembled and taken apart and packed for transportation in army wagons. It should be capable of being assembled and put into flying condition in about one hour.
3. The flying machine should be designed to carry two persons having a combined weight of about 350 pounds, also sufficient fuel for a flight of 125 miles.
4. The flying machine should be designed to have a speed of at least forty miles per hour in still air, but bidders must submit quotations in their proposals for cost depending on the speed attained during the trial flight, according to the following scale:
   > 40 miles per hour, 100 per cent
   > 39 miles per hour, 90 per cent
   > 38 miles per hour, 80 per cent
   > 37 miles per hour, 70 per cent
   > 36 miles per hour, 60 per cent
   > Less than 36 miles per hour rejected
   > 41 miles per hour, 110 per cent
   > 42 miles per hour, 120 per cent
   > 43 miles per hour, 130 per cent
   > 44 miles per hour, 140 per cent
5. The speed accomplished during the trial flight will be determined by taking an average of the time over a measured course of more than five miles, against and with the wind. The time will be taken by a flying start, passing the starting point at full speed at both ends of the course. This test subject to such additional details as the Chief Signal Officer of the Army may prescribe.
6. Before acceptance a trial endurance flight will be required of at least one hour during which time the flying machine must remain continuously in the air without landing. It shall return to the starting point and land without any damage that would prevent it immediately starting upon another flight. During this trial flight of one hour, it must be steered in all directions without difficulty and at all times under perfect control and equilibrium.
7. Three trials will be allowed for speed as provided for in paragraphs 4 and 5. Three trials for endurance as provided in paragraph 6, and both tests must be completed within a period of thirty days from the date of delivery. The expense of the tests shall be bourne by the manufacturer. The place of delivery to the Government and trial flights shall be Fort Meyer, Va.
8. It should be designed as to ascend in any country which may be encountered in field service. The starting device must be simple and transportable. It should also land in a field without requiring a specially prepared spot and without damaging its structure.
9. It should be provided with some device to permit a safe descent in case of an accident to the propelling machinery.
10. It should be sufficiently simple in its construction and operation to permit an intelligent man to become proficient in its use within a reasonable length of time.
11. Bidders must furnish evidence that the Government of the United States has the lawful right to use all patented devices or appurtenances which may be part of the flying machine, and that the manufacturers of the flying machine are authorized to convey the same to the Government. This refers to the unrestricted right to use the flying machine sold to the Government, but does not contemplate the exclusive purchase of the patent rights for duplicating the flying machine.

JAMES ALLEN
Brigadier General, Chief Signal Officer of the Army

SIGNAL OFFICE
Washington, D.C., December 23, 1907

Figure 2-3 U.S. Army Signal Corps Mission Specification for First U.S. Military Airplane

WESTERN UNION
RYAN AIRLINES INC. ANGLUM MO.
SAN DIEGO CALIFORNIA   FEB. 3,1927

CAN YOU CONSTRUCT WHIRLWIND ENGINE
PLANE CAPABLE FLYING NONSTOP BETWEEN
NEW YORK AND PARIS STOP IF SO PLEASE
STATE COST AND DELIVERY DATE

ROBERTSON AIRCRAFT CORP.

WESTERN UNION
SAN DIEGO CALI F.
FEB. 4 1927
ROBERTSON AIRCRAFT CORP.
ANGLUM MO.

CAN BUILD PLANE SIMILAR M ONE BUT LARGER WINGS
CAPABLE OF MAKING FLIGHT COST ABOUT SIX
THOUSAND WITHOUT MOTOR AND INSTRUMENTS
ABOUT THREE MONTHS
RYAN AIRLINES

WESTERN UNION
RYAN AIRLINES INC.   ANGLUM MO.
SAN DIEGO CALIFORNIA   FEB. 5 1927

COMPETITION MAKES TIME ESSENTIAL CAN YOU
CONSTRUCT PLANE IN LESSTHAN THREE MONTHS
STOP PLEASE WIRE GENERAL SPECIFICATIONS

ROBERTSON AIRCRAFT CORP.

WESTERN UNION
SAN DIEGO CALIFORNIA
3 PM FEB. 5 1927
ROBERTSON AIRCRAFT CORP.
ANGLUM MO.

GAS CAPACITY THREE HUNDRED EIGHTY GALLONS
CRUISING SPEED ONE HUNDRED MILES PER HOUR
LOADING ONLY TWELVE AND A HALF POUNDS PER
FOOT AND TWENTY POUNDS PER HORSEPOWER
STOP CAN COMPLETE IN TWO MONTHS FROM DATE
OF ORDER IF NECESSARY STOP WILL REQUIRE
FIFTY PERCENT DEPOSIT

RYAN AIRLINES

Figure 2-4 Development of Lindbergh's Mission Specification for New York-Paris Airplane

Reprinted with permission from Reference 2.3

March 1966
> Purpose: Medium range wide body let transport for low cost operation on high density short to medium range high density routes
> General medium range mission
> Payload: 250 single class coach passengersand bags plus 5000 lbs. of revenue cargo
> Range: 1850 n.mi. with full payload
> Cruise Altitude: No greater than 31,000 ft.
> Cruise Speed: Mach 0.80
> Takeoff Distance: Less than 9,000 ft. for 600 ft airport altitude at 90°F
> Specific short range mission (LaGuardia-Chicago)
> Payload: 250 single class coach passengers and bags plus 5000 lbs of revenue cargo
> Range: 675 n.mi. with full payload
> Cruise Altitude: No greater than 31,000 ft
> Cruise Speed: Mach 0.82
> Takeoff Distance: 7,000 ft for sea level airport at 90°F (LaGuardia)
> Maximum takeoff weight for LaGuardia-Chicago mission no greater than 250,000 lbs
> Stalling speed, landing configuration at maximum landing weight, to be 96 kts or less
> Fuel tank capacity to provide range capability of 2400 n.mi.
> Powerplants: 2 Turbofan engines

July 1967
> Purpose: Medium range wide body let transport with luxury interior for mixed first class and coach service on short to medium range high density routes
> General medium range mission
> Payload: 230 mixed class passengers and bags plus 5000 lbs of revenue cargo
> Range: 1850 n.mi. with best eflorts toward reasonable transcontinental capability
> Cruise Altitude: 35,000 ft
> Cruise Speed: Mach 0.82 or greater
> Takeoff Distance: 9,000 ft for 600 ft airport aftitude at 90°F
> Specific short range mission (LaGuardia-Chicago) unchanged
> Maximum takeoff weight for LaGuardia-Chicago mission no greater than 285,000 lbs
> Fuel tank capacity to provide range capability of 2500 n.mi.
> Overall length 165 ft or less; Wing span 155 ft or less
> Structural capability to increase MTOGW for 2500 n.mi range with design payload
> Powerplants: 3 Turbofan engines

March 1968 (Contractual mission specification)
> Purpose: Unchanged
> Payload: 254 mixed class passengers and bags
> Range: 3000 n.mi.
> Cruise Altitude: 35,000 ft
> Cruise Speed: Mach 0.85
> Takeoff Distance: 8200 ft at sea level 90°F for primary payload-range mission
>   5600 ft at sea level 90°F for LaGuardia-Chicago mission
> Maximum takeoft weight for LaGuardia-Chicago mission, 360,000 lbs
> Stalling speed, landing configuration, at maximum landing weight, 102 kts
> Overall length, 180 ft

Figure 2-5 Development of Mission Specification for Medium Range Wide-Body Transport

Adapted with permission from Reference 2.1

performed by both Douglas and Lockheed, the mission specification gradually evolved over a two year period into a longer range, three-engine aircraft which became the DC-10-10, initially purchased by American Airlines, and later by United Airlines. The nearly identical Lockheed L-1011-1 was not selected by American Airlines, but was procured by Eastern, Delta, and later TWA. It should be noted that both aircraft, designed to the final American Airlines mission specification, have had long and productive careers in airline service throughout the world.

The starting point, then, for any new aircraft, is a design mission specification, with the associated mission profile. Examples of a design specification and mission profiles for civil aircraft are shown in Figs. 2-6, 2-7 and 2-8. An example of a design mission specification and mission profile for a military attack aircraft is shown in Fig. 2-9.

Some comments on specified values for key mission parameters for various types of aircraft are as follows.

Payload

- For personal and utility aircraft, payload usually includes the pilot as well as passengers and baggage

- For business jets, commuters, and commercial transports, payload does not include the flight or cabin crew, only the passengers, their baggage, and revenue cargo

- For military fighter/attack and bomber aircraft, payload consists of expendable ordnance such as bombs, rockets, missiles, and ammunition for onboard guns.

- For military cargo aircraft, payload is made up of the military cargo designed to be carried, but not the related tie down and restraining equipment needed to secure the cargo.

Range

The choice of the design range for a new aircraft design is one of the most difficult decisions to be made, and has a major impact on the gross weight required to perform the design mission. If the aircraft is to operate between specific pairs of cities, the design range must be great enough to cover practical operational aspects, such as operating on prescribed airways, and overcoming adverse headwinds that are likely to be present. Figs. 2-10 and 2-11 present data on the shortest or "great circle" distances between major cities in North America and the entire world. For operation between specific cities, the design

Purpose: Reasonably fast, convenient, personal business transportation

Payload: Pilot plus five passengers at 175 lbs each plus 240 lbs total baggage

Range: 1000 nautical miles with maximum payload

Reserve fuel: 25% of required mission fuel

Cruise Altitude: 10,000 feet

Cruise Speed: 250 knots true airspeed at 10,000 feet

Takeoff Distance: 1500 feet over a 50 foot obstacle at sea level standard day conditions at maximum takeoff gross weight

Landing Distance: 1500 feet over a 50 foot obstacle at sea level standard day conditions at maximum landing weight

Powerplants: Piston Propeller

Pressurization: None

Certification Basis: FAR Part 23

Mission Profile:

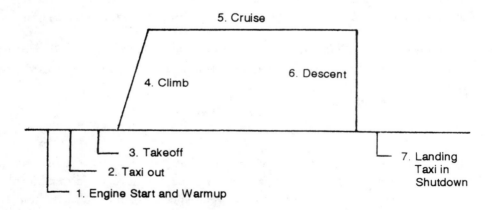

Figure 2-6 Mission Specification for Personal/Utility Twin Engine Propeller Driven Aircraft

Purpose: Competitive alternative to Embraer EMB-145 and Canadair RJ

Payload: 50 passengers at 175 lbs each plus 30 lbs of baggage each

Crew: 2 pilots at 175 lbs each plus baggage at 30 lbs each

       2 cabin attendants at 130 lbs each plus baggage at 30 lbs each

Range: 800 nautical miles

Reserve fuel: 100 nautical mile flight to alternate, followed by 45 minute loiter

Cruise Altitude: 30,000 feet

Cruise Speed: Mach number = 0.74

Climb: Direct to 30,000 feet at maximum takeoff weight

Takeoff Field Length: 5,000 feet at sea level, 90°F, at maximum takeoft weight

Landing Field Length: 4,500 feet at sea level, 90°F, at maximum landing weight

Powerplants: 2 Turbofans

Pressurization: 5,000 foot cabin altitude at 30,000 feet

Certification Basis: FAR Part 25

Mission Profile:

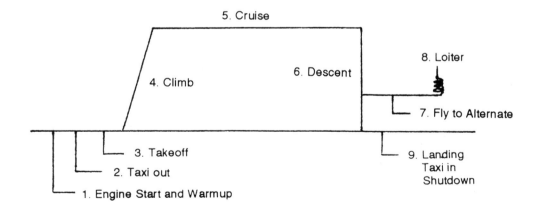

Figure 2-7 Mission Specification for Regional Jet Transport

Purpose: Competitive alternative to MD-90, A-320, and B 737-400

Payload: 150 passengers at 175 lbs each plus 30 lbs of baggage each

Crew: 2 pilots at 175 lbs each plus baggage at 30 lbs each
        3 cabin attendants at 130 lbs each plus baggage at 30 lbs each

Range: 1500 nautical miles

Reserve fuel: 150 nautical mile flight to alternate, followed by 45 minute loiter

Cruise Altitude: 35,000 feet

Cruise Speed: Mach number = 0.82

Climb: Direct to 35,000 feet at maximum takeoff weight

Takeoff Field Length: 5.000 feet at sea level, 90°F, at maximum takeoff weight

Landing Field Length: 4,500 feet at sea level, 90°F, at maximum landing weight

Powerplants: 2 Turbofans

Pressurization: 5,000 foot cabin altitude at 35,000 feet

Certification Basis: FAR Part 25

Mission Profile:

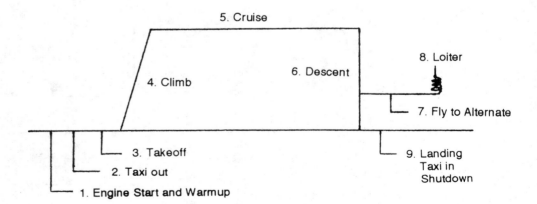

Figure 2-8 Mission Specification for Short Range Jet Transport

Purpose: Attack enemy ground installations with bombs and cannon fire

Payload: 20 500 lb bombs carried externally
                  2000 lbs of ammunition for a GAU-81A multi-barrel cannon
Crew: 1 Pilot at 200 lbs

Range: Radius mission; 400 nautical miles to target and return.
                               300 nautical mile subsonic cruise out,
                               100 nautical mile subsonic dash to target
                               100 nautical mile subsonic dash from target
                               300 nautical mile subsonic cruise back to base

Altitude: Subsonic cruise at 40,000 feet
                  High speed dash in and out at sea level

Cruise Speed: Mach number = 0.80 at 40,000 feet with external stores
                  Mach number = 0.85 at 40,000 feet clean
                  Mach number = 0.85 at sea level with external stores
                  Mach number = 0.90 at sea level clean

Climb: Direct to 40,000 feet in 8 minutes at maximum takeoff weight. One engine
                  inoperative rate of climb at least 500 ft/min at maximum takeoff weight at sea
                  level 95°F

Takeoff: MIL C 5011A takeoft of 2000 ft or less at sea level 95°F

Landing: MIL C 5011A landing of 2000 ft or less at sea level 95°F

Powerplants: 2 Turbofans with afterburner

Pressurization: 5000 ft cockpit altitude at 40,000 ft

Certification Basis: MIL SPECS

Mission Profile:

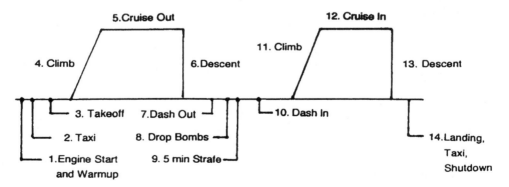

Figure 2-9 Mission Specification for Military Attack Aircraft

range must be increased to account for the practical aspects noted above. A useful rule of thumb to determine the design range required to practically operate between a pair of cities is to increase the great circle distance by 2% and add 10% of the distance for adverse headwinds. For personal/utility aircraft, and for turboprop commuters, a design range of 500 to 1000 nautical miles is usually sufficient to meet the needs of operation between major cities in certain regions of the country, or to provide the capability for longer trips with intermediate stops. Referring to Fig. 2-10, a design range of 500 n. mi. would provide the capability to operate between Los Angeles and San Francisco, or Boston and Washington, for example. A design range of 1000 n. mi. would provide the capability to operate between Los Angeles and Denver or Philadelphia and Miami.

For regional turboprops and the new regional jets, the design range is usually chosen from 800 to 1200 n. mi. to provide the flexibility to operate between the smaller cities and the major hub cities in a specific region. Business jets and jet transports both have a wide variation in design range, usually aimed at a specific segment of the market. The smaller, and less expensive, of these aircraft usually have design ranges of 1500 to 1800 n. mi. suitable for operation between cities such as New York and Dallas, or San Diego and St. Louis. Larger, more costly models in this category, have design ranges from 2500 to 3500 n.mi. which provides true transcontinental non-stop capability across the U.S., and referring to Fig. 2-11, transatlantic capability from East Coast U.S. cities to the coastal cities of Western Europe. Larger models currently have design ranges from 6500 to 7200 n. mi. which provides the capability to operate non-stop from cities in the interior of the U.S. to cities in Eastern Europe, or to operate non-stop from the West Coast of the U.S. to cities in the Pacific Rim. It is interesting to note that in Fig. 2-11, the longest great circle distances shown are only slightly over 10,000 n. mi. and there are only two major city pairs that are that far apart. That, coupled with the long times involved in making such a non-stop flight at current transonic cruise speeds, suggests that design ranges much beyond 8000 to 9000 n. mi. are not too likely to occur.

Cruise Speed and Altitude

- Unpressurized propeller driven aircraft are usually designed to cruise at speeds between 150 and 250 knots at an altitude of 10,000 ft, while pressurized designs cruise at speeds between 250 and 300 knots at altitudes ranging from 25,000 to 35,000 ft.

- For business jets and commercial jet transports, the cruise speeds are usually specified in terms of Mach number, and the cruise altitudes range from 30,000 to 45,000 ft, depending on the type of jet. Early short to medium range business jets cruised at Mach numbers between Mach 0.70 and Mach 0.75, while the newer, longer range models cruise at Mach numbers beyond Mach 0.80. For short and medium range commercial jet transports, there is not much of a payoff for flying faster than Mach 0.80, but the longer range jet transports are now designed to cruise at Mach 0.84 or slightly faster.

- For military jet fighters and attack aircraft, the mission usually involves a subsonic cruise portion, typically at Mach 0.85 to 0.90 at 35,000 ft, and a supersonic portion usually at Mach numbers in excess of 2.0.

Takeoff Distance

- For personal and utility propeller driven aircraft, which must operate out of small airfields, the takeoff distance over a 50 ft obstacle varies from 1200 ft to 2000 ft at sea level.

- For larger twin engine business and commuter propeller driven aircraft, which operate out of larger airports, the takeoff distance over a 50 ft obstacle at sea level may vary from 3000 ft for the larger twins to 5000 ft for the commuters.

- For business jets which may have to operate out of smaller city airports, takeoff distances are usually around 5000 ft. For smaller commercial jet transports, the takeoff distances vary from 5500 to 7500 ft over the obstacle at sea level. For larger jet transports, the takeoff distances vary from 8,000 ft to as much as 11,000 ft for the very largest. For commercial jet transports, takeoff distance is usually specified at sea level. Figs. 2-12 and 2-13 present data on the major commercial airports throughout the world, while Fig. 2-14 shows data on smaller U.S. airports.

- For military jet fighters and attack aircraft, takeoff distance is not usually at critical requirement when operating from established military bases since runway lengths available are always much greater than current takeoff distance requirements. For these types afterburner takeoff distances are on the order of 2000 to 2500 ft. For military transports and bombers, the takeoff distances when operating from established bases vary from 7500 to 10,000 ft. For operations close to the battle area, transport takeoff distances may be as low as 3000 ft.

Figure 2-10 Air Distance Between Major North American Cities

nautical miles

	Atlanta	Boston	Chicago	Dallas	Denver	Detroit	Houston	Kansas City	Los Angeles	Miami	Minneapolis	Montreal	New Orleans	New York	Oklahoma City	Philadelphia	Phoenix	St. Louis	Salt Lake City	San Diego	San Francisco	Seattle	Toronto	Vancouver	Washington
Atlanta		821	526	626	1049	516	598	591	1689	516	786	908	369	651	661	577	1378	420	1379	1641	1857	1894	679	2024	462
Boston	821		753	1350	1534	549	1391	1088	2266	1092	976	220	1187	162	1306	244	1996	908	1827	2246	2347	2167	333	2145	359
Chicago	526	753		693	782	204	803	350	1515	1039	290	644	727	642	602	589	1250	215	1084	1496	1602	1493	373	1606	512
Dallas	626	1350	693		568	852	188	399	1082	963	740	1309	379	1200	157	1123	763	474	877	1026	1281	1450	1029	1565	1009
Denver	1049	1534	782	568		985	750	471	737	1489	602	1436	926	1416	434	1362	519	678	331	729	830	884	1156	996	1271
Detroit	516	549	204	852	985		950	547	1718	995	458	458	812	425	791	393	1459	382	1292	1706	1805	1677	179	1776	334
Houston	598	1391	803	188	750	950		641	1379	812	881	1627	302	1420	401	1149	881	579	1045	1135	1420	1627	1143	1774	1032
Kansas City	591	1088	350	399	471	547	641		1183	1075	399	995	599	1096	271	902	905	199	798	1161	1300	1292	713	1474	805
Los Angeles	1689	2266	1515	1082	737	1718	1379	1183		2033	1333	2160	1450	2446	1030	2084	321	1382	512	95	293	828	1888	937	1986
Miami	516	1092	1039	963	1489	995	812	1075	2033		1333	1407	585	1092	1062	1005	1712	927	1968	2033	2244	2365	1071	2530	798
Minneapolis	786	976	290	740	602	458	881	399	1333	1333		957	1026	908	602	851	1102	389	860	1330	1379	1214	677	1325	789
Montreal	908	220	644	1309	1436	458	1627	995	2160	1407	957		1246	289	1235	342	2152	834	1745	2171	2160	2123	279	2083	426
New Orleans	369	1187	727	379	926	812	302	599	1450	585	1026	1246		1230	492	950	1129	524	1240	1388	1450	1812	992	1916	841
New York	651	162	642	1200	1416	425	1420	1096	2446	1092	908	289	1230		1101	82	1807	706	1677	2062	2188	2068	302	2122	199
Oklahoma City	661	1306	602	157	434	791	401	271	1030	1062	602	1235	492	1101		1200	723	401	751	950	1200	1319	956	1430	1005
Philadelphia	577	244	589	1123	1362	393	1149	902	2084	1005	851	342	950	82	1200		1860	851	1677	2245	2188	2101	302	2177	118
Phoenix	1378	1996	1250	763	519	1459	881	905	321	1712	1102	2152	1129	1807	723	1860		1102	440	264	565	963	1630	1266	1698
St. Louis	420	908	215	474	678	382	579	199	1382	927	389	834	524	706	401	851	1102		1003	1351	1506	1483	555	1674	603
Salt Lake City	1379	1827	1084	877	331	1292	1045	798	512	1968	860	1745	1240	1677	751	1677	440	1003		543	520	598	1465	711	1596
San Diego	1641	2246	1496	1026	729	1706	1135	1161	95	2033	1330	2171	1388	2062	950	2245	264	1351	543		388	914	1891	1034	1956
San Francisco	1857	2347	1602	1281	830	1805	1420	1300	293	2244	1379	2160	1450	2188	1200	2188	565	1506	520	388		589	1984	694	2100
Seattle	1894	2167	1493	1450	884	1677	1627	1292	828	2365	1214	2123	1812	2068	1319	2101	963	1483	598	914	589		1844	111	2002
Toronto	679	333	373	1029	1156	179	1143	713	1888	1071	677	279	992	302	956	302	1630	555	1465	1891	1984	1844		1804	317
Vancouver	2024	2145	1606	1565	996	1776	1774	1474	937	2530	1325	2083	1916	2122	1430	2177	1266	1674	711	1034	694	111	1804		2134
Washington	462	359	512	1009	1271	334	1032	805	1986	798	789	426	841	199	1005	118	1698	603	1596	1956	2100	2002	317	2134	

	Athens	Bangkok	Beijing	Berlin	Cairo	Cape Town	Caracas	Chicago	Hong Kong	Honolulu	London	Madrid	Mexico City	Montreal	Moscow	Nairobi	New Delhi	New York	Paris	Rio de Janeiro	Rome	San Francisco	Singapore	Sydney	Tokyo
Athens		4278	4127	971	581	4302	5046	4726	4613	7249	1290	1278	6093	4110	1202	2451	2706	4284	1131	5232	566	5894	4883	8065	5139
Bangkok	4278		1758	4643	3922	5468	9171	7436	932	5736	5145	5496	8499	7235	3812	3888	1521	7523	5100	8667	4766	6882	768	3973	2485
Beijing	4127	1758		3989	4067	6972	7789	5747	1036	4411	4416	4997	6744	5676	3147	4963	2038	5959	4458	9354	4404	5149	2389	4887	1131
Berlin	971	4643	3989		1542	5170	4548	3830	4723	6355	502	1007	5253	3245	866	3424	3121	4353	475	5386	636	4922	5351	8617	4822
Cairo	581	3922	4067	1542		3913	5499	5307	4388	7652	1871	1794	6662	4688	1535	1923	2386	4857	1711	5339	1131	6453	4462	7550	5152
Cape Town	4302	5468	6972	5170	3913		5520	7367	6402	10010	5196	4604	7390	6873	5447	2206	5006	6769	5016	3273	4540	8894	5211	5578	7944
Caracas	5046	9171	7789	4548	5499	5520		2168	8828	5226	4046	3775	1937	2119	5358	6229	7669	1842	4107	2432	4511	3389	9900	8420	7648
Chicago	4726	7436	5747	3830	5307	7367	2168		6766	3692	3436	3637	1463	645	4324	6954	6495	618	3596	4586	4185	1613	8137	8389	5479
Hong Kong	4613	932	1036	4723	4388	6402	8828	6766		4821	5193	5689	7627	6713	3855	4726	2029	6995	5199	9549	5010	5991	1394	3995	1554
Honolulu	7249	5736	4411	6355	7652	10010	5226	3692	4821		6284	6834	3289	4268	6116	9321	6432	4311	6467	7198	6977	2079	5840	4772	3349
London	1290	5145	4416	502	1871	5196	4046	3436	5193	6284		680	4822	2824	1348	3669	3625	3013	185	4990	773	4659	5855	9119	5168
Madrid	1278	5496	4997	1007	1794	4604	3775	3637	5689	6834	680		4896	2992	1856	3331	3929	3163	564	4377	735	5038	6143	9343	5817
Mexico City	6093	8499	6744	5253	6662	7390	1937	1463	7627	3289	4822	4896		2008	5789	7999	7914	1809	4966	4138	5531	1638	8966	7307	6106
Montreal	4110	7235	5676	3245	4688	6873	2119	645	6713	4268	2824	2992	2008		3816	6306	6085	287	2977	4409	3559	2206	7990	9017	5614
Moscow	1202	3812	3147	866	1535	5447	5358	4324	3855	6116	1348	1856	5789	3816		3408	2344	4061	1344	6215	1280	5106	4545	7780	4046
Nairobi	2451	3888	4963	3424	1923	2206	6229	6954	4726	9321	3669	3331	7999	6306	3408		2924	6391	3487	4821	2897	8330	4024	6212	6071
New Delhi	2706	1521	2038	3121	2386	5006	7669	6495	2029	6432	3625	3929	7914	6085	2344	2924		6351	3561	7591	3196	6674	2232	5501	3156
New York	4284	7523	5959	4353	4857	6769	1842	618	6995	4311	3013	3163	1809	287	4061	6391	6351		3156	4169	3725	2232	8278	8984	5863
Paris	1131	5100	4458	475	1711	5016	4107	3596	5199	6467	185	564	4966	2977	1344	3487	3561	3156		4929	595	4841	5967	9062	5253
Rio de Janeiro	5232	8667	9354	5386	5339	3273	2432	4586	9549	7198	4990	4377	4138	4409	6215	4821	7591	4169	4929		4949	5744	8484	7131	10011
Rome	566	4766	4404	636	1131	4540	4511	4185	5010	6977	773	735	5531	3559	1280	2897	3196	3725	595	4949		5431	5407	8626	5328
San Francisco	5894	6882	5149	4922	6453	8894	3389	1613	5991	2079	4659	5038	1638	2206	5106	8330	6674	2232	4841	5744	5431		7332	6812	4467
Singapore	4883	768	2389	5351	4462	5211	9900	8137	1394	5840	5855	6143	8966	7990	4545	4024	2232	8278	5967	8484	5407	7332		3268	2866
Sydney	8065	3973	4887	8617	7550	5578	8420	8389	3995	4772	9119	9343	7307	9017	7780	6212	5501	8984	9062	7131	8626	6812	3268		4399
Tokyo	5139	2485	1131	4822	5152	7944	7648	5479	1554	3349	5168	5817	6106	5614	4046	6071	3156	5863	5253	10011	5328	4467	2866	4399	

nautical miles

Figure 2-11 Air Distance Between Major World Cities

City	Airport	Code	Elev. (ft)	Runway (ft)
Athens	Athens	ATH	90	11,483x197
Bangkok	Bangkok	BKK	12	11,647x200
Beijing	Beijing Int'l	PEK	115	10,500x150
Berlin	Tegel	TXL	121	10,138x151
Cairo	Cairo Int'l	CAI	381	13,123x148
Capetown	D F Malan	CPT	151	10,512x200
Caracas	Simon Bolivar Int'l	CCS	235	11,483x150
Chicago	O'Hare Int'l	ORD	667	11,600x200
Hong Kong	Hong Kong Int'l	HKG	15	11,130x200
Honolulu	Honolulu Int'l	HNL	13	12,357x150
London	Heathrow Int'l	LHR	80	12,802x299
Madrid	Barajas	MAD	1998	13,452x148
Mexico City	Licen Benito Juarez	MEX	7341	12,796x148
Montreal	Dorval Int'l	YUL	117	11,000x200
Moscow	Sheremetyevo	SVO	623	12,140x197
Nairobi	Jomo Kenyetta Int'l	NBO	5327	13,507x150
New Delhi	Indira Gandhi Int'l	DEL	744	12,500x150
New York	Kennedy Int'l	JFK	12	13,574x148
Paris	Charles De Gaulle	CDG	387	11,861x148
Rio de Janeiro	Rio de Janeiro Int'l	GIG	30	13,124x148
Rome	Leonardo daVinci Int'l	FCO	14	12,796x148
San Francisco	San Francisco Int'l	SF0	11	11,870x200
Singapore	Singapore Changi	SIN	65	13,200x200
Sydney	Sydney Int'l	SYD	21	13,000x150
Tokyo	Narita Int'l	NRT	135	13,124x197

Figure 2-12   Airport Data for Major International Airports

Adapted with permission from reference 2.4

City	Airport	Code	Elev.(ft)	Runway (ft)
Atlanta	Hartsfield Int'l	ATL	1026	11,889x150
Boston	Logan Int'l	BOS	20	10,081x148
Chicago	O'Hare Int'l	ORD	667	11,600x200
Dallas	Dallas - Ft. Worth Int'l	DFW	596	11,387x200
Denver	Denver Int'l	DEN	5431	12,000x150
Detroit	Detroit Metropolitan	DTW	639	12,000x200
Houston	Houston Intercontintal	IAH	98	12,000x150
Kansas City	Kansas City Int'l	MCI	1026	10,801x150
Los Angeles	Los Angeles Int'l	LAX	126	12,091x150
Miami	Miami Int'l	MIA	10	13,002x200
Minneapolis	Minn-St Paul Int'l	MSP	841	10,000x200
Montreal	Dorval Int'l	YUL	117	11,000x200
New Orleans	New Orleans Int'l	MSY	6	10,080x150
New York	Kennedy Int'l	JFK	12	14,574x148
Oklahoma City	Will Rogers	OKC	1295	9,802x150
Philadelphia	Philadelphia Int'l	PHL	21	10,499x200
Phoenix	Sky Harbor Int'l	PHX	1133	11,001x150
St. Louis	Lambert Int'l	STL	605	11,019x200
Salt Lake City	Salt Lake City Int'l	SLC	4227	12,003x150
San Diego	Lindbergh	SAN	15	9,400x200
San Francisco	San Francisco Int'l	SF0	11	11,870x200
Seattle	Seattle - Tacoma Int'l	SEA	429	11,900x150
Toronto	Toronto Int'l	YYZ	569	11,000x150
Vancouver	Vancouver Int'l	YVR	9	11,000x200
Washington	Dulles Int'l	IAD	313	11,500x451

Figure 2-13 Airport Data on Major North American Airports

City	State	Airport	Code	Elev(ft)	Runway (ft)
Tuscaloosa	AL	Tuscaloosa Municipal	TCL	170	6499x150
Nome	AK	Nome	OME	36	6001x150
Sedona	AZ	Sedona	SEZ	4827	5131x75
Fayetteville	AR	Fayetteville Municipal	FYV	1251	6006x100
Santa Ana	CA	John Wayne Airport	SNA	54	5700x150
Greely	CO	Greely-Weld County	GXY	4658	6200x100
New Haven	CT	Tweed-New Haven	HVN	14	5600x150
Wilmington	DE	New Castle County	ILG	80	7165x150
Key West	FL	Key West Int'l	EYW	4	4800x100
Macon	GA	Middle Georgia Regional	MCN	354	6501x150
Lihue	HI	Lihue	LIH	153	6500x150
Lewiston	ID	Lewiston-Nez Perce	LWS	1438	6512x150
Decatur	IL	Decatur	DEC	682	8496x150
Elkhart	IN	Elkhart Municipal	EKM	778	6500x120
Dubuque	IA	Dubuque Regional	DBQ	1076	6498x150
Emporia	KS	Emporia Municipal	EMP	1206	5000x100
Paducah	KY	Barkley Regional	PAH	410	6499x150
Lake Charles	LA	Lake Charles Regional	LCH	15	6500x150
Portland	ME	Portland Int'l	PWM	74	6800x150
Salisbury	MD	Salisbury-Wicomico	SBY	52	5500x150
Hyannis	MA	Barnstable Municipal	HYA	55	5430x150
Muskegon	MI	Muskegon County	MKG	628	6501x150
Hibbing	MN	Chisholm-Hibbing	HIB	1353	6758x150
Tupelo	MS	Tupelo Municipal	TUP	346	5499x100
Joplin	MO	Joplin Regional	JLN	981	6503x150
Miles City	MO	Frank Wiley Field	MLS	2628	5680x100
Grand Island	NE	C'ntr'l Nebraska Regional	GRI	1846	7188x150
Ely	NV	Ely Airport	ELY	6255	5998x150
Nashua	NH	Boire Field	ASH	200	5550x100
Trenton	NJ	Mercer County	TTN	213	6006x150
Farmington	NM	Four Corners Regional	FMN	5503	6702x100
Poughkeepsie	NY	Dutchess County	POU	166	5001x100
Winston-Salem	NC	Smith Reynolds	INT	970	6655x150
Grand Forks	ND	Grand Forks Int'l	GFK	844	7349x150
Akron	OH	Akron Fulton Int'l	AKR	1068	6338x150
Stillwater	OK	Stillwater Municipal	SWO	986	6002x100
Medford	OR	Rouge Valley Int'l	MFR	1331	6700x150
Allentown	PA	Lehigh Valley Int'l	ABE	394	7600x150
Providence	RI	Theodoer F. Green	PVD	55	7166x200
Hilton Head	SC	Hilton Head Island	HXD	20	4300x75
Pierre	SD	Pierre Regional	PIR	1742	6891x150
Chatanooga	TN	Lovell Field	CHA	682	7401x150
College Station	TX	Easterwood Field	CLL	320	7000x150
Logan	UT	Logan-Cache	LGU	4454	5931x100
Rutland	VT	Rutland State	RUT	787	5000x150
Roanoke	VA	Roanoke Regional	ROA	1176	6802x150
Wenatchee	WA	Pangborn Memorial	EAT	1245	5499x150
Morgantown	WV	Morgantown Municipal	MGW	1248	5199x150
Racine	WI	John H. Batten	RAC	674	6556x100
Jackson Hole	WY	Jackson Hole	JAC	6445	6299x150

Figure 2-14 Airport Data for Smaller U.S. Airports

Domestic Reserve Fuel

Minimum reserve fuel requirement for operation in the Continental United States is for the aircraft to be able to fly from destination to the alternate , then continue to hold at normal cruise fuel consumption for 45 minutes.

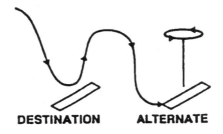

DESTINATION   **ALTERNATE**

International Reserve Fuel

For international operation, the aircraft must have sufficient fuel after reaching destination to fly for an additional 10 percent of the total flight time at normal cruising speed, and then fly to the alternate, and then hold for 30 minutes at 1500 feet above the alternate airport.

Part I - Fly additional 10% of flight time
Part II - Fly to alternate and hold

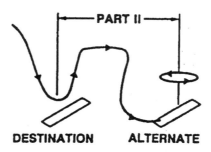

DESTINATION   **ALTERNATE**

Fig. 2-15 FAA Reserve Fuel Requirements for Transport Category Aircraft

Landing Distance

In general, the landing distance should be the same or less than the takeoff distance for the design mission, to make the design compatible for operation out of a given airport.

Reserve Fuel

Most mission specifications include some requirement for reserve fuel; that is, fuel which must be carried in reserve for contingencies at the end of the defined mission, but which may not be used to accomplish the design mission. For personal and utility propeller driven airplanes, reserve fuel is usually specified as 20% to 25% of the required mission fuel. For business jets, commuters, and commercial transports, reserve fuel requirements are specified in the appropriate Federal Aviation Regulations, as noted in Fig. 2-15. For military fighter and attack aircraft, mission specifications call for minimal reserves, usually 5% of mission fuel plus a 10 minute loiter at best endurance sea level. Military design missions usually specify performance without aerial refueling, even though in actuality, nearly all military aircraft except trainers and personnel transports are equipped for aerial refueling.

FEDERAL AVIATION REGULATIONS

Preliminary design efforts must also consider the many different specifications, standards, and regulations that must be met by the final aircraft design. Civil aircraft designed, built, and operated in the U.S. must comply with the provisions of the Federal Aviation Regulations, (FAR's) which cover all aspects of aircraft design , construction, and operation. Of particular interest to the preliminary designer are the Airworthiness Standards, Noise Standards, and the rules governing flight operations, the pertinent sections of which are listed below.

Airworthiness standards

- Airplanes
  - Part 23 - Normal, Utility, Acrobatic, Commuter
  - Part 25 - Transport
- Engines
  - Part 33

52

- Propellers
  - Part 35

Noise standards

- Part 36

General operating and flight rules

- Part 91

Operations

- Part 121 - Domestic, Flag and supplemental commercial operators of large aircraft.
- Part 123 - Air Travel Clubs using large aircraft
- Part 135 - Air Taxi & Commuter Operators
- Part 137 - Agricultural aircraft

The FAR's are continuously being modified to incorporate additional requirements, usually as a result of an accident or serious incident. As such, they represent a comprehensive body of design requirements based on actual operational experience. For example, the Airworthiness Standards at the time of certification of the DC-3 comprised 57 pages contained in the Department of Commerce Aeronautics Bulletin 7-A. The latest version of the FAR Airworthiness Standards has over 320 pages of requirements.

It should be noted that in the airworthiness standards for non-transport aircraft covered by Part 23, there are various types identified, with different design and performance requirements as noted in Fig. 2-16.

	Normal	Utility	Acrobatic	Commuter
Passenger seats (excluding pilot seats)	9 or less	9 or less	9 or less	19 or less
Maximum Takeoff weight	12,500 lb or less	12,500 lb or less	12,500 lb or less	19,000 lb or less
Maneuvers	Non-acrobatic	Limited acrobatics	No restrictions	Non-acrobatic
Other	_____	_____	_____	Propeller-driven multi-engine

Fig. 2-16 FAR Part 23 Aircraft Type Categories

MILITARY SPECIFICATIONS

For many years, U.S. military aircraft had to meet the provisions of the U.S. Military Services Specifications (Mil-Specs) which were comprised of thousands of detailed requirements applicable the aircraft, its systems, and all of the parts used in the aircraft. A very small listing of the Mil-Specs that have a major impact on design is presented in Fig. 2-17. In 1994, the Secretary of Defense announced that in the future, the Military Services would no longer require weapon systems components to meet the Mil-Specs if they met a comparable commercial specification. The impact of this new approach on new military aircraft designs has yet to be seen, but in all probability the Mil-Specs that govern the overall configuration will remain in use. The impact of this has yet to be fully realized. The few Mil-Specs that have a major influence on preliminary design, especially those associated with airworthiness and performance, are very similar to the FAR's.

Spec Number	Title
MIL-C-5011	Charts, Standard Aircraft Characteristics
MIL-F-8785	Flying Qualities of Piloted Aircraft
MIL-F-83300	Flying Qualities of Piloted V/STOL Aircraft
MIL-F-9490	Flight Control Systems - Design, Installation & Test
MIL-S-8369	Stall-Post Stall-Spin Demonstration Requirements
MIL-C-18244	Control and Stabilization Systems, Automatic
MIL-D-8708	Demonstration Requirements for Airplanes
MIL-A-8860	Airplane Strength and Rigidity, General Specification
MIL-P-26366	Propellers, Type Test of
MIL-I-8700	Installation and Test of Electronics Equipment
MIL-S-18471	Seat System, Ejectable, Aircraft
MIL-W-25140	Weight and Balance Control Data
MIL-M-7700	Manuals, Flight
MIL-STD-757	Reliability Evaluation from Demonstration Data
MIL-STD-850	Aircrew Station Vision Requirements
MIL-STD-88i	Work Breakdown Structure

Fig. 2-17 Partial Listing of Military Specifications and Standards for Aircraft Design

DESIGN EXERCISE

Select an aircraft type for your design project. Develop a mission specification, and sketch the mission profile. Your design mission should be realistic based on current state of the art, and competitive with current designs.

REFERENCES

2.1 Shevell, Richard S., Aerospace Systems Synthesis and Analysis, Course Notes, Stanford University. Palo Alto. CA. 1985

2.2 Swihart, John M., Design Choice and Marketing of Commercial Jet Airplanes, Boeing Commercial Airplane Company, 1978

2.3 Lindbergh, Charles A., The Spirit of St. Louis, Scribners, New York, 1953.

2.4 Anonymous, AOPA Airport Directory for 1999, Aircraft Owners and Pilots Association, Frederick, MD, 1999

2.5 U. S. Code of Federal Regulations, Title 14, Aeronautics and Space, Parts 1-199, Federal Aviation Administration, published by Office of the Federal Register, revised 1999

2.6 Nicolai, Leland M., Fundamentals of Aircraft Design, METS, San Jose, CA 1984

3

PRELIMINARY ESTIMATE OF MAXIMUM TAKEOFF WEIGHT

GENERAL PROCEDURE

The usual first step in the Preliminary Design Process, following the definition of the mission requirement, is the determination of the Maximum Takeoff Gross Weight (MTOGW) and the Operating Weight Empty (OWE) to perform the specific design mission. The procedure outlined is a general solution that involves:

- "Hard" numbers - Mission requirements (payload, range, speed, altitude)
- Assumptions - Cruise SFC (Powerplant appropriate to mission)
  - Cruise L/D (general type & configuration)
- Empiricism - W_{empty}/W_{to} data for actual similar aircraft

A key concept in estimating the takeoff weight and the empty weight for a specific design mission is "Weight Fractions."

- The maximum takeoff weight required for a specific design mission (Wto) may be written as

$$W_{to} = W_{empty} + W_{payload} + W_{fuel} \qquad (3\text{-}1)$$

or

$$\frac{W_{empty}}{W_{to}} + \frac{W_{payload}}{W_{to}} + \frac{W_{fuel}}{W_{to}} = 1 \qquad (3\text{-}2)$$

57

where $\dfrac{W_{empty}}{W_{to}}$ = Weight Empty Fraction

$\dfrac{W_{payload}}{W_{to}}$ = Payload Fraction

$\dfrac{W_{fuel}}{W_{to}}$ = Fuel Fraction

where W_{empty} = Operating Weight Empty (OWE), the basic aircraft hardware plus other items required to allow the aircraft to perform the design mission.

$W_{payload}$ = Passengers+Bags+Revenue Cargo (Commercial)

or

Bombs, Missiles, Cargo (Military)

W_{fuel} = Total fuel to do mission; that is fuel burned + reserve fuel

Figure 3-1 shows a simple bar chart illustrating the elements of the weight buildup to the maximum takeoff weight, W_{to}, required for a specific design mission. Also noted to the right of the bar chart are some important structural weight definitions that are related to the weight buildup, for a typical commercial jet transport. Other aircraft types have similar structural weight definitions. Note that the Operating Weight Empty involves both the Manufacturers Weight Empty (MWE), plus the operators items, which include the flight crew, cabin crew, food, galley service items, drinkable water, cargo containers and pallets, plus life vests, life rafts, emergency transmitters and the unusable fuel trapped in the fuel system and unavailable for the use by the engines.

When all the payload is loaded, that is, all available passenger seats filled at the "standard" passenger + baggage weight, usually 205 lb for domestic flights and 215 lb for international flights, and all the available revenue cargo volume is filled at some selected cargo density, usually taken as 10 lb/cu.ft, the aircraft has reached its space limit payload (SLPL), which coincides with another key weight definition, the maximum zero fuel weight (MZFW), the maximum design weight for the aircraft with no fuel on

$$W_{to} = W_{empty} + W_{payload} + W_{fuel}$$

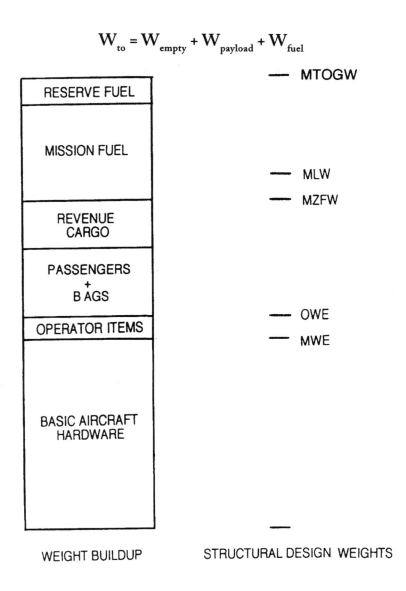

WEIGHT BUILDUP   STRUCTURAL DESIGN WEIGHTS

Figure 3-1 Jet Transport Weight Buildup and Important Structural Design Weights

board. Loading on the fuel required to perform the mission, the mission fuel, plus the required reserves, brings the aircraft to the W_{to}, the maximum takeoff gross weight required to perform the specified design mission. The design maximum landing weight (MLW) for most smaller aircraft, such as private propeller driven aircraft and short range commuters is usually the same as the MTOGW. However, for larger, long range aircraft, where the mission fuel is a large percentage of the MTOGW, a somewhat lower MLW is selected to minimize the structural weight impact of designing all the structure to withstand the loads associated with landing at MTOGW. For this design choice, a fuel dump system, which allows fuel to be jettisoned overboard in an emergency following a high gross weight takeoff, allows the aircraft to reduce its weight to the MLW without having to burn off large amounts of mission fuel. Trend data showing MLW as a fraction of MTOGW related to design range for modern jet transports is shown in Figure 3-2.

The procedure for estimating W_{to} and W_{empty} as a starting point for the preliminary design process involves working with the weight fractions to arrive at consistent W_{empty}, $W_{payload}$, W_{fuel} and W_{to} that meet the design mission requirements.

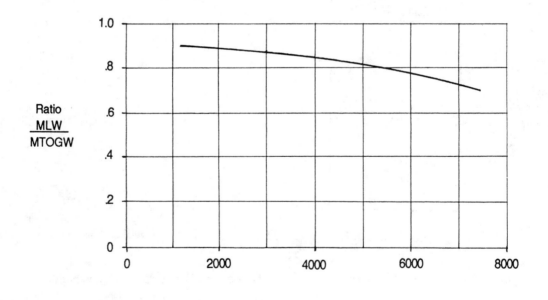

Design Range ~ N. Mi.

Figure 3-2 Trend Data on Ratio of Maximum Landing Weight to Maximum Takeoff Weight

DETAILED PROCEDURE

Fuel Fraction

The fuel fraction is usually estimated first. For most mission specifications, the fuel fraction is dominated by the design mission cruise requirement, with partial fuel fractions for other phases of the mission obtained from empirical data such as that of Figure 3-3.

Fortunately, the cruise fuel required to perform a specific mission may be estimated quite well by using an extremely simple relationship called the Breguet range equation. It should be noted that the form of the Breguet range equation is slightly different for props and jets, which has some implications on the cruise conditions for maximum range.

For propeller driven aircraft, maximum range is obtained by operating the aircraft at its maximum lift-to-drag ratio, $(L/D)_{max}$, since the propeller efficiency, η, and the cruise specific fuel consumption, C, are essentially constant during cruise.

	Engine Start and Warmup	Taxi out	Takeoff	Accelerate and Climb	Landing and Taxi in
Personal/Utility	.0005	.0003	.0010	.0060	.0010
Commuters	.0008	.0004	.0015	.0080	.0020
Regional Turboprops	.0010	.0005	.0020	.0100	.0030
Business Jets	.0010	.0005	.0020	.0130	.0030
Jet Transports	.0010	.0010	.0020	.0160	.0030
Military Fighter/Attack	.0010	.0010	.0020	.0180	.0300

Figure 3-3   Trend Data on Partial Fuel Fractions for Various Mission Phases

For Propeller Driven Aircraft

$$\text{Range} \quad (\text{N. Mi.}) = 325 \left(\frac{\eta}{C}\right)\left(\frac{L}{D}\right) \ln \frac{W_{initial}}{W_{final}} \tag{3-3}$$

where

325	is a constant to convert BHP from ft-lbs/min to ft-n.mi/hr
η	is the cruise propeller efficiency
C	is the engine specific fuel consumption in lb/BHP-hr
L/D	is the aircraft lift-to-drag ratio at cruise conditions
$W_{initial}$	is the total aircraft weight at the start of cruise
W_{final}	is the total aircraft weight at the end of cruise

For Jet Powered Aircraft

$$\text{Range} \quad \text{(N.Mi)} \quad = \quad \left(\frac{V}{C}\right)\left(\frac{L}{D}\right) \, \ln \, \frac{W_{initial}}{W_{final}} \tag{3-4}$$

where

V	is the true cruise speed in knots
C	is the engine specific fuel consumption in lb/hr/lb of thrust
L/D	is the aircraft lift-to-drag ratio at cruise conditions
$W_{initial}$	is the total aircraft weight at the start of cruise
W_{final}	is the total aircraft weight at the end of cruise

For jet powered aircraft, maximum range is obtained by operating the aircraft at the condition where (V L/D) is a maximum. Since the true cruise speed can be expressed in terms of Mach number as $V = aM$, where a is the speed of sound at cruise altitude, for jet powered aircraft, maximum range is achieved by operating at (M L/D)max. These range parameters will be discussed further in Chapter 12 under detailed drag buildup for cruise.

In the Brequet range equation, the term $W_{initial}/W_{final}$ is directly related to the fuel fraction for cruise. By solving for this quantity, the cruise fuel fraction may be determined. Note that the values in the equation must be in compatible units.

For Propeller Driven Aircraft

$$\ln \, \frac{W_{initial}}{W_{final}} \, = \, \ln \, \frac{W_{start\,of\,cruise}}{W_{end\,of\,cruise}} \, = \, \frac{\text{Range}}{325\left(\frac{\eta}{C}\right)\left(\frac{L}{D}\right)} \tag{3.5}$$

Range in N.Mi
V in Knots
C in Lb/BHP-Hr

For Jet Powered Aircraft

$$\ln \, \frac{W_{initial}}{W_{final}} \, = \, \ln \, \frac{W_{start\,of\,cruise}}{W_{end\,of\,cruise}} \, = \, \frac{\text{Range}}{\left(\frac{a}{C}\right)\left(\frac{L}{D}\right)} \tag{3-6}$$

Range in N.Mi
a in Knots
C in Lb/Hr/Lb Thrust

To estimate the fuel fraction for the cruise phase of the mission, one needs to estimate only a few parameters for your type of aircraft.

For propeller driven aircraft

η ~ propeller efficiency in cruise
C ~ engine SFC in cruise
(L/D) ~ lift to drag ratio in cruise at $(L/D)_{max}$

For jet powered aircraft

C ~ engine SFC in cruise
(L/D) ~ lift to drag ratio in cruise at $(M\ L/D)_{max}$

Typical propulsion parameters for propeller driven aircraft are presented in Fig. 3-4.

Aircraft Type	Propeller Efficiency η	Engine SFC C
Personal, Utility	.80	.60
Commuters	.82	.55
Regional Turboprops	.85	.50

Figure 3-4 Propeller Efficiency and Engine SFC for Propeller Driven Aircraft

For jet powered aircraft, the installed SFC at cruise for jet engines is primarily related to bypass ratio, defined in Fig. 3-5. Early jet engines had bypass ratios ranging from 0 to 2.0. The engines for current jet transports, business jets and military cargo transports have bypass ratios ranging from 4.5 to 6.5, while experimental ducted propellers and unducted fans have bypass ratios ranging from 15 to 35. Current military fighter engines equipped with afterburners have bypass ratios around 1.0. Trend data on cruise SFCs for jet powered aircraft are shown in Fig. 3-6.

Representative cruise (L/D)'s for propeller driven aircraft are shown in Fig. 3-7, while data on cruise (L/D)'s for jet powered aircraft are presented in Fig. 3-8 and 3-9. Three views of these aircraft are shown in Figs. 3-10 through 3-18. Use this information to estimate the cruise L/D.

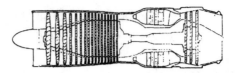

Single Spool Axial flow Turbojet ~ BPR = 0

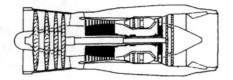

Twin Spool By-Pass Turbojet ~ BPR 1.0 to 2.0

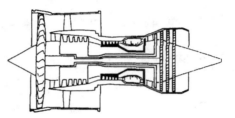

Triple Spool High By-Pass Turbofan ~ BPR 4.5 to 8.0

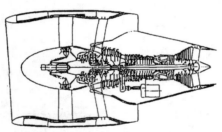

High By-Pass Ducted Prop ~ BPR 11.0 to 15.0

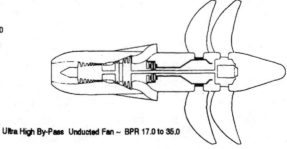

Ultra High By-Pass Unducted Fan ~ BPR 17.0 to 35.0

In by-pass jet engines, not all of the air entering the inlet goes through the engine core where the main compression, combustion and turbine components are found. The By-Pass Ratio (BPR) is the ratio of the by-passed or secondary airflow to the the primary or core airflow through the engine.

Fig. 3-5 Types of Jet Engines

Courtesy of Rolls Royce plc and Pratt & Whitney

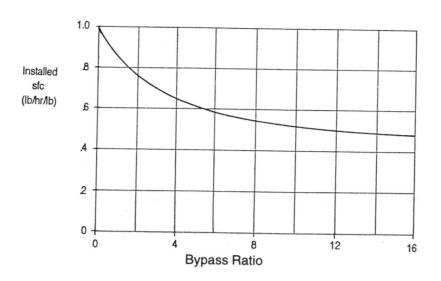

Fig. 3-6 Trend Data on Cruise Specific Fuel Consumption for Jet Aircraft

Historical Record Setters
Single engine, fixed landing gear

Ryan NYP	9.8
Lockheed Vega 5C	11.4

Personal/Utility Aircraft
Single engine, fixed landing gear

Piper J-3 Cub	9.6
Piper PA-28 Cherokee	10.1

Single engine, retractable landing gear

Beech Model 35 Bonanza	13.8
Cessna 177 RG Cardinal	14.2

Twin engine, retractable landing gear

Cessna 310	12.5
Cessna 402	12.6

Commercial Transports

Douglas DC-3	15.3
Saab 340	13.8
Fokker F27	17.6
Douglas DC-7C	18.5

Military Transports

Lockheed C-130	13.0

Fig. 3-7 Cruise $(L/D)_{max}$ Values for Representative Propeller Driven Aircraft

Business Jets
    Learjet 35   13.0
    Gulfstream GIII   15.6

Single Aisle Twinjet Transports
    McDonnell Douglas MD-80   15.6
    Boeing 737-300   15.1
    Airbus A320   17.6
    Boeing 757-200   17.1

Single Aisle Trijet Transport
    Boeing 727-200   16.2

Single Aisle Four Engine Jet Transport
    Boeing 707-320   18.6

Twin Aisle Twinjet Transports
    Airbus A300 B4   15.0
    Boeing 767-200   18.1

Twin Aisle Trijet Transports
    Lockheed L1011-100   16.0
    McDonnell Douglas DC-10-30 17.2
    McDonnell Douglas MD-11   18.2

Twin Aisle Four Engine Jet Transport
    Boeing 747-400   17.4

Fig. 3-8 Cruise $(L/D)_{max}$ Values for Representative Civil Jet Powered Aircraft

Military Transports
    Lockheed C-141B   17.5
    Lockheed C-5A   18.7

Military Bombers
    Boeing B-47   18.8
    Boeing B-52   20.5

Military Fighters (Subsonic Cruise)
    Lockheed F-104   9.2
    McDonnell F-4   10.2
    Northrop F-5   10.8
    General Dynamics F-111   13.9

Fig. 3-9 Cruise $(L/D)_{max}$ Values for Representative Military Jet Aircraft

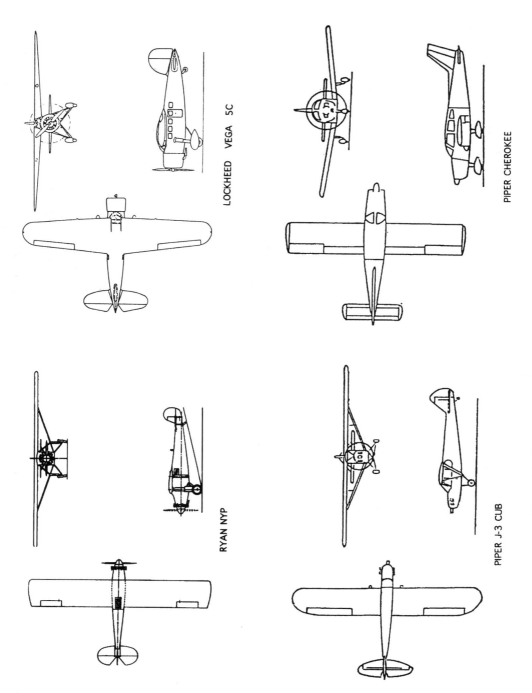

LOCKHEED VEGA 5C

PIPER CHEROKEE

RYAN NYP

PIPER J-3 CUB

Fig. 3-10 Three views of Representative Prop Driven Aircraft

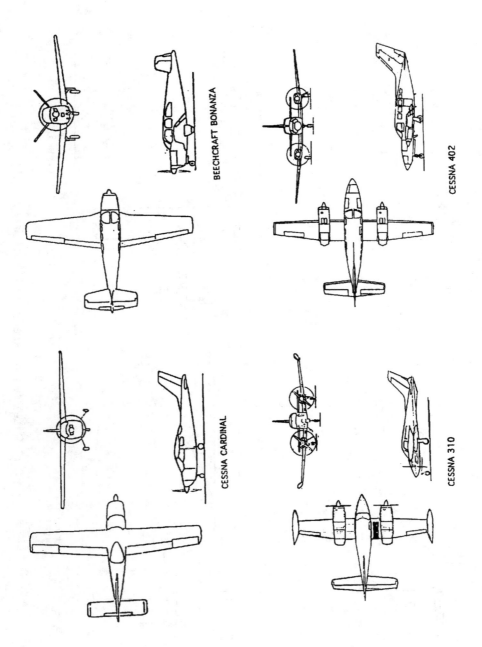

BEECHCRAFT BONANZA

CESSNA 402

CESSNA CARDINAL

CESSNA 310

Fig. 3-11 Three views of Representative Prop Driven Aircraft

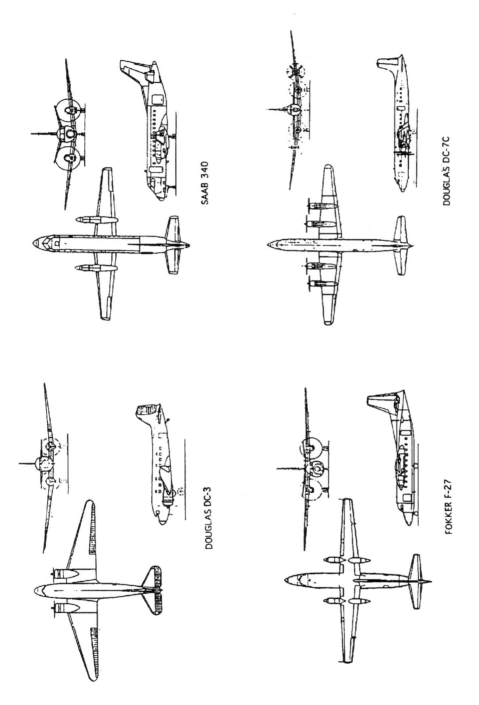

SAAB 340

DOUGLAS DC-7C

DOUGLAS DC-3

FOKKER F-27

Fig. 3-12 TThree views of Representative Prop Driven Aircraft

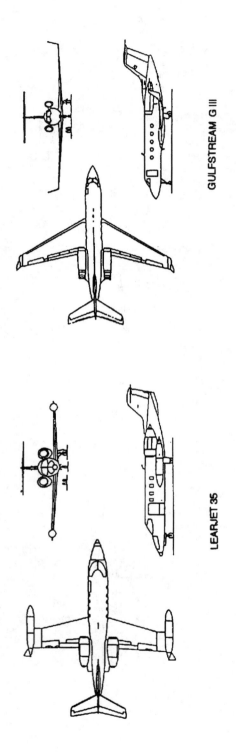

GULFSTREAM G III

LEARJET 35

Fig. 3-13 Three views of Representative Civil Jet Aircraft

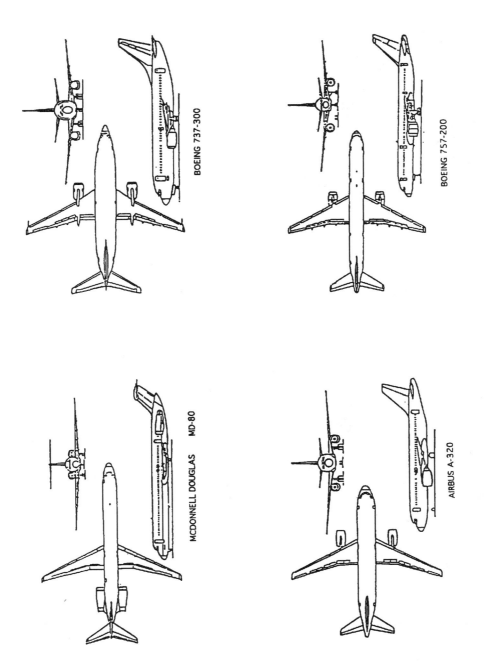

Fig. 3-14 Three views of Representative Civil Jet Aircraft

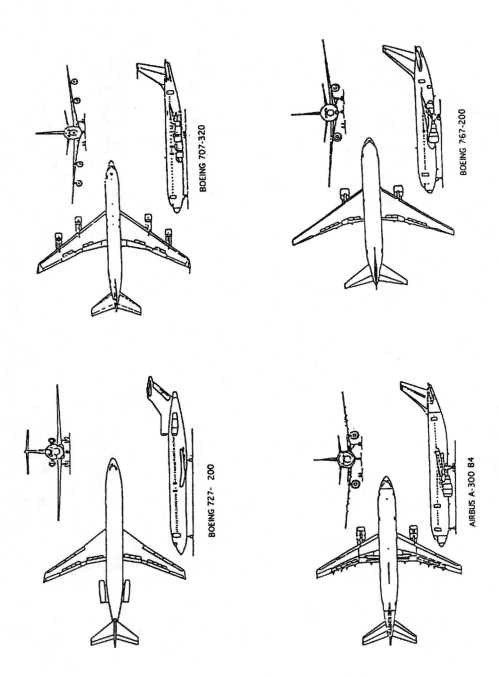

Fig. 3-15 Three views Representative of Civil Jet Aircraft

BOEING 707-320

BOEING 767-200

BOEING 727- 200

AIRBUS A-300 B4

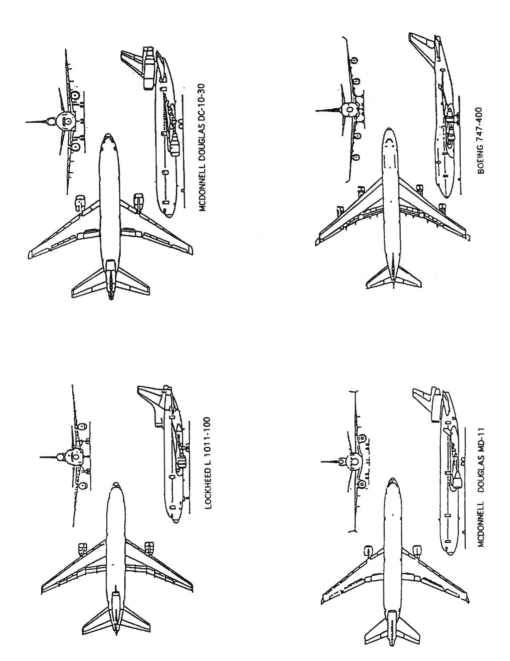

MCDONNELL DOUGLAS DC-10-30

BOEING 747-400

LOCKHEED L 1011-100

MCDONNELL DOUGLAS MD-11

Fig. 3-16 Three views of Representative Civil Jet Aircraft

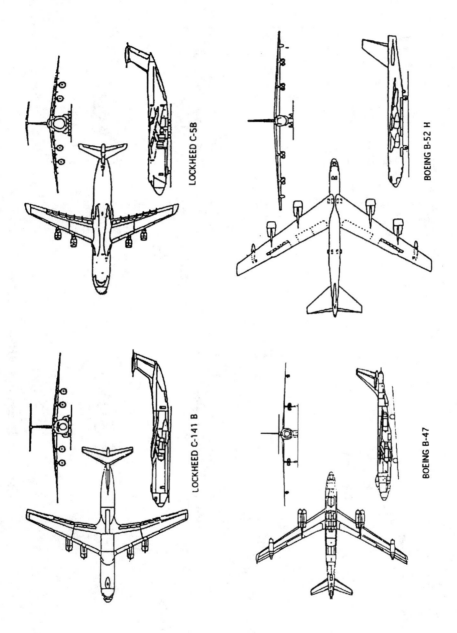

LOCKHEED C-5B

BOEING B-52 H

LOCKHEED C-141 B

BOEING B-47

Fig. 3-17 Three views of Representative Military Jet Aircraft

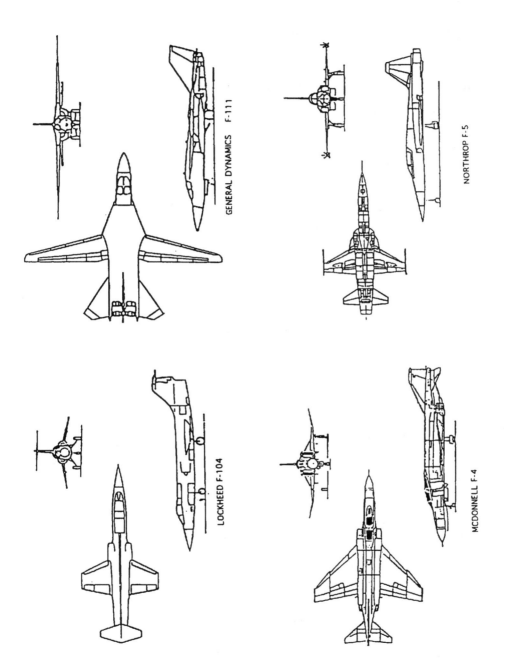

GENERAL DYNAMICS F-111

NORTHROP F-5

LOCKHEED F-104

MCDONNELL F-4

Fig. 3-18 Three views of Representative Military Jet Aircraft

Example Problem

An example to illustrate the procedure for estimating the cruise fuel fraction using the short range jet transport mission specification and mission profile of Fig. 2-8 is outlined below.

The cruise fuel is in the Breguet range equation notation

$$W_{fuel\ cruise} = W_{to} - W_{end\ of\ cruise} = W_{to} - W_{final} \qquad (3\text{-}7)$$

$$\frac{W_{fuel\ cruise}}{W_{to}} + 1 - \left(\frac{W_{final}}{W_{to}}\right) = 1 - \frac{1}{\left(\dfrac{W_{to}}{W_{final}}\right)} \qquad (3\text{-}8)$$

$$\ln \frac{W_{initial}}{W_{final}} = \frac{Range}{\left(\dfrac{a}{C}\right)\left(\dfrac{ML}{D}\right)} \qquad (3\text{-}9)$$

From the mission specification

Range = 1500 n.mi.
Cruise Mach = 0.82
Cruise altitude = 35,000 ft.   a = 576.4 kts from Fig. 1-9

From Fig. 3-5
C is estimated to be 0.60 for BPR 6.0

From Fig. 3-7 and 3-13
L/D is estimated to be 17.6

$$\ln \frac{W_{initial}}{W_{final}} = \frac{1500}{\dfrac{(576.4)\ (0.82)\ (17.6)}{(0.60)}} \qquad (3\text{-}10)$$

$$\ln W_{initial} / W_{final} = .1082 \qquad W_{initial} / W_{final} = 1.142$$

$$\frac{W_{fuel\ cruise}}{W_{to}} = 1 - \frac{1}{1.142} = 0.124 \qquad (3\text{-}11)$$

The total fuel fraction is the sum of all the partial fuel fractions for the mission. Note that the partial fuel fraction for each segment of the mission is the ratio of the fuel weight used for that phase of the mission to the takeoff weight. As noted previously, a table of empirical partial fuel fractions is shown on Fig. 3-3.

Phase 1	Engine start & warm-up	$W_{F1}/W_{to} = .001$
Phase 2	Taxi	$W_{F2}/W_{to} = .001$
Phase 3	Takeoff	$W_{F3}/W_{to} = .002$
Phase 4	Accelerate and climb to cruise altitude	$W_{F4}/W_{to} = .016$
Phase 5	Cruise	$W_{F5}/W_{to} = .124$
	Assume cruise range is the total mission range.	
	No distance credit for climb to cruise altitude.	
Phase 6	Descent	$W_{F6}/W_{to} = .000$
	Assume no range credit for descent, no fuel burned	
	in descent.	
Phase 7	Landing and Taxi in	$W_{F7}/W_{to} = .003$
Reserve	Although it is not used in performing the design	
Fuel	mission, the reserve fuel must be included in the	
	fuel fraction. Based on an average value for FAR 121	
	reserve fuel requirements use	$W_{F\,Res}/W_{to} = .049$

The total fuel fraction for this example is

$$\frac{W_{Fuel}}{W_{to}} = \frac{W_{F1}}{W_{to}} + \frac{W_{F2}}{W_{to}} + \frac{W_{F3}}{W_{to}} + \frac{W_{F4}}{W_{to}} + \frac{W_{F5}}{W_{to}} + \frac{W_{F6}}{W_{to}} + \frac{W_{F7}}{W_{to}} + \frac{W_{Fres}}{W_{to}} \qquad (3\text{-}12)$$

$$\frac{W_{Fuel}}{W_{to}} = .001 + .001 + .002 + .016 + .124 + .003 + .049 = .196 \qquad (3\text{-}13)$$

Weight Empty Fraction

For the weight empty fraction, the usual approach is to rely on an empirical data correlation of W_{empty} vs. W_{to} for state-of-the-art aircraft with similar mission requirements. Figs. 3-19 through 3-26 present data on W_{to} and W_{empty} for a number of aircraft in similar mission categories.

Payload Fraction

The payload fraction for any value of W_{to} is simply the design payload divided by the W_{to}.

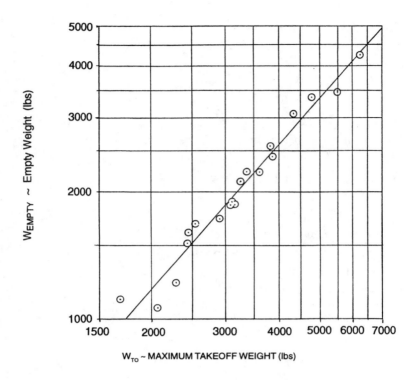

W$_{TO}$ ~ MAXIMUM TAKEOFF WEIGHT (lbs)

Aircraft	W$_{TO}$	W$_{EMPTY}$
Katana Xtrema	1698	1201
Piper PA -18A -150 Super Cub	2070	1060
Piper PA - 25 -150 Pawnee	2300	1220
Piper PA - 28 -161 Warrior III	2440	1514
Cessna 172 Skyhawk	2450	1600
Piper PA - 28 -181 Archer III	2550	1683
Mooney MSE	2900	1726
Aerospatiale Trinidad TC	3086	1860
Cessna 182 Skylane	3100	1882
Beech 35 Bonanza	3125	1855
Commander 114B	3250	2102
Mooney Ovation	3368	2225
Piper PA -32 -235 Cherokee Six	3400	2026
Cessna 206 Stationair	3616	2227
Piper PA -44 -180 Seminole	3800	2576
Beech B36TC	3850	2410
Piper PA - 46 -350P	4300	3080
Piper PA -34 -220 Seneca V	4750	3386
Beech 58 Baron	5500	3481
Aero Commander 500A	6250	4255

Fig. 3-19   Weight Trend Data ~ Personal/Utility Aircraft

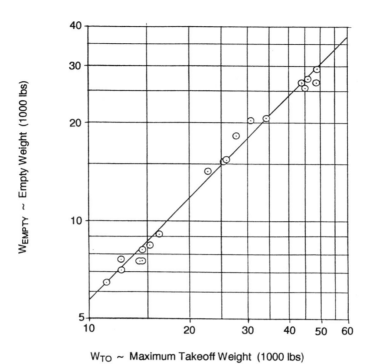

W_{TO} ~ Maximum Takeoff Weight (1000 lbs)

Aircraft	W_{TO}	W_{EMPTY}
Beech C99	11,300	6494
Embraer EMB-110 Banderante	12,500	7837
DeHavilland DHC-6 Twin Otter	12,500	7065
Antonov An-28	14,330	7716
Fairchild Metro III	14,500	8387
British Aerospace BAe Jetstream 31	14,500	7606
Beech 1900 Airliner	15,245	8500
CASA C 212-200	16,424	9072
Shorts SD 330	22,900	14,175
Embraer EMB-120 Brasilia	25,353	15,032
Saab 340	26,000	15,510
Dornier Do 328-100	27,558	18,023
DeHavilland DHC-8	30,500	20,176
Aerospatiale/Alenia ATR-42	34,720	20,580
DeHavilland DHC-7	44,000	27,000
Aerospatiale/Alenia ATR-72	44,070	26,950
Fokker F27 Mk 200	45,000	25,525
Fokker 50	45,900	27,600
British Aerospace BAe 748	48,500	26,560
Saab 2000	48,500	29,770

Fig 3-20 Weight Trend Data ~ Turboprop Commuter Aircraft

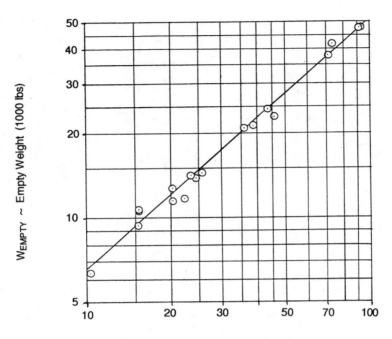

Aircraft	W_{TO}	W_{EMPTY}
Cessna Citation Jet	10,400	6315
Cessna Citation Ultra	16,300	9395
Beechjet 400A	16,300	10,850
Learjet 31A	16,500	10,641
Learjet 45	20,200	12,850
Saberliner 60	20,372	11,500
Cessna Citation VII	22,450	11,770
Learjet 60	23,500	14,038
Saberliner 80	23,500	13,600
Israel Aircraft Industries Astra SPX	24,650	13,700
British Aerospace BAe 700	25,500	14,400
British Aerospace BAe 800	25,500	14,400
Dassault Falcon 2000	36,000	20,735
Dassault Falcon 50	38,800	21,100
Canadair Challenger CL-601	43,250	24,600
Dassault Falcon 900B	45,500	22,611
Gulfstream Aerospace G III	70,200	38,000
Gulfstream Aerospace G IV	73,600	42,500
Gulfstream Aerospace G V	90,900	48,000
Canadair Global Express	93,750	48,250

Fig. 3-21 Weight Trend Data ~ Business Jet Aircraft

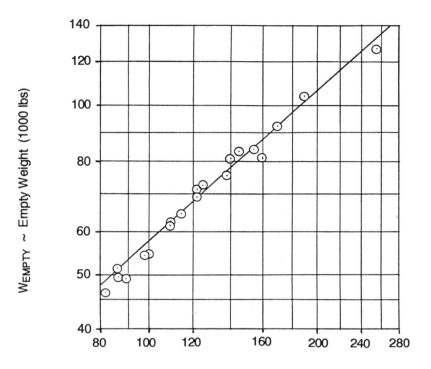

W_{TO} ~ Maximum Takeoff Weight (1000 lbs)

Aircraft	W_{TO}	W_{EMPTY}
British Aerospace BAe 146-100	82,250	47,000
Douglas DC-9-10	85,700	51,900
British Aircraft Corporation BAC-111	87,000	49,600
British Aerospace BAe 146-200	89,500	49,300
Fokker F 100	98,000	53,975
British Aerospace BAe 146-300	100,000	54,500
Douglas DC-9-30	108,000	61,400
Boeing 737-200	109,000	63,000
Douglas DC-9-40	114,000	64,600
Douglas DC-9-50	121,000	69,200
Boeing 717-200	121,000	70,790
Boeing 737-300	124,500	72,360
Boeing 737-400	138,500	76,180
McDonnell Douglas MD-81	140,000	80,700
Boeing 737-600	144,500	80,360
Boeing 737-700	154,500	83,790
McDonnell Douglas MD-83	160,000	80,968
Airbus A 320-200	169,800	92,400
Airbus A 321-100	187.400	105,600
Boeing 757-200	255,000	128,730

Fig. 3-22 Weight Trend Data ~ Single Aisle Jet Transports

81

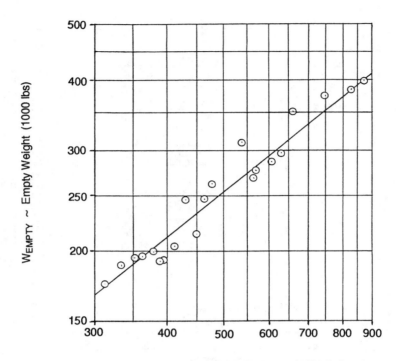

W_{TO} ~ Maximum Takeoff Weight (1000 lbs)

Aircraft	W_{TO}	W_{EMPTY}
Airbus A 310-200	313,100	174,700
Boeing 767-200	335,000	186,900
Boeing 767-300	351,000	193,700
Airbus A 300- B4	363,800	195,100
Airbus A 300-600R	378,500	199,000
Boeing 767-200ER	395,000	190,000
Boeing 767-300ER	412,000	203,400
Douglas DC-10-10	430,000	245,467
Boeing 767-400ER	450,000	227,300
Lockheed L 1011-100	466,000	246,466
Airbus A 330-300	478,400	262,460
Boeing 777-200	545,000	310,100
Douglas DC-10-30	565,000	267,996
Airbus A 340-200	568,800	275,800
Airbus A 340-300	606,300	285,300
McDonnell Douglas MD-11	630,500	295,600
Boeing 777-300	660,000	352,200
Boeing 747-100	750,000	373,300
Boeing 747-300	833,000	383,000
Boeing 747-400	875,000	399,280

Fig. 3-23 Weight Trend Data ~ Twin Aisle Jet Transport

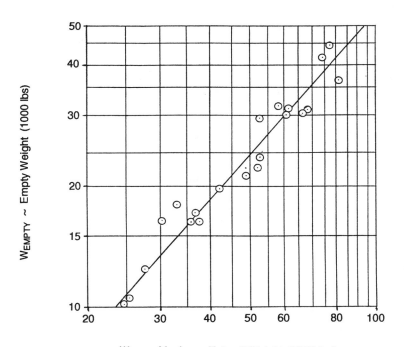

W_{TO} ~ Maximum Takeoff Weight (1000 lbs)

Aircraft	W_{TO}	W_{EMPTY}
Douglas A-4F	24,500	10,100
Northrop F-5F	25,220	10,567
Saab JAS 39 Gripen	27,557	12,900
Dassault Mirage 3E	30,200	16,300
Dassault Mirage F-1C	32,900	17,900
Israel Aircraft Industries Kfir C2	35,715	16,060
Dassault Mirage 2000	36,375	17,000
General Dynamics F-16 A/B	37,500	16,291
Vought A-7D	42,000	19,792
Fairchild A-10A	48,560	22,141
McDonnel Douglas F/A-18 A/B	51,900	23,050
Lockheed F-117A	52,500	29,500
McDonnell F-4E	58,000	31,360
Grumman A-6E	60,400	30,000
Panavia Tornado	61,600	31,900
McDonnell Douglas F/A-18E/F	66,000	30,600
McDonnell Douglas F-15 C/D	68,000	31,000
Grumman F-14D	74,349	41,780
Mikoyan MiG-25P	77,000	44,500
McDonnell Douglas F-15E	81,000	37,000

Fig. 3-24 Weight Trend Data ~ Military Fighter/Attack Aircraft

83

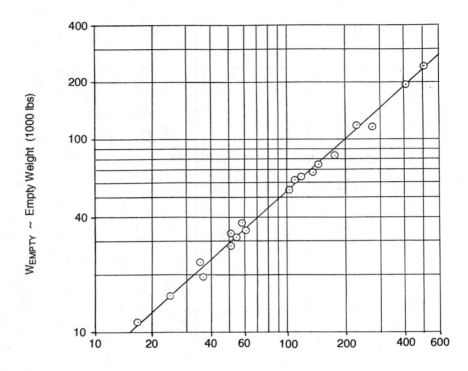

W_{TO} ~ Maximum Takeoff Weight (1000 lbs)

Aircraft	W_{TO}	W_{EMPTY}
CASA C-212-400	17,860	10,030
Short Brothers C-23B	25,600	16,194
Grumman VC-4 A Gulfstream	36,000	23,693
CASA/Nusantara CN-235M	36.376	19,400
Antonov An-26	50,706	33,113
British Aerospace HS 780	51,000	28,650
Grumman C-2A	54,830	31,154
Antonov An-32	59,525	38,200
Aeritalia G-222	61,730	33,950
Dassault/Breguet Atlantic II	102,000	55,100
Aerospatiale/Daimler C160NG	112,435	61,730
Antonov An-12	121,475	63,540
Lockheed P-3C	139,760	67,486
Lockheed C-130 H	155,000	73,877
Bristol Type 175 Britannia	185,000	82,537
Short Brothers SC5 Belfast	230,000	127,000
Douglas C-133 B	286,000	120,363
Tupolev Tu-95 Bear	414,470	198,432
Antonov An-22	551,160	251,325

Fig. 3-25 Weight Trend Data ~ Military Turboprop Transport

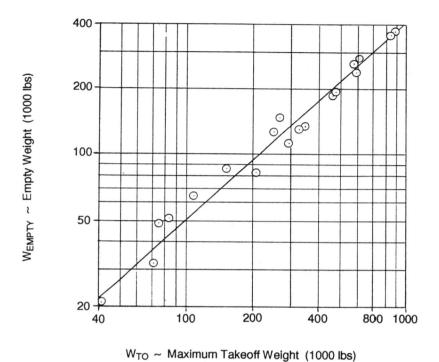

W_{TO} ~ Maximum Takeoff Weight (1000 lbs)

Aircraft	W_{TO}	W_{EMPTY}
Lockheed C-140 A	40,921	21,455
Gulfstream C-20 E	70,200	32,200
Gulfstream C-20 G	75,000	49,500
Kawasaki C-1	85,320	51,190
Douglas VC-9C	110,000	65,269
Boeing C-22 B	161,000	87,000
Boeing B-47 E	206,700	80,756
Boeing C-23	255,000	124,370
Tupelov Tu-223 M Backfire	273,370	163,140
Boeing KC-135 E	297,000	114,000
Boeing VC-137 C	328,000	138,000
Lockheed C-141 B	343,000	140,882
Rockwell B-1 B	477,000	186,234
Boeing B-52 H	488,000	189,600
McDonnell Douglas C-17	585,000	274,400
McDonnell Douglas KC-10 A	590,000	241,027
Tupelov Tu-160 Blackjack	606,260	279,980
Lockheed C-5 B	837,000	374,000
Antonov An-124	892,872	384,653

Fig. 3-26 Weight Trend Data ~ Military Jet Transports and Bombers

Graphical Solution for W_{to} and W_{empty}

For a specific design mission, the following procedure will allow a preliminary estimate of the W_{to} and W_{empty}.

- Select three "trial" takeoff weights that cover the range of the anticipated takeoff weight, based on similar aircraft.

- For each "trial" takeoff weight
    - Calculate W_{fuel} from W_{fuel} = (W_{fuel} / W_{to}) x W_{to}
    - Add $W_{payload}$ from the mission requirements
    - Subtract the sum of these from the "trial" W_{to}

  The remainder is the "available" W_{empty} for the "trial" W_{to}

$$W_{empty\ avail} = W_{to\ trial} - W_{fuel} - W_{payload}$$

- Plot W_{empty} avail vs. W_{to} for the three "trial" W_{to}'s on the empirical data correlation of W_{empty} vs. W_{to} for similar state-of-the-art aircraft.

The intersection of these two lines yields a preliminary estimate of the W_{to} and W_{empty} for a specific design mission.

For the short range jet transport of the example problem select 3 trial takeoff weights and follow the graphical procedure.

W_{to}	100,000 lbs	140,000 lbs	180,000 lbs
W_{fuel}	19,600 lbs	27,440 lbs	35,280 lbs
$W_{payload}$	30,750 lbs	30,750 lbs	30,750 lbs
$W_{empty\ avail}$	49,650 lbs	81,810 lbs	113,970 lbs

Plotting these values on Fig. 3-22 for single aisle jet transports, the $W_{empty\ avail}$ and the W_{empty} from the trend data fairing coincide at W_{empty} = 74,000 lbs and W_{to} = 131,00 lbs as shown in Fig. 3-27.

Check W_{empty} 74,000 lbs

                         W_{fuel} 25,676 lbs

                         $W_{payload}$ <u>30,750 lbs</u>

                                      130,426 lbs

Adjusting the W_{empty} to 74,574 lbs yields a consistent set of weight sand weight fractions

	Weights	Fractions
W_{empty}	74,574	.569
W_{fuel}	25,676	.196
$W_{payload}$	<u>30,750</u>	<u>.235</u>
	131,000	1.000

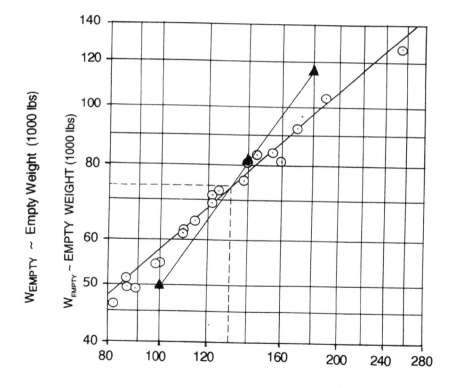

W_{TO} ~ MAXIMUM TAKEOFF WEIGHT (1000 lbs)

Weight Trend Data ~ Single Aisle Jet Transports

Fig. 3-27 Graphical Solution for W_{to} and W_{empty}

Some examples of weights and weight fractions:

| | Ryan NYP "Spirit of St. Louis" | | Rutan "Voyager" | | Concorde SST | | Boeing 747-400 | |
	weights	*fractions*	*weights*	*fractions*	*weights*	*fractions*	*weights*	*fractions*
OWE	2535	(.494)	2448	(.252)	172,500	(.443)	392,032	(.450)
Payload	0	0	0	0	21,000	(.054)	88,410	(.102)
Fuel	2600	(.506)	7247	(.748)	195,500	(.503)	389,558	(.448)
Wto	5135	1.000	9695	1.000	389,000	1.000	870,000	1.000

Some observations may be made from these examples. Since all of these aircraft were designed for a range dominated mission, the fuel fractions are all quite high from about 45% of the MTOGW for the 747-400, to nearly 75% of the MTOGW for the unique "Voyager." The weight empty fraction for the three more or less conventional designs ranges from about 45% to 50% of MTOGW, while for the Voyager, it is only 25% of MTOGW, showing the need for an extremely light weight aircraft with large amounts of fuel, to meet the extreme range mission. Also note that the payload fraction for all examples is quite low, ranging from 0% to 10% of MTOGW.

DESIGN EXERCISE

For your design project estimate the maximum takeoff gross weight and the operating weight empty using the procedures of Chapter 3.

REFERENCES

3.1 Loftin, Laurence K. Jr, Subsonic Aircraft. Evolution and the Matching of Size to Performance., NASA Reference Publication 1060, 1980.

3.2 Raymer, Daniel P., Aircraft Design. A Conceptual Approach, AIAA, Washington, D.C.. 1989.

3.3 Roskam, Jan, Airplane Design. Part I, Preliminary Sizing of Airplanes, Roskam Aviation and Engineering, Ottawa, KS, 1989

3.4 Aviation Week and Space Technology, Aerospace Source Book, McGraw- Hill, New York, January 11, 1999.

3.5 Taylor, J. W. R., Jane's All the World Aircraft, published annually by Jane's Publishing Company, London, England

4

PRELIMINARY WING DESIGN

Preliminary wing design involves the determination of wing area, sweep angle, average thickness ratio, aspect ratio, and taper ratio that meet the mission requirements. Other elements of the preliminary wing design are the definition of the high lift system, that is the trailing edge flaps, the leading edge flaps or slats, as well as the lateral control system elements, such as ailerons and spoilers that are located within the wing planform.

WING AREA

Having determined the takeoff weight, Wto, for a specific design mission, the next step in the preliminary design process is the estimation of an appropriate wing area for the design mission. The selection of the wing area for an aircraft is usually the subject of a fairly comprehensive study that considers the effect of wing area on a number of performance, weight, and cost parameters. These trade studies will be covered in more detail in Chapter 21. For now, a relatively simple procedure will be used to select the wing area for a specific design mission.

The aircraft gross weight divided by the wing area, or wing loading, (W/S) in pounds per square foot, has a characteristic range of values for current aircraft with similar missions. These wing loading trends can be used in making preliminary estimates of the wing area appropriate to a specific mission. The range of takeoff wing loadings for current aircraft with like missions are shown in Fig. 4-1.

Aircraft Type and Mission	(W/S) ~ psf
Personal/Utility Aircraft	10-30
Commuters - short range	30-50
Regional Turboprop Transports - short range	40-90
Business Jets - short to medium range	45-95
Jet Transports - short to medium range	80-120
Jet Transports - long range	120-160
Military Fighter Aircraft	60-110
Military Attack Aircraft	95-115

Fig. 4-1 Takeoff Wing Load Trends

Wing area is a major factor in determining several aspects of mission performance, namely
- Initial cruise altitude capability
- Takeoff field length
- Landing approach speed
- Landing field length
- Wing internal fuel volume

Unfortunately, other parameters are also involved along with wing area in determining the performance levels in some of these areas. The two most direct determinants of the wing area required for a given mission specification are the initial cruise altitude and the landing approach speed. A simple procedure for determining an appropriate wing area for a specific design mission, using these parameters, as well as wing loading trend data, using a short range jet transport, as an example, will be described in the following paragraphs.

Detailed Procedure

First, prepare a graph of wing area vs. gross weight as shown in Fig. 4-2, and note the related data from the mission specification and the takeoff weight data from the Chapter 3 Design Exercise. The related data shown in Fig. 4-2 is for the short range jet transport of the example. Then, plot lines of constant takeoff wing loading at the upper and lower range for the type of aircraft of interest. In the case of the short range jet transport, the wing loading range is from 80 psf to 120 psf. The corresponding wing area, based on this trend data, may be found from

$$S = \frac{W_{to}}{(W/S)_{to}} \qquad (4\text{-}1)$$

Preliminary Wing Area Selection

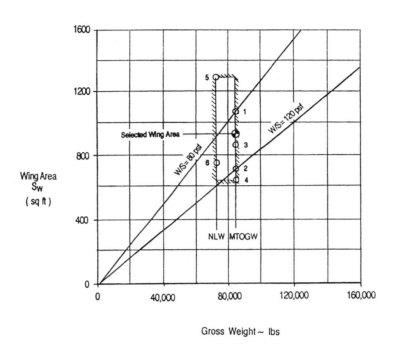

Gross Weight ~ lbs

Related Data

Cruise Mach number	0.76
Cruise Altitude	31,000 ft
MTOGW	85,000 lb
OEW	50,000 lb
Payload (80 pass)	16,400 lb
Reserve Fuel	5,800 lb
NLW	72,200 lb
V_{APP}	125 kts
q @ V_{APP}	53.2 psf
q @ ICA	349.5 psf

Fig. 4-2 Preliminary Wing Area Selection Chart

For $(W/S)_{to}$ = 80 psf

$$S_1 = \frac{85,000}{80} = 1062.5 \text{ sq ft}$$

For $(W/S)_{to}$ = 120 psf

$$S_2 = \frac{85,000}{120} = 708.3 \text{ sq ft}$$

Now determine the wing area required to meet the initial cruise altitude stated in the mission specification. The wing area should be large enough to allow initial cruise at the $C_{L(L/D)max}$ at the specified cruise speed or Mach number and altitude. At initial cruise conditions,

$$C_{L(L/D)max} = \frac{W}{Sq} \tag{4-2}$$

or
$$S = \frac{W}{C_{L(L/D)max} \, q} \tag{4-3}$$

For personal/utility aircraft, commuters, and regional turboprops, the $C_{L(L/D)max}$ usually ranges between C_L's of 0.60 and 0.75. For business jets, commercial jet transports and military cargo transports, the $C_{L(L/D)max}$ usually ranges between 0.40 and 0.55. For military fighter attack aircraft, the $C_{L(L/D)max}$ for high subsonic cruise is usually between 0.32 and 0.40. For supersonic transports or supersonic bombers, the $C_{L(L/D)max}$ at supersonic cruise usually ranges between 0.12 and 0.15. The weight at initial cruise altitude is usually taken conservatively as the takeoff weight for reasons that we shall see later. Now calculate the wing area for each of the $C_{L(L/D)max}$ values that cover the range for the type of aircraft of interest and plot these wing areas on the wing area vs. gross weight graph at the takeoff gross weight. For the example, the C_L's that cover the range of $C_{L(L/D)max}$ for this type of aircraft are 0.40 and 0.55. At these C_L's the required wing area for initial cruise at M = 0.76 at 31,000 ft. at a GW = 85,000 lbs is from Eq. 4-2

For $C_{L(L/D)max}$ = 0.40

$$S_3 = \frac{85,000}{0.40 \times 242.8} = 875.2 \text{ sq ft}$$

For $C_{L(L/D)max}$ = 0.55

$$S_3 = \frac{85,000}{0.55 \times 242.8} = 636.5 \text{ sq ft}$$

Next, determine the wing area required, in conjunction with the aircraft maximum lift coefficient in the landing configuration, to meet the maximum landing approach speed at the normal landing weight for the type of aircraft of interest. Operational experience over many years has led to some specific values for the maximum landing approach speed for various aircraft types at their normal landing weight. These speeds are shown in Fig. 4-3.

Aircraft Type	Speed (kts)
Personal/Utility Aircraft	75
Turboprop Commuters	105
Regional Turboprops	110
Business Jets	120
Short Range Jet Transports	125
Long Range Jet Transports	150
Military Fighter/Attack Aircraft	150

Fig. 4-3 Maximum Landing Approach Speeds

The landing approach speed is defined as

$$V_{APP} = 1.3\, V_S \tag{4-4}$$

Normal landing weight may be defined as

$$NLW = OWE + Full\ Payload + Reserve\ Fuel \tag{4-5}$$

For approach conditions

$$C_L = \frac{W_{NLW}}{S q_{APP}} \tag{4-6}$$

$$S = \frac{W_{NLW}}{C_L q_{APP}} \tag{4-7}$$

The wing area required to meet the maximum landing approach speed depends on the normal landing weight, the q at the maximum landing approach speed, and the C_L at landing approach condition of $1.3\, V_S$. It can be shown that the C_L at $1.3\, V_S$ is

$$C_L = \frac{C_{L_{MAX}}}{(1.3)^2} \tag{4-8}$$

93

The range of maximum lift coefficients for various types of aircraft are indicated by the trend data of Fig. 4-4. As we shall see later, the higher values of maximum lift coefficient in the landing configuration are associated with more complex high lift systems.

AIRCRAFT TYPE	$C_{L_{MAX}}$ Clean	$C_{L_{MAX}}$ Takeoff	$C_{L_{MAX}}$ Landing
Personal/Utility	1.3-1.8	1.3-1.8	1.6-2.3
Commuters	1.3-1.8	1.4-2.0	1.6-2.5
Regional Turboprops	1.5-1.8	1.7-2.2	1.9-2.7
Business Jets	1.4-1.8	1.6-2.2	1.8-2.6
Jet Transports	1.4-1.8	1.6-2.2	1.8-3.0
Military Fighter/Attack	1.2-1.8	1.4-2.0	1.6-2.4

Fig. 4-4 Maximum Lift Coefficient Trends

Now calculate the wing area required to meet the maximum landing approach speed for the range of $C_{L_{MAX}}$ values in the landing configuration for the type of aircraft of interest. For the example short range jet transport, the values range from 1.8 to 3.0, and the maximum landing approach speed is 125 knots.

For $C_{L_{MAX}} = 1.8$ $\quad S_5 = \dfrac{72,200}{(1.8 / 1.69)\,53.2} = 1274.2$ sq ft

For $C_{L_{MAX}} = 3.0$ $\quad S_6 = \dfrac{72,200}{(3.0 / 1.69)\,53.2} = 764.5$ sq ft

Plot these values on the wing area vs. gross weight graph at the normal landing weight. At this point, using trend data on takeoff wing loading, and specific calculations based on a range of key parameters involved in attaining a specified initial cruise altitude and a maximum landing approach speed, a number of possible wing areas have been identified. To recap, the range of wing areas from

Wing loading trends	$S_{1,2} = 708$ sq ft to 1062 sq ft
Initial cruise altitude	$S_{3,4} = 635$ sq ft to 874 sq ft
Landing approach speed	$S_{5,6} = 764$ sq ft to 1274 sq ft

The concept that there are a range of wing areas, which combined with other parameters, will meet the mission specification is consistent with the fact that there is no exact value of wing area that can be calculated to meet all the requirements of the design mission.

94

However, some practical considerations and some judgment can lead to the selection of an appropriate wing area. From the wing loading standpoint, it is not usually a good idea to start a new design with a wing area that results in a takeoff wing loading at the top of the wing loading range.

Since takeoff gross weight tends to grow because of increases in weight empty, payload and fuel as the design matures, a wing area that cannot accommodate modest increases in takeoff gross weight above the initial value can result in severe performance limitations. A reasonable approach might be to consider a wing area that results from an average of the trend wing loadings, for the example short range jet transport, a (W/S) of 100 psf, which yields a wing area of 850 sq ft. This wing area is reasonably close to the wing area of 874 sq ft needed for the initial cruise altitude condition if the $C_{L(L/D)max}$ turns out to be as low as 0.40. These values of wing area are both greater than the wing area of 764 sq ft needed to meet the maximum approach speed requirement at the highest value of the landing maximum lift coefficient of 3.0 shown in the trend data. A wing area of 850 to 875 sq ft would provide a slightly lower landing approach speed at NLW at a landing C_{LMAX} of 3.0, or require a slightly lower C_{LMAX} than 3.0 to meet the 125 knot requirement. One final consideration on wing area is the probable development of growth versions of the initial design, that is derivatives with more payload, more range (more fuel) or both. This is especially important in commercial jet transport design, where history has shown that market demand invariably requires growth derivatives of the basic design, resulting in higher takeoff and landing weights that still must meet the initial cruise altitude and landing approach speed requirements.

From all of the considerations discussed above, it appears that a reasonable wing area would be 850 sq ft to meet the requirements of the basic design, with perhaps a 10% increase in wing area to accommodate some increase in takeoff and landing weights associated with growth versions of the initial design, without incurring performance limitations, or without having to increase the wing area, an extremely difficult and costly change. So a reasonable wing area choice for the example short range jet transport is

$$S = 850 (1.1) = 935 \text{ sq ft}$$

Wing Airfoil Sections

Wing airfoil sections are the cross-sectional shapes of the wing in planes parallel to the airplane center line and normal to the wing reference plane. The wing airfoil sections provide the wing lift by creating suctions on the wing upper surface and pressures on the wing lower surface. The wing airfoil geometry determines the detailed pressure distribution on the wing upper and lower surfaces, which in turn have a significant influence on some of the important aerodynamic characteristics of the wing. Airfoil geometric parameters are defined in Fig. 4-5.

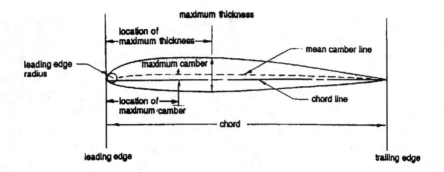

Fig. 4-5 Airfoil Section Geometric Parameters

Since the days of the Wright Brothers, many hundreds of airfoil sections have been designed. Some of the more well known airfoils have been defined in a rationally related family or series, usually with a common generalized thickness distribution along the mean camber line, but with variations in mean line shape and maximum thickness. Early airfoil development was done by Gottingen in Germany, Eiffel in France, the Royal Aircraft Factory in Britain, and later by the NACA in the U.S. Of these, the airfoils developed and tested by the NACA were the most widely used. Some examples of airfoils from the three most used NACA families are the 4-digit series, the 5-digit series, and the 6 series, which are discussed below. It should be noted that the numbering system for the NACA airfoils began with the 4-digit series as a fairly simply way to describe the main features of the airfoil geometry, but became increasingly more complicated as more numbers were added to describe features of the aerodynamic characteristics as well as the basic geometry. There is however, one common aspect of the numbering system for all NACA family series. The last two digits denote the thickness ratio in percent chord.

4-digit Series

The first of the NACA airfoil families was developed in the early 1930s. All airfoils have the same basic thickness distribution, but the mean camber line varies with respect to the chordwise location of the maximum camber. The 24XX airfoils were used on the DC-1, DC-2, and DC-3, and the symmetrical 00XX series are still widely used as horizontal and vertical tail airfoils for many personal/utility, commuter, regional turboprop, and business jet aircraft.

5-digit Series

Developed in the mid 1930s to improve the airfoil section maximum lift coefficients, these airfoils have the same basic thickness distribution as the 4-digit series, but with a different mean camber. The 230XX series were used on the DC-4, DC-6, DC-7, and nearly all of the aircraft produced in the U.S. during World War II. These sections are still used on a number of subsonic propeller driven aircraft.

6 Series

These airfoils were developed in the late 1930s to achieve lower values of section drag coefficient through pressure distributions that produced extensive regions of laminar flow over the forward portion of the airfoil. Wind tunnel tests of these sections confirmed the lower values of section drag coefficient as long as the airfoils were smooth and fair. However, wind tunnel tests with sections that had the waviness and joints found in practical metal aircraft construction showed no lower values of section drag coefficient than the earlier NACA series. In spite of this situation, the 6-series have been used on a number of propeller driven aircraft, and some early jet transports, business jets, and military fighter/attack aircraft.

"Peaky" Airfoils

Developed in the 1960s, by the major airframe manufacturers in the U.S. and Great Britain, these airfoils have improved M_{DIV} over the NACA 6-series. The shapes were designed to produce a narrow peak in the upper surface suction very far forward on the airfoil. These airfoils were used on the DC-10, C-5A, and VC-10 jet transports.

Supercritical Airfoils

This airfoil concept was developed by Dr. Richard T. Whitcomb at the NASA Langley Research Center in the 1970s. These airfoil shapes have very little curvature over much of the upper surface, which leads to more distributed high levels of suction without strong shocks, and a highly cambered aft portion to produce positive pressure lift over the aft lower surface. Wind tunnel and flight experiments showed that for any given thickness ratio, supercritical airfoils can provide a higher M_{DIV} by about 0.06 than the "peaky" airfoils. One of the first applications of these airfoils to a new design was the McDonnell Douglas YC-15, followed later by the C-17, A-330/340, Boeing 777, and a number of new business jets.

A comparison of the shapes of the airfoil types discussed above is shown in Fig. 4-6.

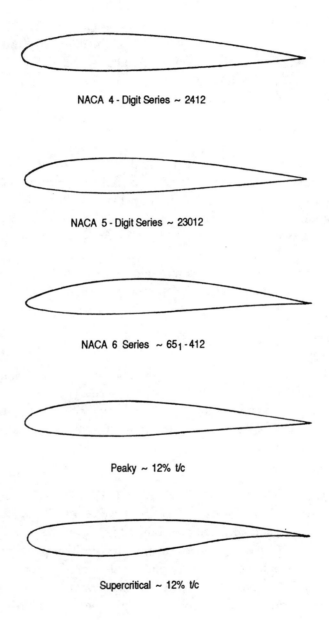

NACA 4 - Digit Series ~ 2412

NACA 5 - Digit Series ~ 23012

NACA 6 Series ~ 65_1 - 412

Peaky ~ 12% t/c

Supercritical ~ 12% t/c

Fig. 4-6 Wing Airfoil Section Types

With the advent of modern computational methods for designing and analyzing airfoil section characteristics, more and more airplane designs have specifically designed airfoil sections created by aerodynamicists for a particular application.

Wing Airfoil Selection

The selection of the wing airfoil section type is dependent primarily on the flight speed regime that the aircraft is to operate in. For subsonic personal/utility, commuter, and regional turboprop aircraft, the NACA 5-digit series are probably the best choice, since they have high section maximum lift coefficients and good thickness distribution that allows ample spar depth for the wing structure. For high subsonic speed business jets, commercial jet transports, and military cargo jets, the favored choice is the supercritical type, because of superior drag divergence characteristics. For supersonic military fighter/attack aircraft, the usual choice is a thin NACA 6-series airfoil, which shows reasonable characteristics at both subsonic and supersonic speeds. For supersonic transports, the wing is usually developed as an integrated surface with extensive camber and twist to achieve minimum wave drag, so that the selection of airfoil types does not have any real significance.

Wing Sweepback Angle and Average Thickness Ratio

Two very important wing geometric parameters, especially for airplanes that cruise at high subsonic speeds, are the wing sweepback angle and average thickness. Wing sweepback or sweep angle is defined in the plan view as the angle between a line perpendicular to the airplane center line and the constant 25% chord line of the wing airfoil sections, as shown in Fig. 4-7. Nearly all high subsonic speed aircraft have wings have some amount of sweep, because sweep increases the wing drag divergence Mach number, M_{DIV}, for given streamwise airfoil thickness.

As shown in Fig. 4-7, the component of the freestream velocity parallel to the 25% chord line is not subjected to the airfoil contours that produce variations in the local velocities that create lift. Only the component of velocity perpendicular to the 25% chord line is effective in producing lift. Therefore, on a wing with a sweep angle, Λ,

$$V_{eff} = V \cos \Lambda \qquad (4\text{-}9)$$

$$M_{eff} = M \cos \Lambda \qquad (4\text{-}10)$$

$$q_{eff} = q \cos^2 \Lambda \qquad (4\text{-}11)$$

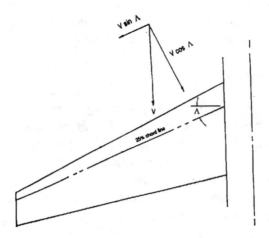

Fig. 4-7 Velocity Components Related to a Swept Wing

After taking into account the usual practice of defining airfoil sections and thickness ratios in the streamwise direction, and the angle of attack and dynamic pressure defined in the normal manner, the variation of M_{DIV} with sweep angle for a given thickness ratio and lift coefficient is of the form

$$M_{DIV} \sim \frac{1}{\cos^m \Lambda} \qquad (4\text{-}12)$$

where m is a function of the lift coefficient, C_L.

Selection of Wing Sweepback Angle and Average Thickness Ratio

The selection of wing sweepback angle and average thickness ratio must be compatible with the cruise speed or Mach number specified in the design mission. For personal/utility aircraft and commuters which cruise at speeds below the compressibility drag rise, zero wing sweepback angle and average thickness ratios around .15 (15%) usually meet the aerodynamic and structural requirements. For business jets and jet transports which want to cruise at $(ML/D)_{max}$ for best range, the designer must select a combination of wing sweepback angle and average thickness ratio that will just reach M_{DIV} at the cruise conditions specified in the design mission. In general, it is desirable to select the minimum sweepback angle consistent with reasonable thickness ratios for the wing design. The average thickness ratios for business jets and jet transports usually turn out to be in the range of 10% and 12%, after optimization studies which consider weight, drag, and fuel volume. Design charts for transonic cruise aircraft using supercritical airfoils, Fig. 4-8, have been prepared for use in selecting the sweep angle and average thickness ratio for this type of aircraft. For supersonic fighter/attack aircraft, the key wing design parameter is average thickness ratio, with most aircraft of this type having average thickness ratios around 3.5%

Wing Aspect Ratio and Taper Ratio

Two other important wing plan form parameters are aspect ratio and taper ratio. Wing aspect ratio, AR, is defined as the square of the wing span, b, divided by the wing area, S.

$$AR = \frac{b^2}{S} \qquad (4\text{-}13)$$

Aspect ratio selection is basically a compromise between aerodynamic efficiency, in the form of high cruise L/D, and wing structural weight associated with the bending moments due to airloads for a given wing area. Taper ratio, λ is defined as the ratio of the chord at the tip of the wing, c_t , to the chord at the airplane centerline, called the root chord, c_r .

$$\lambda = \frac{c_t}{c_r} \qquad (4\text{-}14)$$

Taper ratio is also a compromise between aerodynamic considerations, primarily span load distribution, important for cruise efficiency, and stall characteristics, and structural considerations, associated primarily with the bending moments. Fig. 4-9 summarizes the range of aspect and taper ratios for several modern aircraft types.

Aircraft type	Aspect Ratio	Taper Ratio
Personal/Utility	5.0 - 8.0	1.0 - 0.6
Commuters	9.0 - 12.0	1.0 - 0.5
Regional Turboprops	11.0 - 12.8	0.6 - 0.4
Business Jets	5.0 - 8.8	0.6 - 0.4
Jet Transports	7.0 - 9.5	0.4 - 0.2
Military Fighter/Attack	2.4 - 5.0	0.5 - 0.2

Fig. 4-9   Wing Aspect Ratio and Taper Ratio Trends

Wing Thickness Distribution

Another wing geometric characteristic is the variation of airfoil thickness ratio across the span of each wing panel. The simplest wing geometry, still found on many small personal/

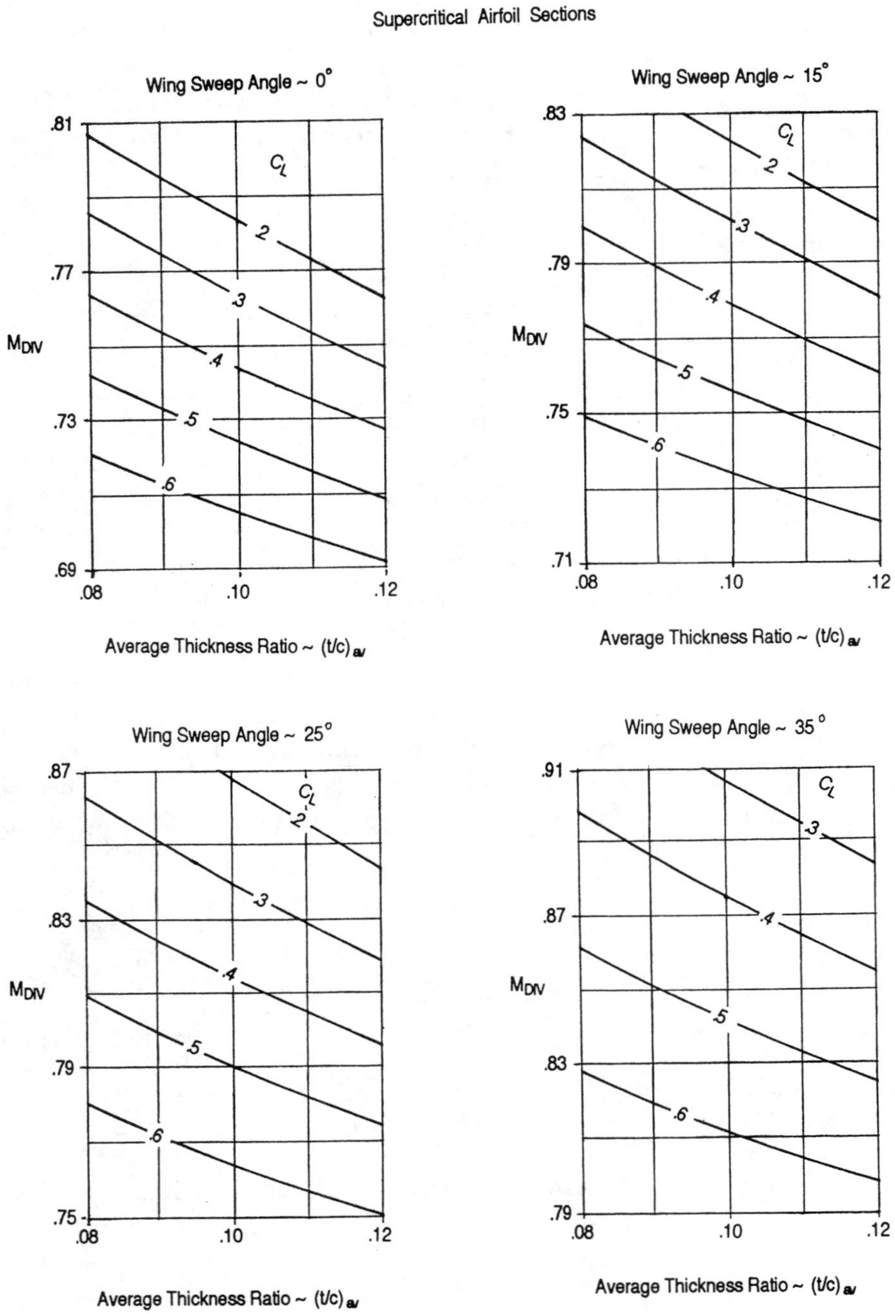
Supercritical Airfoil Sections
Wing Sweep Angle ~ 0°
.81
.77
.73
.69
MDIV
CL
.2
.3
.4
.5
.6
.08
.10
.12
Average Thickness Ratio ~ (t/c)av
Wing Sweep Angle ~ 15°
.83
.79
.75
.71
MDIV
CL
.2
.3
.4
.5
.6
.08
.10
.12
Average Thickness Ratio ~ (t/c)av
Wing Sweep Angle ~ 25°
.87
.83
.79
.75
MDIV
CL
.2
.3
.4
.5
.6
.08
.10
.12
Average Thickness Ratio ~ (t/c)av
Wing Sweep Angle ~ 35°
.91
.87
.83
.79
MDIV
CL
.3
.4
.5
.6
.08
.10
.12
Average Thickness Ratio ~ (t/c)av

Fig. 4-8 Wing Design Charts for Transonic Cruise Aircraft

PRELIMINARY WING DESIGN

utility airplanes, is a constant chord, constant thickness ratio configuration. More sophis-
ticated personal/utility aircraft, as well as commuters, regional turboprops, business jets and
jet transports have wing designs which vary the airfoil section thickness ratio, (t/c), across
the span, primarily to obtain greater depth for the airfoil sections at the wing root. This
greater depth provides for a more efficient structural beam to resist the bending moments
due to wing airloads. For straight wing, propeller driven aircraft, the wing is usually defined by two airfoil sections, one at the wing root, and one at the wing tip, connected by
straight line elements through the constant percent chord points. Typical airfoil sections
are the NACA 23018 for the root and the NACA 23010 for the tip.

For business jets and jet transports which cruise at high subsonic speed the wing is
usually defined by three or more airfoil sections, one at the side of the fuselage, one at the
tip, and one or more at intermediate spanwise locations. The purpose of the additional
defining airfoils is to produce wing upper surface pressure distributions which maintain
insofar as possible uniformly swept lines of constant pressure, or isobars at cruise conditions, so that the entire wing reaches its M_{DIV} at the same point. A typical wing thickness
distribution for a jet transport is shown in Fig. 4-10.

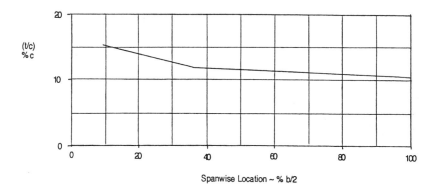

Fig. 4-10 Typical Wing Thickness Distribution for a Jet Transport

It can be shown that the average thickness ratio of the wing, weighted for the wing area
affected, with linear thickness distribution, is

$$(t/c)_{av} = \frac{t_{root} + t_{tip}}{c_{root} + c_{tip}} \qquad (4\text{-}15)$$

The same equation is valid on any portion of the wing with linear thickness distribution when the wing has more than two defining airfoil sections. The entire wing $(t/c)_{av}$ can
then be determined by averaging the $(t/c)_{av}$ for each portion.

103

AERODYNAMIC TWIST

Nearly all wing designs incorporate some degree of aerodynamic twist, that is, a change in the orientation of the airfoil section chord lines from root to tip, with the tip airfoils having less of an angle of incidence than the root, as shown in Fig. 4-11. The aerodynamic twist is used to avoid initial stalling at the wing tip as the airplane $C_{L_{MAX}}$ is reached. Typical values of wing twist vary from 3 degrees for personal/utility, commuters, and regional turboprops, to as much as 7 degrees for business jets and jet transports. Supersonic military fighter/ attack aircraft usually have little or no twist, depending on other means to provide satisfactory stall characteristics.

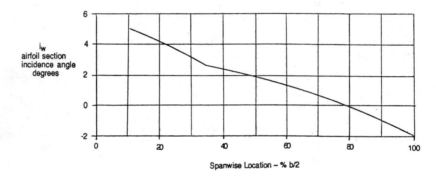

Fig. 4-11 Typical Wing Twist Distribution for a Jet Transport

HIGH LIFT SYSTEMS

Nearly all modern aircraft incorporate devices that fit within the wing planform to increase the maximum lift coefficient of the airplane in the takeoff and landing configurations. These devices collectively are called the airplane's high lift system, and are defined early in the preliminary design process. Wing sections of currently used high lift devices, in order of complexity, are shown in Fig. 4-12. High lift devices fall into two categories: trailing edge devices located on the rear portion of the wing, and leading edge devices located on the forward portion of the wing. The effectiveness of high lift devices in increasing the maximum lift coefficient of the airplane is related primarily to the dimensions of the device, expressed in terms of percentage of the local wing chord, and the angle to which the device is deflected. The simplest high lift device is the plain trailing edge flap. While not used on current aircraft as a high lift device, it finds application as a lift increasing (and decreasing) lateral control device, the aileron. Aileron chords are usually around 15% to 20% of the local wing chord, and are deflected to a maximum angle of 25 degrees. Most

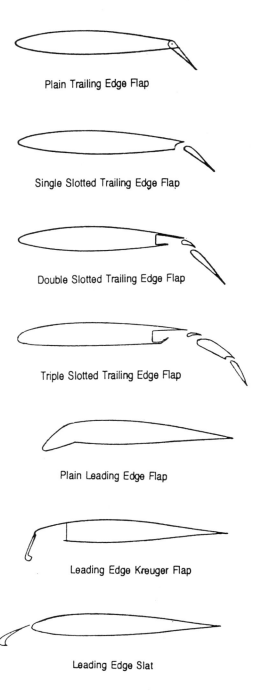

Plain Trailing Edge Flap

Single Slotted Trailing Edge Flap

Double Slotted Trailing Edge Flap

Triple Slotted Trailing Edge Flap

Plain Leading Edge Flap

Leading Edge Kreuger Flap

Leading Edge Slat

Fig. 4-12 Typical Wing High Lift Devices

modern aircraft are equipped with slotted trailing edge flaps. Single slotted flaps are standard for personal/utility aircraft. Single slotted flap chords are usually in the range of 25% to 30% of chord, and have a maximum deflection of 35 degrees. For commuters, regional turboprops, business jets and jet transports, more powerful double slotted trailing edge flaps are usually employed. Double slotted flap chords are in the range of 30% to 35% chord with maximum deflections of 45 degrees to 50 degrees. Some jet transports with design mission specifications that called for extremely low landing approach speeds and short landing distances have utilized triple slotted trailing edge flaps to achieve very high $C_{L_{MAX}}$ values in the landing configuration. Flap chords up to 40% may be used in triple slotted flap designs, with maximum deflections of the aft flap of up to 55 degrees. The effectiveness of trailing edge flaps may be enhanced by selecting as large a percent of chord dimension for the flap, and utilizing as much flap span as possible, considering the need for lateral control ailerons on the outboard wing trailing edge.

Significant increases in $C_{L_{MAX}}$ can also be achieved through the application of leading edge high lift devices. The simplest leading edge device is the plain leading edge flap, used on a number of military fighter/attack aircraft. Some jet transports have used leading edge Kreuger flaps over some portion of the span. A more effective, but more complicated leading edge device is the slat, which is used on nearly all modern jet transports. The maximum effectiveness of leading edge flaps and slats is usually achieved with flap and slat percent chords of 12% to 15%, with deflections ranging from 20 degrees for slats to 30 degrees for plain leading edge flaps, to 60 degrees for Kreuger flaps. Leading edge flaps and slats must extend for the full span of the wing to be effective in increasing $C_{L_{MAX}}$. Referring back to Fig. 4-4, the lower values of $C_{L_{MAX}}$ in the landing configuration are associated with the simpler high lift systems with no leading edge devices, while the higher values are consistent with the more complex systems using triple slotted flaps and leading edge devices.

LATERAL CONTROL DEVICES

An additional consideration for the preliminary wing design is the provision for lateral control devices which produce rolling moments about the airplane's X-axis. The most common lateral control devices are ailerons, essentially plain trailing edge flaps, and spoilers, basically a portion of the wing upper surface, hinged at its leading edge, which reduces lift in the affected area of the wing when the spoiler is deflected. When deflected asymmetrically, spoilers can produce significant rolling moments, especially if they are located ahead of deflected trailing edge flaps. Spoilers have additional uses when deflected symmetrically as drag producing devices to allow the airplane to slow down in level flight, or to increase the rate of descent at the end of cruise. Spoilers are also used symmetrically to reduce the airplane's lift during landing ground roll, which improves braking effectiveness.

For personal/utility, commuters, and regional turboprops, the usual lateral control device is the aileron, with aileron spans typically occupying the trailing edge area from 60% to 90% of the wing semispan. For business jets and jet transports, spoilers are generally used in conjunction with ailerons. Furthermore, since ailerons located on the outer part of the wing trailing edge tend to twist the wing as they are deflected to produce rolling moments at high dynamic pressure, or high q conditions, thereby reducing their effectiveness, some jet transports utilize smaller ailerons located further inboard for high q lateral control and trim, in addition to the outboard ailerons.

WING SPAR LOCATIONS

The next consideration in the preliminary wing design is the location of the wing front and rear spars. The spars, along with the upper and lower wing skins, are the major elements of the wing structural "box", which resists the applied wing air loads in bending and torsion. The distance between the spars has a significant impact on the space available for high lift and lateral control devices, and on the volume available for wing internal fuel tankage. Depending on the demands of the high lift system and lateral control elements, typical locations for the front spar are between 16% and 22% of chord, while typical rear spar locations range from 60% to 75% of chord.

WING INBOARD TRAILING EDGE EXTENSIONS

Wing inboard trailing edge extensions are often used on business jets and jet transports with wing sweep angles greater than 30 degrees. The need for an inboard trailing edge extension arises from the required main landing gear leg upper pivot point location, which would be very near the wing trailing edge on a trapezoidal planform. By incorporating an inboard trailing edge extension, a suitable structural arrangement involving an additional rear spar may be designed to provide the necessary gear pivot location. This situation is shown in Fig. 4-13.

AVAILABLE WING FUEL VOLUME

It is highly desirable, especially for transports and business jet designs, to carry all the mission fuel in the wing. The available wing fuel volume is the space between the front and rear spars, and the upper and lower wing skins, including the volume in the wing structural

107

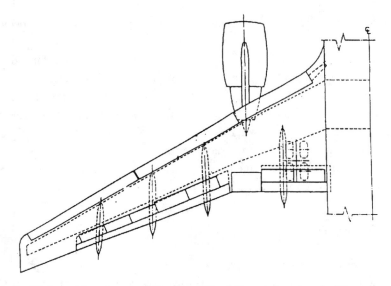

Fig. 4-13 Wing Inboard Trailing Edge Extension for Jet Transport

"box" that carries through the fuselage. A preliminary check on available wing fuel volume may be made by plotting the cross sectional area between the front and rear spar and the upper and lower wing skins vs. wing spanwise dimension. As a first approximation, the area between the front and rear spars and the upper and lower wing skins is 80% of the rectangle defined by the spar locations and the maximum thickness of the airfoil section. The area under this curve of cross sectional area vs. wing spanwise dimension is the available wing fuel volume. The wing fuel volume, converted into pounds of fuel should at least be equal to the mission fuel weight and it is desirable to have more volume to add fuel for growth (longer range) versions of the design. Standard weight for aviation gasoline is 6.0 lbs/gal and the standard weight for jet fuel is 6.7 lbs/gal.

WING m.a.c. DETERMINATION

A geometric parameter often used in preliminary design procedures is the wing mean aerodynamic chord, (m.a.c.). The m.a.c. is the chord of an imaginary wing, with constant chord, that has the same aerodynamic characteristics as the actual wing. Although called the mean aerodynamic chord, the m.a.c. is defined geometrically as shown in Fig. 4-14. A graphical method of determining the length and spanwise location of the m.a.c. is as follows. On the wing planform diagram, mark off a line which is one root chord in length forward of the tip chord, and another line which is one tip chord in length aft of the root chord. Connect the end points of these lines. Where this line intersects the 50% chord line

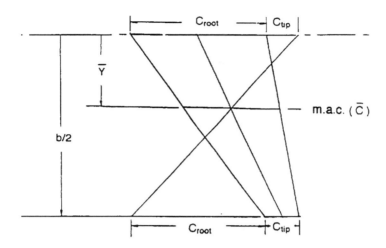

Fig. 4-14 Wing m.a.c. Determination

of the wing establishes the spanwise location of the m.a.c., and the wing chord at this location is the m.a.c. The length and location of the m.a.c. can also be found from Equations 4-19 and 4-20.

The wing span, b, is
$$b = \sqrt{AR \cdot S} \qquad (4\text{-}16)$$

where AR is the wing aspect ratio and S is the reference wing area. The root chord length is

$$C_{root} = \frac{2S}{b(1+\lambda)} \qquad (4\text{-}17)$$

where λ is the wing taper ratio.

The tip chord length is
$$C_{tip} = \lambda \, C_{root} \qquad (4\text{-}18)$$

The wing m.a.c. length is
$$\overline{C} = \left(\frac{2}{3}\right) C_{root} \left[1 + \lambda - \frac{\lambda}{1+\lambda}\right] \qquad (4\text{-}19)$$

The distance from the centerline to the m.a.c. location is

$$\overline{Y} = \left(\frac{b}{6}\right) \frac{1+2\lambda}{1+\lambda} \qquad (4\text{-}20)$$

WING LINE DIAGRAM

After all of the considerations associated with the preliminary wing design are resolved into specific geometric values, a wing line diagram is drawn. The line diagram is a scaled drawing of the wing planform and shows the location of the high lift devices, lateral control devices, and wing spar locations. Some typical examples are shown in Figs. 4-15, 4-16, and 4-17.

DESIGN EXERCISE

Make a drawing of your preliminary wing design. Show locations of front and rear spar planes, leading and trailing edge high lift devices, lateral control devices, and note on the drawing the specific geometry of the wing (span, aspect ratio, taper ratio, sweep, average thickness ratio). Also make a graph of wing airfoil thickness ratio across the span of the wing. Also, graphically determine the wing mean aerodynamic chord location (m.a.c.) on the wing.

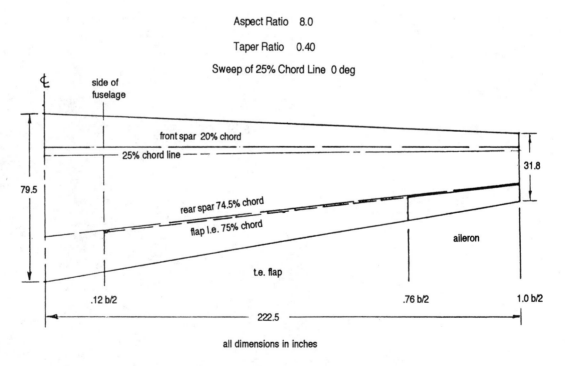

Fig. 4-15 Wing Planform Diagram for Personal/Utility Aircraft

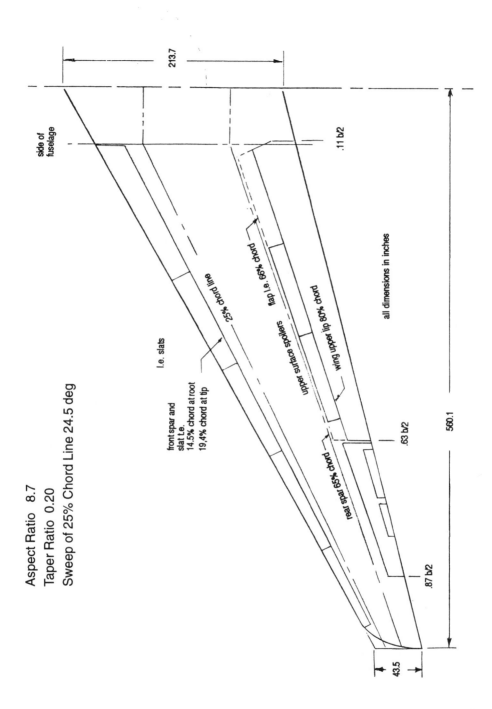

Aspect Ratio 8.7
Taper Ratio 0.20
Sweep of 25% Chord Line 24.5 deg

213.7

side of fuselage

.11 b/2

l.e. slats

25% chord line

flap l.e. 66% chord

upper surface spoilers

wing upper lip 80% chord

front spar and
slat t.e.
14.5% chord at root
19.4% chord at tip

all dimensions in inches

.63 b/2

560.1

rear spar 65% chord

.87 b/2

43.5

Fig. 4-16 Wing Planform Diagram for Short Range Jet Transport

111

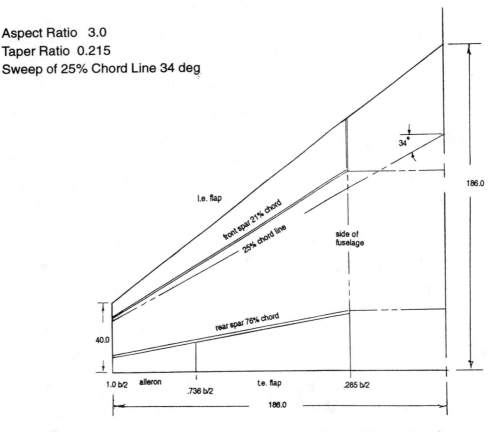

Aspect Ratio 3.0
Taper Ratio 0.215
Sweep of 25% Chord Line 34 deg

Fig. 4-17 Wing Planform Diagram for Military Fighter/Attack Aircraft

REFERENCES

4.1 Abbott, Ira H., and Von Doenhoff, Albert F., Theory of Wing Sections, Dover, New York, 1959.

4.2 Shevell, Richard S., Fundamentals of Flight, Prentice Hall, Englewood Cliffs, NJ, 1989

4.3 Lynch, Frank T., Commercial Transports - Aerodynamic Design for Cruise Performance Efficiency, Transonic Aerodynamics, Vol. 81, Progress in Astronautics and Aeronautics, AIAA, Washington, D.C., 1982.

4.4 Rudolph, Peter K. C., High Lift Systems on Commercial Subsonic Airliners, NASA Contractor Report 4746, 1996

4.5 Schaufele, Roger D., and Ebeling, Ann W., Aerodynamic Design of the DC -9 Wing and High Lift System, SAE Paper No. 67-0846, presented to the Aeronautics and Space Engineering Meeting, Los Angeles, CA, October, 1967

5

PRELIMINARY FUSELAGE DESIGN

GENERAL CONSIDERATIONS

Primary considerations for preliminary fuselage design are for providing accommodation for the crew station, passengers, and other payload to be carried in the fuselage, and for some designs, accommodating the engine/propulsion system as well.

The fuselage design varies somewhat, depending on the type of aircraft. For single engine propeller driven personal/utility aircraft, the fuselage accommodates the engine/propeller installation forward, the pilot and passenger compartment, followed by the aft fuselage, which serves mainly as a convenient structure to attach the horizontal and vertical tails. For light twin engine aircraft, the engine-propeller installation is usually located on the inboard portion of each wing panel, , and the fuselage nose is used for baggage space. Examples of the general arrangement and dimensions of the pilot and passenger compartment for these types are shown in Fig. 5-1.

For commuters, regional turboprops, business jets and commercial jet transports, the fuselage is made up of three distinct sections: (1) Constant section passenger compartment, (2) Nose section, and (3) Afterbody or tail-cone.

CROSS SECTION

For smaller commuters, where flight lengths are on the order of 1to 2 hours, and there is no real requirement to move about in the passenger compartment, the cross section provides for a minimum aisle and a vertical dimension that does not allow an average person to stand fully erect. Usually, these aircraft do not have pressurized cabins, so the cross section shapes tend to be more or less rectangular, the most straight forward way to envelope the passengers. For regional turboprops, larger business jets and jet transports with longer

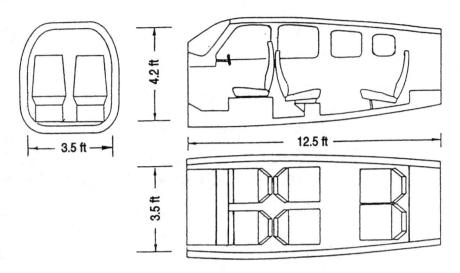

Single Engine Beech Bonanza B 36 TC

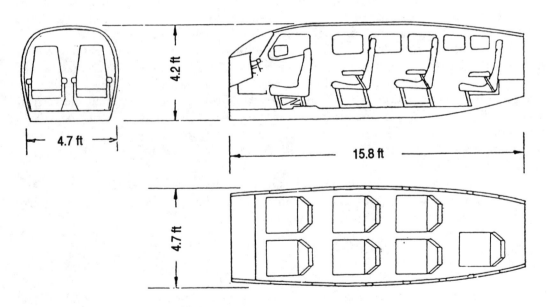

Twin Engine Cessna 402 C

Fig. 5-1 Pilot and Passenger Compartments of Personal/Utility Aircraft

Courtesy of Raytheon Aircraft Co. and Cessna Aircraft Co.

flight durations and where there is need to move about, the aisles are somewhat wider, and the vertical dimensions allow passenger to walk about standing fully erect. These aircraft are usually pressurized and the cross sections are circular, or made up of two circles of different diameter (double bubble) because of the structural weight efficiency of this shape for pressure vessels.

For larger capacity, long range jet transports, two aisles are provided to allow for greater passenger mobility, and for ease of entry and exit from multiple adjacent seats. Furthermore, these larger circular cross sections provide significant space below the passenger deck to carry large amounts of revenue cargo, either in special containers, or stacked on flat pallets.

Figures 5-2 to 5-6 provide data on passenger cross sections for business jets, commuters, regional turboprops, and commercial jet transports, which is summarized in Fig. 5-7.

PASSENGER COMPARTMENT LENGTH

For commuters, regional turboprops, business jets, and jet transports, the length of the passenger compartment must be sufficient to accommodate the design passenger payload, with the appropriate number of seat rows at the selected seat pitch, the distance between the same point on successive seat rows, plus the allowance for passenger entrance and emergency exit doors, galley space, lavatory space, and coat room/wardrobe space, all required on the main passenger deck floor plan.

Business jet passenger compartments are not usually arranged with defined seat rows and regular seat pitch. Instead, these aircraft are configured with more luxurious seats, conference tables, and work stations to accommodate the business executive passengers. Commuters and regional turboprops are usually configured for single class service, so the determination of the required passenger compartment length is relatively straightforward after the seat pitch is defined. For shorter range (up to 2500 N.Mi) jet transports there is usually a 2-class seating arrangement, first class and coach or economy, with different seat pitch, and different numbers of seats across. For longer range jet transports, there is normally a 3-class seating arrangement, first class, business class, and coach/economy class, all with varying seat pitch, number of seats across, and percentage of seats devoted to each class.

It should be noted that while all jet transports have the flexibility to be configured in 1, 2, or 3 class seating arrangements, with any seat pitch selected by the airline operator, there is usually a standard specification seating arrangement, and hence standard passenger payload that is used for performance calculations. Typical arrangements are shown in Figs. 5-8 through 5-11. The resulting constant section passenger compartment length-to-diameter ratios usually range between 4.0 and 9.0 as noted in Fig. 5-12.

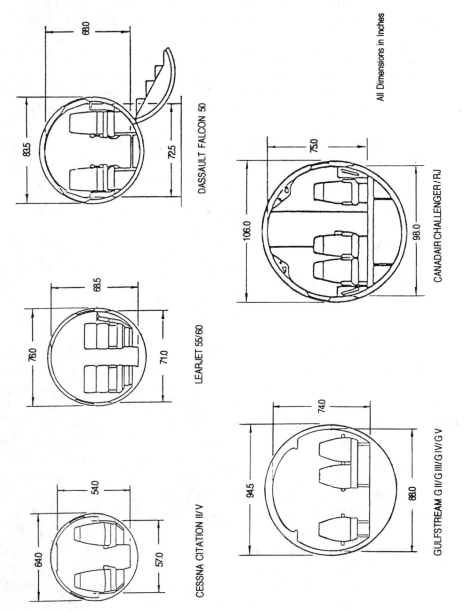

Fig. 5-2 Passenger Compartment Cross Sections - Business Jets

Courtesy of Cessna Aircraft Co., Bombardier Aerospace, Dassault Aviation, Gulfstream Aerospace

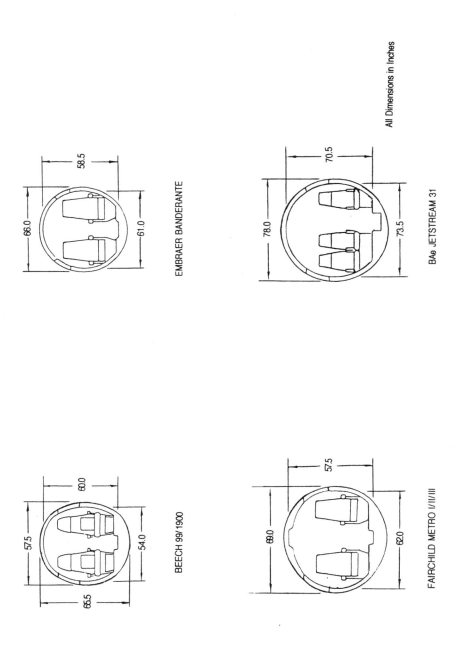

Fig. 5-3 Passenger Compartment Cross Sections - Commuters

Courtesy of Raytheon Aircraft Co., Embraer, Fairchild Aerospace Corp., BAE Systems

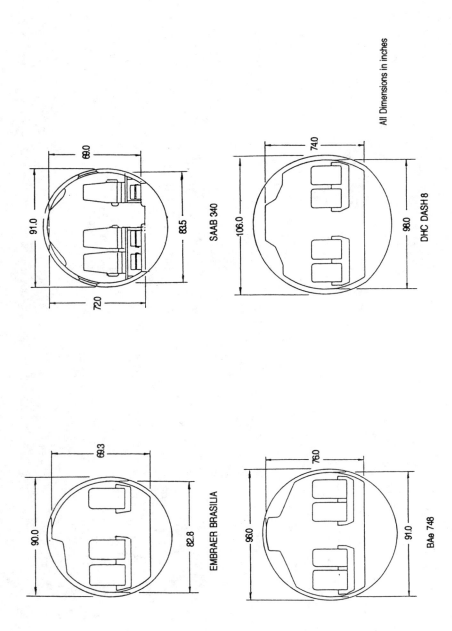

Fig. 5-4 Passenger Compartment Cross Sections - Regional Turboprops

Courtesy of Embraer, Saab AB, BAE Systems, Bombardier Aerospace

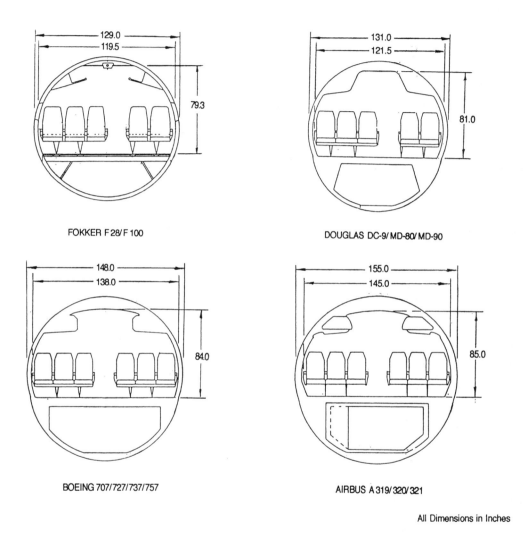

Fig. 5-5 Passenger Compartment Cross Sections - Single Aisle Jet Transports

Courtesy of Fokker N.V., the Boeing Co, Airbus Industrie

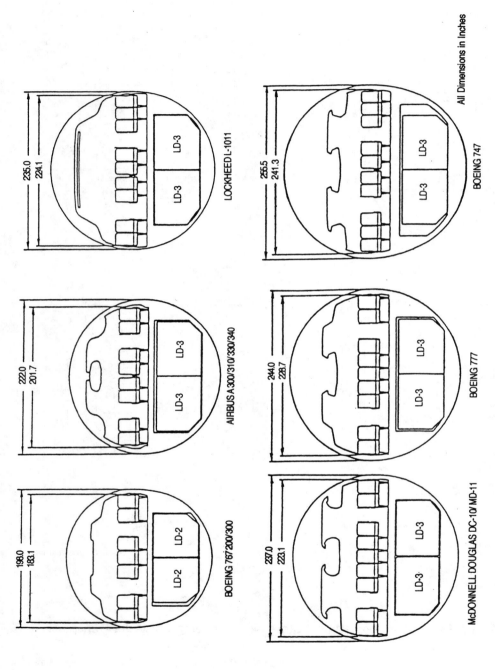

Fig. 5-6 Passenger Compartment Cross Sections - Twin Aisle Jet Transports

Courtesy of the Boeing Co, Lockheed Martin

No. Pass.	Aisles	Seats Across (coach)	Fuselage Dia. (inches).	Examples
4 to 9	1	1+1	64-84	Citation, Learjet, Falcon
10-20	1	1+1	58-78	Beech 1900, Metro III
10-20	1	2+1	94-106	Gulfstream II/III/IV/V, Challenger
20-50	1	2-1	90-91	Saab 340, Brasilia
50-75	1	2+2	96-106	BAe 748, DHC-8
75-190	1	2+3	130	F-28, F-100, DC-9, MD-80
	1	3+3	148	707,727,737,757,A320
190-270	2	2+3+2	198	767
	2	2+4+2	222	A300, A310
270-360	2	2+4+2	222	A330, A340
	2	2+5+2	236	DC-10, MD-11, L1011, 777
360-450	2	3+4+3	256	747
450-700	2	3+4+3	256	747 Stretch
	2	3+5+3	256	Airbus design study
	3	2+4+4+2	338	Boeing design study

Average aisle width = 19 in.

Average coach seat width = 20 in.

Average coach seat pitch = 32 in. (2 or 3 class)

Average first class seat pitch = 36 in. (2 class)

Average business seat pitch = 38 in. (3 class)

Average first class seat pitch = 60 in. (3 class)

Average first/coach split = 10%-90%

Average first/business/coach split = 8%-20%-72%

Fig. 5-7 Fuselage Cross Section Sizing Summary

THE ELEMENTS OF AIRCRAFT PRELIMINARY DESIGN

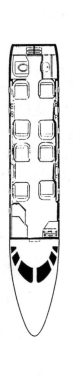

Cessna Citation X

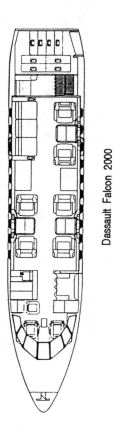

Dassault Falcon 2000

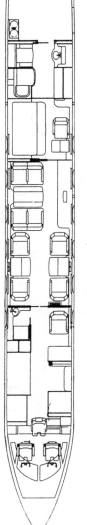

Gulfstream V

Fig. 5-8 Passenger Compartment Arrangements of Business Jets

Courtesy of Cessna Aircraft Co., Dassault Aviation, Gulfstream Aerospace

Courtesy of McDonnel Douglas Corp., now the Boeing Co.

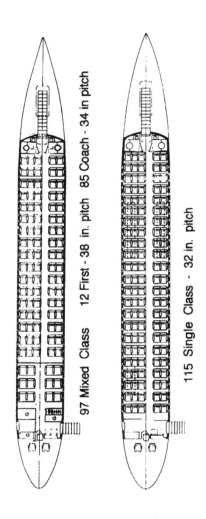

DC-9-30 TYPICAL ARRANGEMENTS

97 Mixed Class   12 First - 38 in. pitch   85 Coach - 34 in pitch

115 Single Class - 32 in. pitch

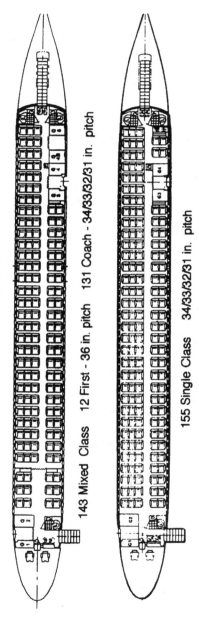

MD-80 TYPICAL ARRANGEMENTS

143 Mixed Class   12 First - 36 in. pitch   131 Coach - 34/33/32/31 in. pitch

155 Single Class   34/33/32/31 in. pitch

Fig. 5-9 Passenger Cabin Layouts of Short Range Jet Transports

757-200 TYPICAL ARRANGEMENTS

194 Mixed Class   12 First - 38 in. pitch   182 Coach - 32 in. pitch

155 Three Class   14 First - 60 in pitch   28 Business - 38 in. pitch   113 Coach - 32 in. pitch

767-300 TYPICAL ARRANGEMENTS

269 Mixed Class   24 First - 38 in. pitch   245 Coach - 32 in. pitch

218 Three Class   18 First - 60 in. pitch   46 Business - 38 in. pitch   154 Coach - 32 in. pitch

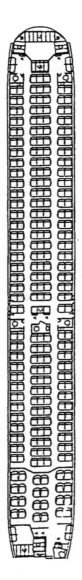
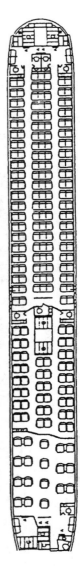

Courtesy of the Boeing Co.

Fig. 5-10 Passenger Cabin Layouts of Medium Range Jet Transports

Courtesy of the Boeing Co.

777-200   305 Passengers ~ 3 Class   24 First   54 Business   227 Coach

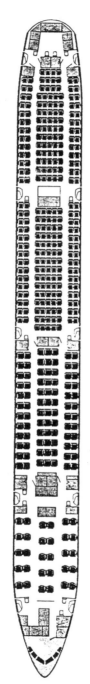

777-300   368 Passengers ~ 3 Class   30 First   84 Business   254 Coach

Upper Deck

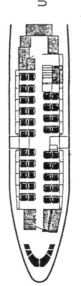

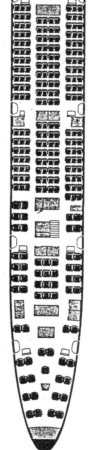

747-400   416 Passengers ~ 3 Class   23 First   78 Business   315 Coach

Fig. 5-11 Passenger Cabin Layouts of Long Range Jet Transports

Constant Section Planforms

L = length of constant section passenger cabin
D = maximum outside fuselage diameter

Aircraft	L/D
BAe 146-200	4.13
737-500	4.75
MD-11	6.39
MD-87	6.67
A330-300	7.16
757-200	8.63
MD-82	8.78

Fig. 5-12 Constant Section Planforms

For all the aircraft types noted above, there are very specific requirements for emergency exists, for use in the event of a survivable accident. The description of the various types of emergency exits, their location, the minimum size of the various exit types, as well as the maximum step heights for non-floor level exits are summarized in Fig. 5-13. The number of pairs of emergency exits required is related to the number of passenger seats installed on the aircraft. Fig. 5-14 provides information on the number and types of exits required by the FARs for various numbers of passengers.

Commuters, regional turboprops, business jets, and jet transports also require space on the passenger compartment floor plan for galleys, lavatories, and closets for coat storage. The usual approach is to allocate galley space on a cubic foot per passenger basis, lavatories on a number of passengers per lavatory basis, and coat closets on the basis of a number of inches of closet space per passenger. Some general data on passenger service and amenities allocations for jet transports is shown in Fig. 5-15.

Another consideration for the passenger compartment is the provision for carrying standard size cargo containers and pallets on the cargo deck below the main passenger deck. Single aisle jet transports usually do not have sufficient below deck volume to accommodate containerized cargo. However, twin aisle jet transports usually have a large volume available for containerized revenue cargo, and the industry has developed a number of standard lower deck containers and pallets for carrying cargo. The most common is the LD-3, used on the majority of the wide-body jet transports, and favored for the ease of interchangeability. The LD-2 is a special smaller version of the LD-3 designed to fit in the 767, but it has had limited success because of its lesser cargo volume when interchanged with aircraft capable of carrying LD-3s. A summary of lower deck container and pallet descriptions is shown in Fig. 5-16.

Types Of Emergency Exits Defined by FAR 25.807 for Transport Category Aircraft

Type	Location	Minimum Size (inches)	Max. Step Height Inside/Outside (inches)
Type I	floor level	24 x 48	N.A.
Type II	floor level	20 x 44	N.A.
	overwing	20 x 44	10/17
Type III	overwing	20 x 36	24/27
Type IV	overwing	19 x 26	29/36
Ventral	through pressure shell and bottom fuselage skin	At least equivalent to TYPE I	N.A.
Tailcone	through pressure shell with openable cone aft of pressure shell	20 x 60	24/27
Type A	floor level	42 x 72	N.A..

Fig. 5-13 Types of Emergency Exits

NOSE SECTION

The nose section of the fuselage on larger aircraft usually contains the crew station, with associated crew seats, control wheel or stick, rudder pedals, instrument panel, glare shield, cockpit enclosure windows, plus a variety of levers, knobs, and switches to operate various aircraft systems.

Number and Type of Emergency Exits Specified by FAR 25.807 for Transport Category Aircraft

For 1-299 Passenger Seats:

Number of passenger seats		Emergency Exits on Each Side			
		Type 1	Type II	Type III	Type IV
1	9				1
10	19			1	
20	39		1	1	
40	79	1		1	
80	109	1		2	
110	139	2		1	
140	179	2		2	

For additional passenger seats greater than 179, additional exits of the following types must be incorporated, so that he additional exit seat credit equals or exceeds the number of additional passenger seats installed.

Additional Seat Credit	Additional Type Exit	
12	Ventral	single
15	Tailcone	single
35	Type III	pairs
40	Type II	pairs
45	Type I	pairs
110	Type A	pairs

For greater than 299 passenger seats:

Emergency exits must be either Type A or Type I, with seat credit as listed in the above table.

Fig. 5-14 Number and Types of Emergency Exits

Aircraft		B757-200	B767-200	A310-200	A300B4	B767-300	DC-10
Seats - Number First Class		16	18	18	24	24	24
- Number Coach		162	192	194	223	224	268
- Total		178	210	212	247	248	292
- Mix	(%)	9.0	8.6	8.5	9.7	9.7	8.2
- First Class Pitch	(in)	38	38	38	39 & 40	38	38
- Coach Pitch	(in)	34	34	34	34	34	34
- Number Abreast First Class		4	6	6	6	6	6
- Number Abreast Coach		6	7	8	8	7	9
Lavatories - Number First Class		1	1	1	1	1	1
- Number Coach		3	4	4	5	5	6
- Pax/Lav First Class		16	18	18	24	24	24
- Pax/Lav Coach		54.0	48.0	48.5	44.6	44.8	44.7
Galleys - Volume First Class	(cu ft)	70	80	119	119	122	120
- CU FT/Psgr First Class		4.4	4.4	6.6	5.0	5.1	5.0
- Equivalent Carts* First Class		4	5	6	6	7	7
- Psgr/Cart First Class		4.0	3.6	3.0	4.0	3.4	3.4
- Volume Coach	(cu ft)	231	264	294	388	361	450
- CU FT/Psgr Coach		1.4	1.4	1.5	1.7	1.6	1.7
- Equivalent Carts* Coach		11	14	15	19	18	21
- Psgr/Cart Coach		14.7	13.7	12.9	11.7	12.4	12.8
Closet - Length First Class	(in)	20	18	20	50	38	42
- Length Coach	(in)	80	70	80	70	116	155
- Inch/Pax First Class		1.2	1.0	1.1	2.1	1.6	1.7
- Inch/Pax Coach		0.49	0.36	0.41	0.31	0.52	0.58
Cabin Attendants - Total Number		5	6	6	7	7	8
- Pax/Attendant		35.6	35.0	35.3	35.7	35.3	36.5

Fig. 5-15 Passenger Cabin Service and Amenities Data for Jet Transports

129

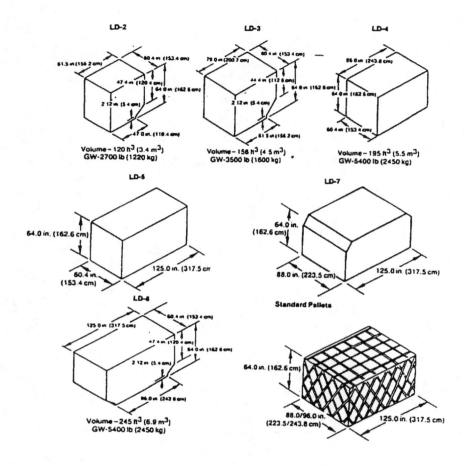

Fig. 5-16 Lower Deck Container and Pallet Dimensions

Requirements for the crew station arrangement are:

- The ability to reach and operate all controls, levers, knobs, and switches from the normal seated position; and
- Must accommodate 5th to 95th percentile men and women.

Another key requirement relates to pilot down vision over the nose, from the <u>Design Pilot Eye Position</u>. The requirement is based on the idea that the pilot should be able to see other aircraft at or slightly below his flight path, without undue maneuvering. This translates to:

Personal/Utility Aircraft	8° - 10°
Commuters/Regional Turboprops	12° - 15°
Business Jets/Jet Transports	18° - 21°

In addition to down vision requirements, there are general field-of-view requirements, from the Design Pilot Eye Position, specified in the FARs.

Blending all of these requirements plus the aerodynamic requirements for low drag and low noise from the nose shape requires considerable attention to the detailed geometry. An overall criterion for high subsonic cruise Mach number aircraft can be obtained from the data of Fig. 5-17, which shows length-to-diameter ratios for a number of business jets and commercial jet transports. The average value of around 1.5 seems to be adequate.

NOSE SHAPES

L = length of nose section forward of constant section
D = maximum diameter of fuselage

Aircraft	$(L/D)_{TOP}$	$(L/D)_{SIDE}$
DC-9/MD-80	1.44	1.46
757-200	1.20	1.53
767-200/300	1.39	1.39
A300/310/330/340	1.50	1.55
DC-10/MD-11	1.46	1.52
777	1.37	1.45
G III / IV / V	1.95	1.44
Average Value	1.48	1.48

Fig. 5-17 Nose Shapes

AFT FUSELAGE SHAPE

The aft fuselage section, or afterbody shape is influenced by conflicting requirements of aerodynamics, structural weight, and pitch attitude during takeoff or landing. The afterbody should be long enough to avoid severe curvature and separation drag, while being as short as possible to avoid the weight of a long and not too useful afterbody. Another factor associated with afterbody design is the amount of upsweep that the mean line of the afterbody has with respect to the constant section as shown in Fig. 5-18. Large upsweep angles can lead to significant drag penalties so upsweep angles are usually limited to 6-1/2 deg. or less. A summary of afterbody data for jet transports is shown in Fig. 5-19.

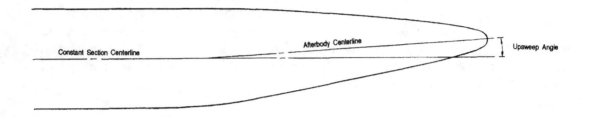

Fig. 5-18 Fuselage Afterbody Upsweep

AFTERBODY SHAPES

L = length of afterbody aft constant section
D = maximum diameter of fuselage

Aircraft	$(L/D)_{TOP}$	$(L/D)_{SIDE}$	"Upsweep" (Deg)
DC-9/MD-80	2.63	2.50	5.50
757-200	3.00	3.25	3.50
767-200/300	2.29	2.48	5.00
A300/310/330/340	3.18	3.40	6.25
DC-10/MD-11	2.56	2.45	5.50
777	2.50	3.52	4.50
G III/IV	3.31	3.84	3.00
Average Value	2.35	3.06	4.75

Fig. 5-19 Afterbody Shapes

MILITARY FIGHTER/ATTACK AND TRAINER CREW STATIONS

Crew station considerations for military fighter/attack and trainer aircraft are similar to civil aircraft as far as the ability of the crew members to reach and operate all controls and switches, and the requirement for good down vision. Down vision is especially important for the rear seat occupant in a military jet trainer, most often the instructor pilot. In addition, there are some special requirements associated with the installation of ejection

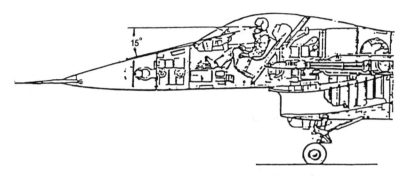

Single Seat Fighter/Attack Aircraft

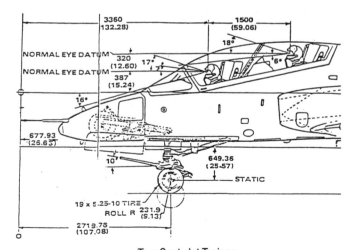

Two Seat Jet Trainer

Fig. 5-20 Typical Military Aircraft Crew Stations

133

seats, which must have proper clearances with the aircraft structure. Fig. 5-20 shows a typical crew station layout for a single seat fighter/attack aircraft, and a two seat tandem layout for a military trainer aircraft. Cockpit clearance dimensions for ejection seat installations are shown in Fig. 5-21.

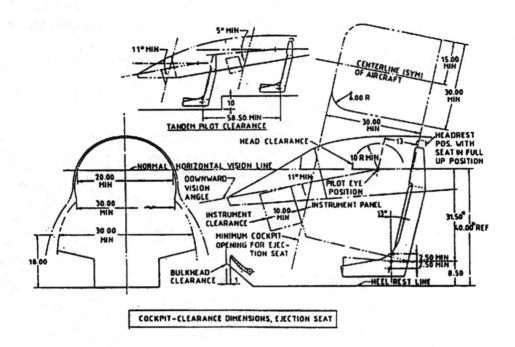

1. THE SEAT SHALL BE PROVIDED WITH VERTICAL ADJUSTMENT AS SHOWN.

2. THE 30 INCH MINIMUM EJECTION CLEARANCE LINE (PARALLEL TO THE EJECTION PATH AND MEASURED PERPENDICULARLY TO THE PLANE OF THE SEAT BACK) SHALL BE PROVIDED FROM THE SEAT REFERENCE POINT. FOR AIRPLANES NOT REQUIRING EJECTION SEATS, THE MINIMUM COCKPIT OPENING SHALL BE 24 INCHES BY 24 INCHES.

3. ALL MEASUREMENTS ARE BASED UPON THE SEAT REFERENCE POINT AT THE CENTERLINE OF THE SEAT IN THE NEUTRAL POSITION

4. THERE SHALL BE NO PROJECTIONS SUCH AS THE THROTTLE, LANDING GEAR CONTROL, INSTRUMENT PANEL, ETC., INTO THE EJECTION SEAT ENVELOPE THAT WOULD INTERFERE WITH SEAT EJECTION.

Fig. 5-21 Ejection Seat Clearance Requirements

Reprinted by perrmission from Ref. 5.6

134

WING POSITION ON THE FUSELAGE
.25 m.a.c. LOCATION IN % OF TOTAL FUSELAGE LENGTH

TYPE OF AIRCRAFT	$\bar{x}$ .25 m.a.c./L_{FUS}
Personal/Utility	.35
Commuters	.42
Regional Turboprops	.42
Business Jets	.56
Jet Transports - Aft Engines	.55
Jet Transports - Wing Engines	.46
Military Fighter/Attack	.59

$\bar{x}$ .25 m.a.c. is the distance from the fuselage nose to the .25 m.a.c. point.

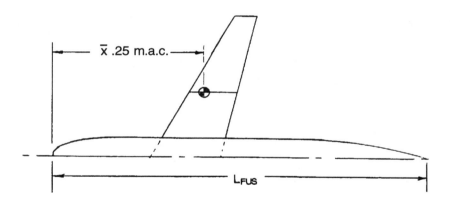

Fig. 5-22   Trend Data of Wing Position on Fuselage

FUSELAGE LOCATION ON THE WING

After the fuselage design is completed, it is necessary to locate the fuselage in a proper location on the wing. This step is required before the horizontal and vertical tails can be designed, and a suitable landing gear arrangement can be developed. Fortunately, there is a significant amount of trend data available for various types of aircraft, summarized in Fig. 5-22, that provides a reasonable basis for locating the wing on the fusselage.

135

DESIGN EXERCISE

Draw a side view and a top view of a preliminary fuselage layout for your design project. Show all important items such as the design pilot's eye position, crew station, passenger seating arrangement, galleys, lavatories, coat closets, as well as size, type, and location, and number of emergency exits.

REFERENCES

5.1 Roskam, Jan, Airplane Design Part III, Layout Design of the Cockpit, Fuselage, and Empennage, Roskam Aviation and Engineering Corporation, Ottawa, KS, 1989

5.2 Anonymous, The DC 9 Handbook, Douglas Aircraft Co. Long Beach, CA. 1991

5.3 Steiner, John E., How Decisions are Made, AIAA Wright Brothers Lecture, Seattle, WA, 1982

5.4 Anonymous, The MD-80 Handbook, Douglas Aircraft Co., Long Beach, CA, 1990

5.5 Anonymous, The Leading Family of Passenger Jet Airplanes, Boeing Commercial Airplane Group, Seattle, WA, 1998

5.6 Anonymous, AFSC Design Handbook, Series DH2-2, Crew Station and Passenger Accommodations, AFWAL, WPAFB,OH, 1984

6

HORIZONTAL AND VERTICAL TAIL SIZING

GENERAL CONSIDERATIONS

Horizontal and vertical tail sizing means determining the geometry of the horizontal and vertical tail surfaces, including their control surface elements, the elevator and rudder. The geometry to be determined includes the tail area, aspect ratio, taper ratio, sweep, thickness ratio, and control surface hinge line location.

For conventional aft tail configurations, the horizontal and vertical tails are the major elements in providing both static aerodynamic stability in pitch and yaw, and aerodynamic control moments in pitch and yaw. For unconventional configurations such as "flying wings" or forward horizontal tail "canards", static aerodynamic stability and control are provided by alternate means.

Before getting into the procedures for sizing the horizontal and vertical tail surfaces, a brief review of the fundamentals of static aerodynamic stability and control in pitch and yaw is in order.

STATIC AERODYNAMIC STABILITY IN PITCH

Static aerodynamic stability in pitch, more commonly known as static longitudinal stability, is most easily achieved through the use of an aft mounted horizontal tail. In concept, static longitudinal stability may be defined as the tendency of the airplane to return to it's original flight condition without pilot input, when disturbed from steady, unaccelerated flight. While not an absolute requirement for sustained, controlled flight, static longitudinal stability has been found over the years to be a desireable characteristic for ease of operation by the pilot. A more specific definition of static longitudinal stability is that the

137

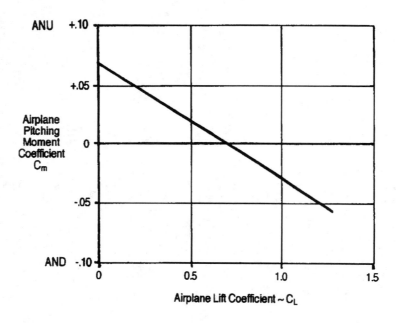

Fig. 6-1 Typical Airplane pitching Moment Diagram

variation of airplane pitching moment coefficient, Cm, with airplane lift coefficient, C_L, have a negative slope as shown on the pitching moment diagram in Fig. 6-1.

It should be noted that the pitching moment coefficient is defined with respect to the airplane center of gravity (c.g.) location, expressed in percent of the wing mean aerodynamic chord (m.a.c.) aft of the leading edge. For example, with a c.g. location expressed as 25% m.a.c., the c.g. is located at a distance of 25% of the m.a.c. length aft of the leading edge of the m.a.c. Using the sign convention noted in Chapter 1, the negative slope of the pitching moment curve means that with the airplane in equilibrium (pitching moment equal to zero) in steady, unaccelerated flight at a given lift coefficient, any disturbance which increases the airplane lift coefficient will result in a negative, or airplane nose down, (AND) pitching moment coefficient.

Effect of c.g. location

It can be shown by analysis of the equation for the airplane pitching moment coefficient versus lift coefficient that the airplane c.g. location has a powerful effect on static longitudinal stability. The results of this analysis show that for every one percent of m.a.c. that the c.g. is moved forward, the slope of the pitching moment curve, dC_m/dC_L, about that c.g. will become more negative by .01. This point is illustrated for a typical airplane

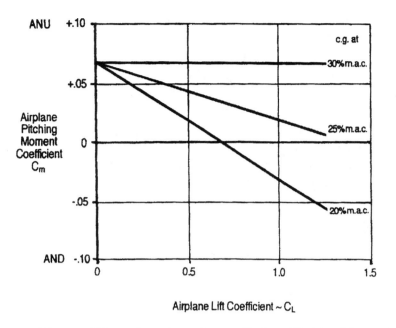

Fig. 6-2 Effect of c.g. Location on Airplane Pitching Moments

configuration in Fig. 6-2. In this figure, the pitching moment curve with the c.g. located at 25% m.a.c. shows a negative (stable) slope of -.05. If the c.g. is moved forward to 20% m.a.c., the pitching moment curve about this c.g. location shows a negative (stable) slope of -.10, indicating that a 5% forward movement in c.g. location results in a pitching moment curve that is more negative by .05. Similarly if the c.g. is moved aft, the pitching moment curve will have a less stable (negative) slope about that c.g. location. In the diagram of Fig. 6-2, if the c.g. location is moved aft to 30% m.a.c., then the slope of the pitching moment curve about this c.g. location is zero. This situation illustrates another important concept in the discussion of static longitudinal stability, that of aerodynamic center.

Aerodynamic Center

From basic aerodynamics the aerodynamic center location for any configuration is defined as the center of constant pitching moments, that is the c.g. location where the pitching moment coefficient remains constant as the lift coefficient varies. In the illustration of Fig. 6-2, the aerodynamic center for the configuration shown is at 30% m.a.c., since for this c.g. location, the pitching moment coeficient, C_m, is constant as the lift coefficient varies.

For any aircraft configuration, the criterion for achieving static longitudinal stability is that the aircraft c.g. must be located forward of the airplane aerodynamic center (a.c.). This criterion applies to all types of configurations, conventional aft tail arrangements as well as canards, three surface layouts, and even flying wings. However, as we shall see, this stability criterion is most easily met using a conventional aft mounted horizontal tail. Again referring to Fig. 6-2, with the c.g. located at 25% m.a.c. and the a.c. located at 30% m.a.c., this configuration meets the criterion for static longitudinal. stability, and with dC_m/dC_L equal to -.05 is said to be stable by 5% m.a.c. With the c.g. located at 20% m.a.c. and the a.c. at 30% m.a.c., dC_m/dC_L is -.10 and the configuration is said to be stable by 10% m.a.c. Expressed in equation form,

$$dC_m/dC_L \;=\; X_{c.g.} - X_{a.c.} \qquad\qquad (6\text{-}1)$$

where X is expressed in terms of percent m.a.c.

Aerodynamic Center Buildup

The aerodynamic center location for a complete airplane configuration is determined by the contribution of the various elements of the configuration in pitch. The contributions of these elements can be calculated with reasonable accuracy, but are usually verified by wind tunnel model tests very early in the preliminary design phase. The major contributors to the complete configuration aerodynamic center are the wing, fuselage, engine nacelles, and the horizontal tail. A typical wind tunnel model buildup to determine the contributions of these elements to the complete configuration a.c. is shown in Fig. 6-3. These data are all referred to a c.g. location of 25% m.a.c. By measuring the slope of the pitching moment curve about this c.g., one can obtain the a.c. location for any configuration made up of the major elements that contribute to the a.c. location, by rearranging Equation 6-1 as

$$X_{a.c.} \;=\; .25 - (dC_m/dC_L) \qquad\qquad (6\text{-}2)$$

Fig. 6-4 summarizes the a.c. locations for the various partial configurations, leading up to the complete configuration a.c. Also shown is the contribution of the various elements to the complete airplane a.c.

The wing alone a.c. is at 22.6% m.a.c. The wing plus fuselage a.c. is at 16.3% m.a.c., indicating that the fuselage has a destabilizing or unstable contribution of .063 or 6.3% m.a.c. The wing plus the fuselage plus the engine nacelles have an a.c. location of 11.0% m.a.c., indicating that the nacelles have an unstable contribution of 5.3% m.a.c. to the a.c.

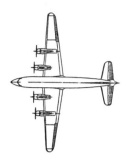

Straight Wing, 4 -Engine, Prop Driven Transport Model

c.g. at 25% m.a.c.

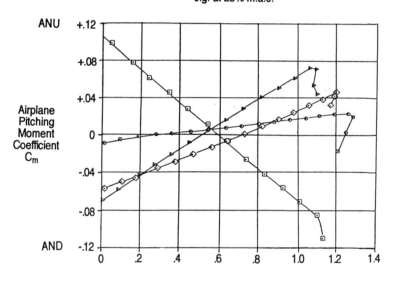

symbol	configuration	notation
—•—	Wing alone	W
—◇—	Wing + Fuselage	W F
—▶—	Wing + Fuselage + Nacelles	W F N
—▫—	Wing + Fuselage + Nacelles + H.T. + V.T.	W F N H V

Fig. 6-3 Typical Wind Tunnel Data for Aerodynamic Center Buildup

141

Typical Aerodynamic Center Buildup
based on wind tunnel test data
c.g. located at 25% m.a.c.

Configurations	p.m. curve slope dC_m/dC_L	a.c. location % m.a.c.	effect of element on a.c. location
W	+.024	22.6	–
W F	+.087	16.3	(-6.3%) fuselage
W F N	+.140	11.0	(-5.23%) nacelles
W F N H V	-.177	42.7	(+31.7%) horiz tail

Fig. 6-4 Summary of Aerodynamic Center Locations and Contributions of Major Elements

location. The addition of the horizontal and vertical tails to the model results in an a.c. location for the complete configuration of 42.7% m.a.c. Since the vertical tail has no aerodynamic contribution in pitch, the horizontal tail provides a strong stabilizing contribution of 31.7% m.a.c. Some generalizations may be made fron the data First, the wing alone a.c. is usually around 25% m.a.c. , not surprising since the a.c. for nearly all airfoil sections which make up the wing is within a per cent m.a.c. or so of the 25% m.a.c. point. Wing sweep may also move the wing alone a.c. a percent or two, usually aft. Secondly, fuselages are destabilizing contributors, tending to move the a.c.location forward. The larger the fuselage is relative to the wing, the more destabilizing will be it's contribution to the complete airplane a.c. Forward mounted nacelles like the ones shown on the model in Fig. 6-3 are also destabilizing, although aft fuselage mounted nacelles are usually stabilizing. Finally, the aft horizontal tail is a major stabilizing contributor to the complete airplane a.c. location. It can be shown that the horizontal tail contribution to static longitudinal stability is dependent on the distance between the 25% chord point on the wing m.a.c. and the 25% m.a.c. point on the horizontal tail, called the horizontal tail length, l_H, and the horizontal tail area, S_H This is quite logical since static longitudinal stability involves the generation of aerodynamic restoring moments which are dependent on an aerodynamic force from the horizontal tail (proportional to the horizontal tail area) and a moment arm (proportional to the horizontal tail length).

LONGITUDINAL CONTROL

In addition to providing a major contribution to static longitudinal stability, the horizontal tail is also a source for longitudinal control moments. These control moments are used by the pilot to achieve equilibrium in pitch (C_m=0) at any desired lift coefficient, allowing control of airspeed in unaccelerated flight, and the curvature of the flight path in accelerated flight. A typical pitching moment diagram is shown in Fig. 6-5. This airplane is stable about it's c.g. with a dC_m/C_L equal to -.10 and is in equilibrium (C_m = 0) at a lift coefficient, C_L= 0.5. This means that the airplane will fly steadily at a speed corresponding to this lift coefficient, and it's static longitudinal stability will resist any disturbances tending to deviate from this speed. If the pilot desires to slow the airplane down, and fly at a C_L = 1.0, he must be equipped with some type of control that can overcome the airplane nose down moment coefficient of -.05 at a C_L= 1.0 as shown in Fig. 6-5 in order to establish equilibrium at C_L = 1.0. Obviously, the more stable the airplane, the more control power that must be provided to change the equilibrium lift coefficient. Thus the designer must achieve a proper balance between the amount of static longitudinal stability provided and the amount of control power available. Longitudinal control power is usually provided through the hinged, moveable aft portion of the horizontal tail (elevators), although in some designs the control power is provided by moving the entire horizontal tail about a fixed pivot point, (all moveable horizontal tail or stabilator).

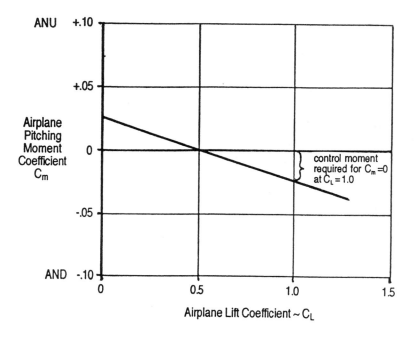

Fig. 6-5 Typical Airplane Pitching Moment Diagram

143

Longitudinal control capability for a specific configuration may be shown on a typical pitching moment diagram, Fig. 6-6, where the pitching moment curves with various control surface deflections show the control deflection required to obtain equilibrium at various lift coefficients. Notice that a negative (trailing edge up) control deflection produces a positive (airplane nose up) pitching moment.

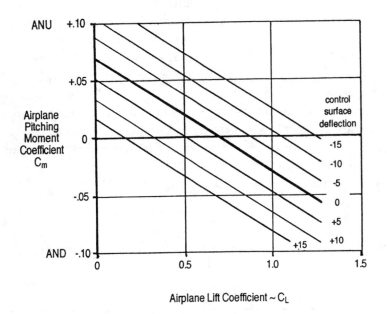

Fig. 6-6 Typical Airplane Pitching Moment Diagram~Effect of Control Deflections

HORIZONTAL TAIL SIZING PROCEDURE

As was noted earlier, the horizontal tail is a major contributor to both static longitudinal stability and longitudinal control. Furthermore, it was pointed out that the airplane c.g. has a powerful effect on both longitudinal stability and longitudinal control. Therefore, a primary task in the preliminary design phase is to specify a horizontal tail that will be adequate to meet airplane stability and control needs over the entire c.g. range expected in service. As a relative measure of the ability of the horizontal tail to provide both longitudinal stability and control, the concept of a non-dimensional horizontal tail volume has been utilized. The horizontal tail volume is defined as

$$V_H = \frac{S_H}{S} \times \frac{l_H}{c} \tag{6-3}$$

144

where S_H = horizontal tail area

S = reference wing area

l_H = distance from .25 c_W to .25c_{HT}

c = wing m.a.c. length

Very early in the preliminary design process, stability and control calculations are made to show the effect of horizontal tail volume on the ability to meet specific aft c.g. static stability requirements and forward c.g. control requirements. These calculations are beyond the scope of this book, but they lead to the development of a chart called the "scissors diagram", shown in Fig. 6-7. As noted earlier, adding horizontal tail volume through an aft tail arrangement moves the complete configuration a.c. aft, so that static longitudinal stability may be achieved at further aft c.g. locations. A fixed amount of static stability (c.g. forward of the a.c.) is selected, usually from 5% to 10% m.a.c. and is called the static margin. Adding horizontal tail volume also increases the ability to provide longitudinal control at forward c.g. locations. The required c.g. range arises from the movement of the c.g. due to variable fuel and passenger loadings. The required ranges can be quite small for a small personal/utility aircraft, but quite large for a commercial jet transport, where large variations in passenger load and seating locations and variations in fuel load can effect the c.g. location. Typical c.g. ranges for various types of aircraft are

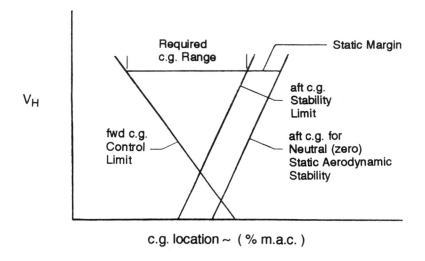

Fig. 6-7 Horizontal Tail Volume "Scissors" Diagram

Aircraft Type	c.g. range (% m.a.c.)
Personal/Utility	10%
Commuters	12%
Regional Turboprops	16%
Business Jets	18%
Jet Transports	32%
Military Fighter/Attack	20%

Fig. 6-8 Typical c.g. Ranges

A relatively straightforward preliminary design method for estimating the horizontal tail volume required, based on the correlation of data from many production airplanes, is outlined as follows. Using the appropriate dimensions of the fuselage determined in Part 5, along with the pertinent wing geometric data from Part 4, calculate the longitudinal fuselage volume parameter, $(W^2_{fus})(L_{fus})/ S_W c_W$ where

W_{fus} is the maximum fuselage width
L_{fus} is the fuselage length
S_W is the reference wing area
c_w is the wing m.a.c. length

Enter Fig. 6-9 to determine the horizontal tail volume required per unit of c.g. range required. With the typical c.g. range for a particular aircraft type, determine the V_H required. With the horizontal tail length derived from the fuselage design and wing placement on the fuselage, the horizontal tail area may be calculated. Note that the longitudinal fuselage volume coefficient is dimensionless. As a check on the estimated horizontal tail volume, the range of horizontal tail volumes for various types of aircraft are shown in Fig. 6-10. The lower values are usually associated with designs that have smaller c.g. ranges.

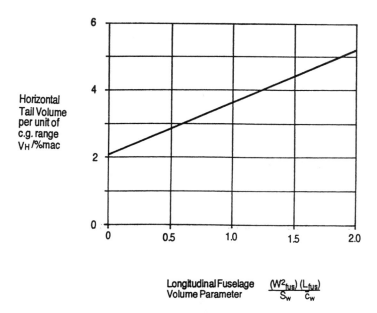

Fig. 6-9 Preliminary Design Chart ~ Horizontal Tail Volume Determination

Aircraft Type	V_H Range
Personal/Utility	.48- .92
Commuters	.46-1.07
Regional Turboprops	.83-1.47
Business Jets	.51 - .99
Jet Transports	.54-1.48
Military Fighter/Attack	.20 - .75

Fig. 6-10   Representative Horizontal Tail Volume Ranges

STATIC DIRECTIONAL STABILITY

Static directional stability for an airplane is defined as it's tendency to develop restoring moments when disturbed from it's equilibrium sideslip angle, normally zero. The static directional stability of an airplane is assessed from a chart of yawing moment coefficient, C_n, versus sideslip angle, β, as shown in Fig. 6-11. Using the sign convention of Fig. 1-3 and 1-5, a positive value of $dC_n/d\beta$ is required for static directional stability. That is, a positive (airplane nose left) sideslip produces a positive (airplane nose right) yawing moment.

147

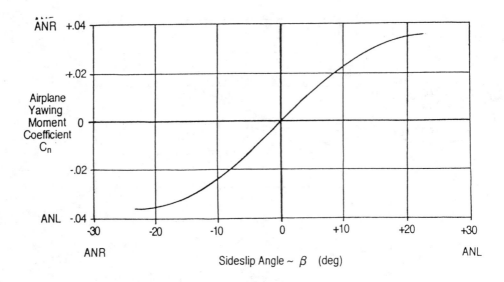

Fig. 6-11 Typical Airplane Directional Stability Diagram

Similar to the longitudinal case, the static directional stability of an airplane may be determined by adding up the contributions of the various elements of the configuration in sideslip. Analysis has shown that the main contributors to the airplane static directional stability are the fuselage and the vertical tail. The wing, a major element in longitudinal stability, has a negligible effect on the directional stability. This is due to the fact that an angle of sideslip produces very small cross wind forces on the wing, whereas an angle of attack can produce very large lift forces. The fuselage is a major contributor to static directional stability, and it's contribution is always unstable (destabilizing). The stabilizing contributor to static directional stability is the vertical tail, in reality a low aspect ratio wing attached to the aft fuselage. The contribution of the major elements is shown in Fig. 6-12. When a sideslip angle develops due to a disturbance, the vertical tail experiences an increase in it's angle of attack, and produces a restoring moment. The loss in directional stability at high sideslip angles, the "roundover" of the directional stability curve, is due to the vertical tail reaching its maximum lift capability, and stalling as the sideslip angle is increased. This roundover is not desireable and is often offset by the addition of a dorsal fin located at the intersection of the vertical tail leading edge and the fuselage. The magnitude of the restoring moment generated by the vertical tail depends on the distance from the airplane c.g. to the 25% m.a.c. point on the vertical tail, called the vertical tail length, l_v and the vertical tail area, S_v. For convenience, l_v is usually taken from the 25% m.a.c. point on the wing, rather than tha c.g.

148

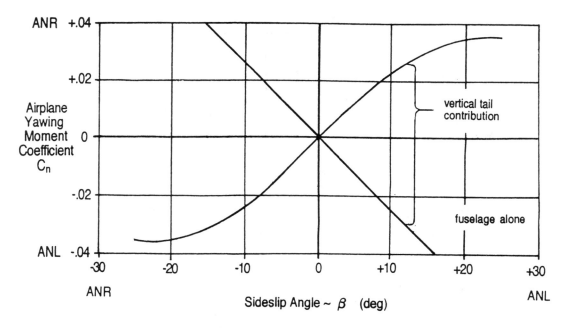

Fig. 6-12 Directional Stability Buildup

DIRECTIONAL CONTROL

The vertical tail also provides the means for directional control. The predominate means is through a hinged, moveable aft portion of the vertical tail (rudder), although some advanced military aircraft use all moveable verticals. As shown in Fig. 6-13, the directional control is used to obtain equilibrium (C_n = 0) in steady sideslips. This figure shows that 30 deg. of left rudder produces about 14 deg. of positive sideslip.

Another requirement for directional control is to offset the asymmetric thrust moment which develops on a multi-engine airplane when one engine becomes inoperative.In this situation, the aerodynamic moment from the vertical tail at or near zero sideslip with the control surface deflected must balance the thrust moment caused by the loss of one engine. This situation is most critical at low speeds during takeoff. The minimum speed for which it is possible to maintain directional equilibrium, (C_n = 0), during takeoff with one engine inoperative is called the mimimum control speed, V_{mc}. It may be obtained graphically by the intersection of the yawing moment due to the inoperative engine and the yawing moment due to full directional control, as shown in Fig. 6-14.

149

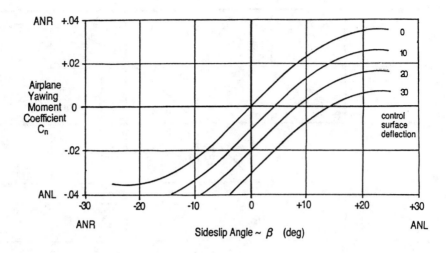

Fig. 6-13 Directional Stability Diagram ~ Effect of Control Surface Deflections

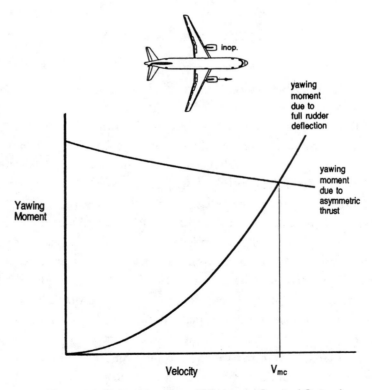

Fig. 6-14 Determination of Minimum Control Speed

VERTICAL TAIL SIZING PROCEDURE

The vertical tail size that is adequate for both directional stability and control is is also defined during the preliminary design phase. Similar to the longitudinal case, the concept of a non-dimensional vertical tail volume is useful. The vertical tail volume is defined as

$$V_V = \frac{S_V}{S} \text{ x } \frac{l_V}{b_W} \qquad (6\text{-}4)$$

where
$\quad S_v$ = vertical tail area
$\quad S$ = reference wing area
$\quad l_V$ = distance from .25 c_W to .25 c_V
$\quad b_W$ = wing span

A simple and useful way to estimate the vertical tail volume required for preliminary design purposes has been used in the industry for some time. The method is based on correlations using many different airplanes. With the fuselage dimensions from Part 5, calculate the non-dimensional directional fuselage volume parameter, $(H_{fus}^2)(L_{fus})/S_W b_W$, where

$\quad H_{fus}$ is the maximum fuselage height
$\quad L_{fus}$ is the fuselage length
$\quad S_W$ is the reference wing area
$\quad b_W$ is the wing span

Use Fig. 6-15 to obtain the estimated vertical tail volume, and with the vertical tail length from the fuselage design, calculate the vertical tail area. A range of vertical tail volumes for various types of aircraft are shown in Fig. 6-16. The lower values of vertical tail volume are usually associated with designs with small fuselages relative to the wing, and for single engine aircraft where directional control following an engine failure is not a critical requirement.

ADDITIONAL GEOMETRIC CHARACTERISTICS

In addition to the horizontal and vertical tail areas obtained by the methods outlined previously, more specific geometric characteristics, such as the tail aspect ratio, taper ratio, sweep angle, thickness ratio, and control surface chords, elevator chord as a percent of the horizontal tail chord, c_e/c, and rudder chord as a percent of vertical tail chord, c_r/c, need to be selected. In the latter stages of preliminary design, these parameters will be analyzed

151

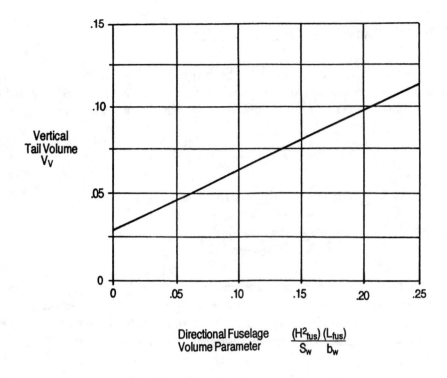

Fig. 6-15 Preliminary Design Chart ~ Vertical Tail Volume Determination

Aircraft Type	V_V Range
Personal/Utility	.024 - .086
Commuters	.041 - .097
Regional Turboprops	.065 - .121
Business Jets	.061 - .093
Jet Transports	.038 - .120
Military Fighter/attack	.041 - .130

Fig. 6-16 Representative Vertical Tail Volume Ranges

in detail in order to obtain proper balance between aerodynamic stability and control requirements, structural weight criteria, manufacturing cost, and other factors. For the initial preliminary design these characteristics are usually set or selected based on the experience of the designer. To assist in the selection of these parameters, a summary of current practice is presented in Figs. 6-17 and 6-18. Although sweep is not presented as a parameter, the sweep on the horizontal and vertical tail is usually set at about 5 deg. more than the wing sweep, to maintain control effectiveness beyond the wing M_{DIV}.

Aircraft Type	AR	λ	c_e/c	t/c
Personal/Utility	3.5-5.0	.50-1.0	.35-.45	.06-.09
Commuters	3.5-5.0	.50-.80	.35-.45	.06-.09
Regional Turboprops	3.5-5.0	.50-.80	.30-.45	.06-.09
Business Jets	3.5-5.0	.35-.50	.30-.40	.06-.09
Jet Transports	3.5-5.0	.25-.45	.30-.35	.06-.09
Military Fighter/Attack	3.0-4.0	.25-.40	.30-1.0	.03-.04

Fig. 6-17 Summary of Horizontal Tail Geometric Characteristics

Aircraft Type	AR	λ	c_r/c	t/c
Personal/Utility	1.2-1.8	.30-.50	.25-.45	.06-.09
Commuters	1.2-1.8	.30-.80	.35-.45	.06-.09
Regional Turboprops	1.4-1.8	.30 -.70	.25-.45	.06-.09
Business Jets	0.8-1.6	.30-.60	.25-.35	.06-.09
Jet Transports	1.4-1.8	.30-.80	.25-.40	.08-.10
Military Fighter/Attack	1.2-1.6	.25-.40	.20-.35	.03-.09

Fig. 6-18 Summary of Vertical Tail Geometric Characteristics

HORIZONTAL AND VERTICAL TAIL LINE DIAGRAMS

Once the geometric characteristics of the horizontal and vertical tail have been established line diagrams showing the geometry to scale are drawn. Examples of typical line diagrams are shown in Figs. 6-19 and 6-20. At this point, preliminary sketches showing the wing, fuselage, and horizontal and vertical tails all joined together are helpful in integrating these elements into a complete configuration.

DESIGN EXERCISE

Define the horizontal and vertical tail geometry for your design, and draw the line diagrams.

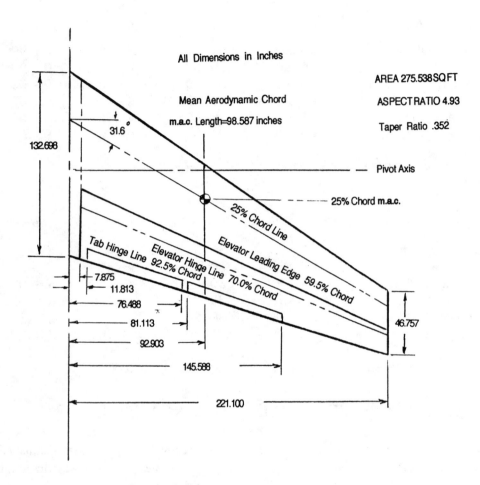

Fig. 6-19 Horizontal Tail Line Diagram

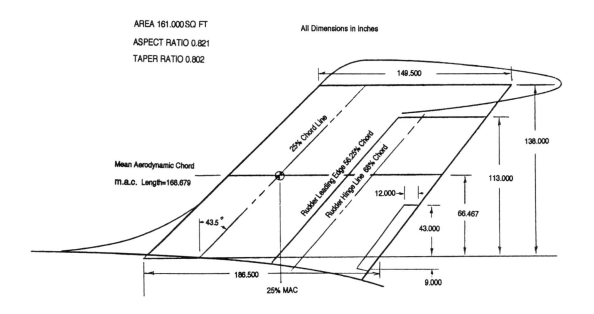

Fig. 6-20   Vertical Tail Line Diagram

REFERENCES

6.1   Perkins, Courtland D., and Hage, Robert E., Airplane Performance Stability and Control, Wiley, New York, 1949.

6.2   Phillips, W. Hewitt, An Appreciation and Prediction of Flying Qualities, NACA TR 927, 1949.

6.3   Etkin, Bernard, Dynamics of Flight, Stability and Control, Wiley, New York, NY, 1982

6.4   Abzug, Malcolm J., and Larabee, E. Eugene, Airplane Stability and Control, Cambridge University Press, Cambridge, England, 1997

7

LANDING GEAR DESIGN

The preliminary design of the landing gear is a task that must be done in conjunction with the preliminary design of the other elements of the configuration, since the landing gear can have a significant impact on weight empty, structural arrangement of the wing and fuselage juncture, and the aircraft performance capability in both landing and takeoff.

GENERAL REQUIREMENTS

The primary purpose of the landing gear is to facilitate the operation of the aircraft in landing, as well as during taxi and takeoff. The landing gear must support the maximum gross weight of the aircraft at rest and during taxi operation and distribute the aircraft weight appropriately through the number and types of wheels and tires used. The landing gear must also accommodate the reaction loads imposed at ground contact during landing.

These reaction loads for civil aircraft are specified for the appropriate aircraft types in FAR 23.471 through 23.499 and FAR 25.473 through 25.511. The requirements for military aircraft, found in the Mil-Specs, are similar. The conditions that are considered are

- Level landing
- Tail down landing
- One wheel landing
- Side load conditions
- Braked roll conditions
- Yawing conditions

157

BASIC ARRANGEMENTS

Three basic types of landing gear arrangements commonly used are shown in Fig. 7-1. Most designs use the tricycle gear arrangement, with the main gear aft, the nose gear forward, and the aircraft c.g. somewhere between. The desirable features of the tricycle gear are:

- Stability during taxi, takeoff, and landing
- Steering during ground operations
- Visibility over the nose during ground operations
- Level floor altitude on the ground
- Simpler takeoff and landing procedure

Some military aircraft have successfully used the bicycle gear arrangement with main wheels forward and aft of the c.g. on the aircraft centerline and outrigger wheels on the wing to prevent the wing tips from striking the ground. The bicycle gear works best on aircraft where the wing is located on top of the fuselage, and the most favorable load paths for the gear reactions are in the fuselage structure. The main disadvantage is the inability to rotate the aircraft from the ground attitude to a flight attitude during takeoff. Bicycle gear aircraft lift off at their ground roll attitude, which results in a much longer takeoff distance than would otherwise be required. This characteristic virtually rules out the use of the bicycle gear for business jets and jet transports, where takeoff field length is a critical performance criterion. Up to the introduction of the tricycle gear, nearly all aircraft used the tail wheel gear arrangement with the main wheels forward and a small wheel aft on the fuselage. Except for some special purpose personal/utility aircraft this arrangement is not being used on new designs.

FIXED VS. RETRACTABLE GEAR

Decisions regarding the use of a fixed vs. retractable gear involve consideration of weight, complexity, maintenance, manufacturing cost, and aircraft performance. For nearly all aircraft except, light personal/utility designs, the tradeoffs favor the use of a retractable gear.

TIP-OVER CRITERIA

A primary consideration in landing gear layout is the avoidance of an inadvertent tip-over during normal ground operations. The key point in avoiding tip-over is maintaining the aircraft weight vector in the proper relationship to the landing gear reaction points. In the

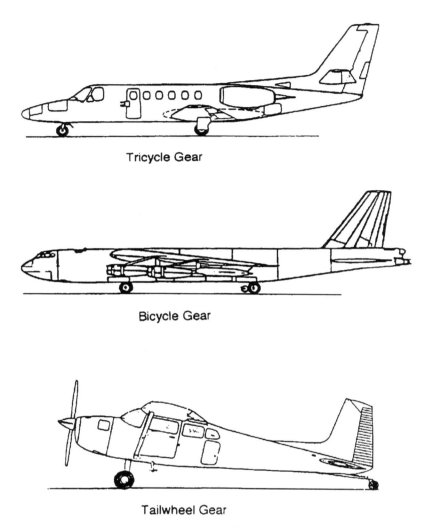

Tricycle Gear

Bicycle Gear

Tailwheel Gear

Fig. 7-1 Basic Types of Landing Gear Arrangements

longitudinal case for tricycle gears, shown in Fig. 7-2, the main gear reaction point must remain aft of the aircraft weight vector at the most aft c.g. location for the most extreme nose up attitude possible for the aircraft on the ground. As a general rule the most aft c.g. locations are around 35% m.a.c. and as indicated in the diagram, the maximum pitch attitude on the ground is usually about 15 deg. For preliminary design purposes, the values are close enough to make a first gear layout, although final resolution of the maximum pitch attitude on the ground will involve considerations of aft fuselage clearance with

159

the runway during takeoff and landing operations. For the tail wheel gear arrangement shown in Fig. 7-2, the same considerations apply, but here the critical angle is that between the main gear reaction point and the aircraft weight vector at the most forward c.g. Again, based on previous experience, an angle of about 15 deg. between the vertical and a line through the main gear reaction point and the most forward c.g. location is a satisfactory starting point for the landing gear layout for this type of aircraft.

The lateral tip-over criteria for tricycle gears involves the location of the aircraft weight

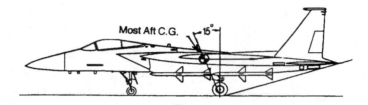

Longitudinal Tipover Criteria For Tricycle Gears

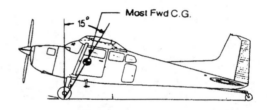

Longitudinal Tipover Criteria For Tailwheel Gears

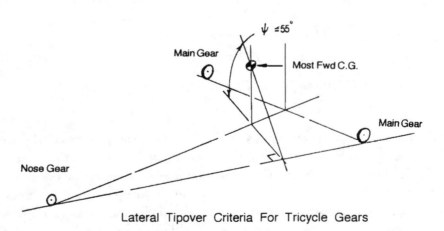

Lateral Tipover Criteria For Tricycle Gears

Fig. 7-2 Tipover Criteria for Landing Gears

Adapted with permission from Ref. 7.3

160

vector relative to a line between the main gear and nose gear reaction points, also shown in Fig. 7-2. With the maximum angle ψ indicated on the diagram, the aircraft weight vector would lie inside the gear reaction points for aircraft roll angles on the ground of 35 deg. which has been found to be acceptable in actual operation. While not shown specifically, a similar lateral tip-over criterion can be applied to tail wheel gear arrangements.

STATIC LOAD CONSIDERATIONS

Landing gear static loads are influenced by the maximum takeoff gross weight and the longitudinal position of the landing gear elements. For tricycle gear arrangements, enough static load must be applied to the nose gear to obtain satisfactory steering through the nose gear for ground operations. A general rule is that the main gear must be located far enough aft of the most aft c.g. location to provide at least 8% of the static load on the nose gear for satisfactory steering. On the other hand, the main gear must not be too far behind the most aft c.g. location such that the longitudinal control power required to rotate the aircraft during takeoff at the most forward c.g. is not excessive. Relationships between the landing gear geometry and the landing gear static loads are shown in Fig. 7-3. For most tricycle landing gear designs, the main gear reaction point is around 55% m.a.c.

GEAR LENGTH CONSIDERATIONS

The length of the main landing gear leg is obviously the prime factor in determining the maximum pitch and roll angles attainable without having some part of the aircraft contact the ground during ground operations. From weight and cost aspects, the main gear should be as short as possible; however, the main gear must be long enough to allow rotation from the ground roll attitude to the takeoff pitch attitude at normal speeds without striking the aft fuselage on the runway. The main gear must be long enough to allow pitch angles associated with normal landings without striking the aft fuselage on the runway. The main gear must also be long enough to allow reasonable roll angles on the ground without striking other parts of the airplane on the runway. Fig. 7-4 shows schematically the pitch and roll clearance angles for a large jet transport. For preliminary design, the maximum pitch attitude is set at 15 deg. and the maximum roll angle is set at 5 deg., until more detailed calculations based on a firmer definition of the aircraft are available.

WHEEL ARRANGEMENTS

In general, the higher the main and nose gear static loads, the more wheels and tires are required to distribute the loads to the runway surface. In order to be compatible with

161

existing runways, the static load on each wheel and tire should not exceed a specified level. This level is dependent on the type of runway construction and the thickness of the paving material. There are two types of runways currently in use.

1. Runways made of asphalt or macadam, called flexible pavement.

2. Runways made of concrete, called rigid pavement, which usually have about half the thickness of flexible pavement runways.

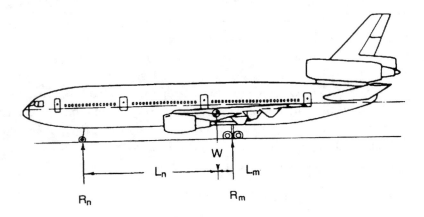

R_n = total static load on nose gear

R_m = total static load on main gear

$$R_n + R_m = W \tag{7-1}$$

N_s = number of main gear struts

To calculate the portion of the weight supported by the main gear,

$$\frac{R_m}{W} = \frac{L_n}{(L_m + L_n)} \tag{7-2}$$

The portion of the weight supported by the nose gear is

$$\frac{R_n}{W} = \frac{L_m}{(L_m + L_n)} \tag{7-3}$$

Fig. 7-3 Geometry for Static Load Calculations

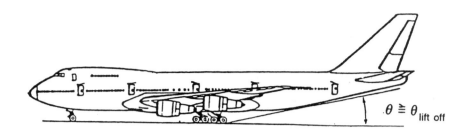

Longitudinal Ground Clearance Criteria

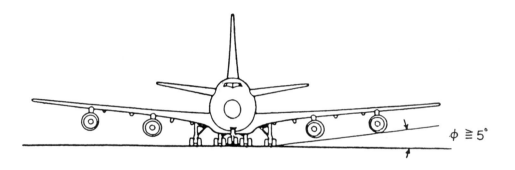

Lateral Ground Clearance Criteria

Fig. 7-4 Ground Clearance Criteria

Personal/utility aircraft normally have one wheel and tire for each landing gear leg, while large jet transports may have three or four main landing legs with four to six wheels per leg. Typical main gear wheel arrangements are shown in Fig. 7-5. Typical runway thickness requirements for jet transport operations is shown in Fig. 7-6. In order to maintain compatibility between the using aircraft and the existing runways, the International Civil Aviation Organization, (ICAO), has established a Load Classification Number, (LCN) method. All of the airport runways in the world can be given an LCN, based on the type and thickness of the pavement. Landing gear designs are also assigned an LCN, and that LCN must not exceed the lowest runway LCN from which that aircraft is to operate.

163

LANDING GEAR WHEEL ARRANGEMENTS

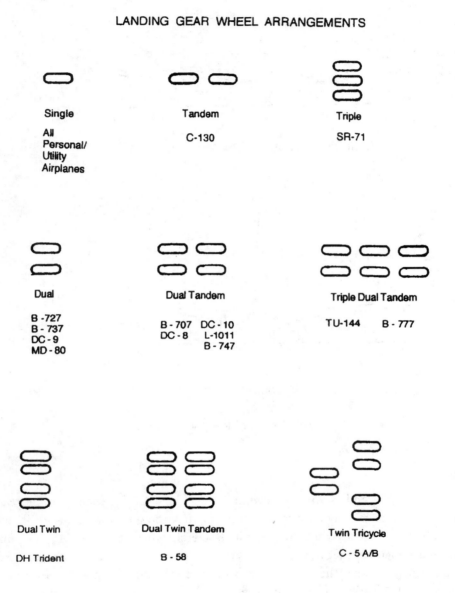

Fig. 7-5 Main Gear Wheel Arrangements

Adapted with permission from Ref. 7.2

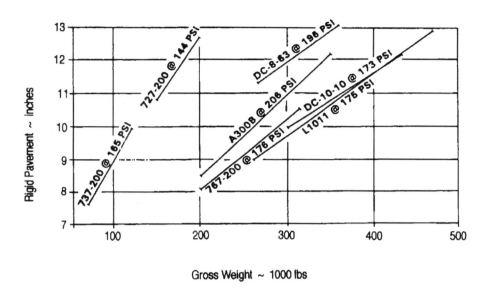

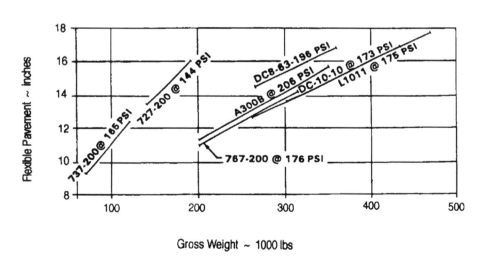

Fig. 7-6 Typical Runway Thickness Requirements

Adapted with permission from Ref. 7.3

165

TIRE SIZE

Aircraft tires are available for a wide range of static load requirements, with appropriate sizes and inflation pressures. For new aircraft designs, tire manufacturers will often produce a new design tire to match the specific requirements of the aircraft, especially if the potential market for the new aircraft is large. Over the years, a number of types of tires have been produced and identified chronologically as Type I through Type VIII. The types still in use are described as follows:

Type I - Smooth Contour- for fixed gear applications

Type III- Low Pressure- basic low pressure tire, still widely used

Type VII- Extra High Pressure- most widely used type for civil and military jets and turboprops

Type VIII- Low Profile High Pressure- newer type for very high speed takeoff requirements

Aircraft tires are defined by their most important dimensions. These are

D_o tire outside diameter

W   tire maximum width

D   rim diameter

Of the several types in use, the size descriptions are given as follows:

Type I	Type III	Type VII	Type VIII
D_o	W-D	$D_o \times W$	$D_o \times$ W-D

For example, a very popular personal/utility tire, used on a number of Beech, Cessna, and Piper aircraft is a Type III 6.00-6, which indicates that the tire maximum width is 6.00 inches, and the rim diameter is 6 inches. The tire specification shows that the tire diameter is 17.5 inches, is rated for 1150 pounds of static load, and the normal inflation pressure is 29 psi, but none of these latter numbers are used in the definition of the tire size. An example of a jet transport tire is the Type VII 40x14 used on the DC-9-30 and the 737-200. The size description indicates that the tire outside diameter of the tire is 40 inches, and the maximum width is 14 inches. The tire specification shows that the tire is rated for 27,700 lbs of static load, the rim diameter is 16 inches, and the inflation pressure is 170 psi. Data for a number of landing gear tire applications is shown in Fig. 7-7

Type	W_{TO} Lbs	Main Gear				Nose Gear			
		$D_t \times b_t$ in.x in	R_m/W_{TO}	PSI	no. tires per strut	$D_t \times b_t$ in.x in	R_n/W_{TO}	PSI	no. tires
Single Engine	1,600	15 x 6	0.80	18	1	16 x 5	0.20	28	1
Prop Driven	2,400	17 x 6	0.84	19	1	12.6 x 5	0.16	22	1
	3,800	16.5 x 6	0.84	55	1	14 x 5	0.16	49	1
Twin Engine	5,000	16 x 6	0.83	55	1	16 x 6	0.17	40	1
Prop Driven	8,000	22 x 6.5	0.88	75	1	17 x 6	0.12	40	1
	12,000	26.6 x 7	0.84	82	1	19.3 x 6.6	0.16	82	1
Regional Turbo-	12,500	18 x 5.5	0.89	105	2	22 x 6.75	0.11	57	1
Propeller Driven	21,000	24 x 7.25	0.90	85	2	18 x 5.5	0.10	65	2
Airplane	26,000	36 x 11	0.92	40	1	20 x 7.5	0.08	40	1
	44,000	30 x 9	0.93	107	2	20.4 x 6.6	0.07	77	2
Business Jets	12,000	22 x 6.3	0.93	90	1	18 x 5.7	0.07	120	1
	23,000	27.6 x 9.3	0.95	155	1	17 x 5.5	0.05	50	2
	39,000	26 x 6.6	0.92	208	2	14.5 x 7.7	0.08	130	2
	68,000	24 x 9.25	0.93	174	2	21 x 7.25	0.07	113	2
Jet Transports	44,000	34 x 12	0.89	75	2	24 x 7.7	0.11	68	2
	73,000	40 x 14	0.92	77	2	29.5 x 6.75	0.08	68	2
	116,000	40 x 14	0.94	170	2	24 x 7.7	0.06	150	2
	220,000	40 x 14	0.94	180	4	29 x 7.7	0.06	180	2
	330,000	46 x 16	0.93	206	4	40 x 14	0.07	131	2
	572,000	52 x 20.5	0.93	200	4*	40 x 15.5	0.07	190	2
	775,000	49 x 17	0.94	205	4**	46 x 16	0.06	190	2
Military Trainers	2,500	17 x 6		36	1	13.5 x 5	0.18	28	1
	5,500	20.3 x 6.5	0.82	60	1	14 x 5	0.09	40	1
	7,500	20.25 x 6	0.91	65	1	17.2 x 5.0	0.08	45	1
	11,000	23.3 x 6.5	0.92	143	1	17 x 4.4	0.10	120	1
Military Fighters									
	9,000	20 x 5.25	0.86	135	1	17 x 3.25	0.14	82	1
	14,000	18.5 x 7	0.87	110	1	18 x 6	0.13	37	1
	25,000	24 x 8	0.91	210	1	18 x 6.5	0.09	120	1
	35,000	24 x 8	0.90	85	2	21.6 x 9.8	0.10	57	1
	60,000	35.3 x 9.3	0.88	210	1	21.6 x 7.5	0.12	120	2
	92,000	42 x 13	0.93	150	1	20 x 6.5	0.07	120	2

*Three main gear struts   ** Four main gear struts

Fig. 7-7 Typical Landing Gear Wheel and Tire Data

Adapted with permission from Ref. 7.3

WHEEL BRAKES

Wheel brakes are also a part of the landing gear, and must be considered during the preliminary design. The primary design requirement for the wheel brakes is for stopping after an aborted takeoff or during a heavy weight landing. Wheel brakes are applied to the main gear only, since the small amount of added braking available from the nose gear is not worth the complication and expense of a nose gear braking system. Nearly all current aircraft use disc type brakes, which fit inside the wheel. Larger and heavier aircraft have several rotor discs which rotate with the wheel between stacks of stators, which contain the brake linings. Upon brake application, hydraulic pressure is applied to the stators which move into contact with the rotors to slow the wheel rotation. This braking action turns kinetic energy into heat, so that aircraft brakes are rated for a demonstrated amount of kinetic energy absorption. Wheels and tires must be compatible with the "heat sink" capabilities of the brakes, since the heat generated in the brake flows into the wheel and tire. Brake material has traditionally been steel, although in the past 20 years, newer jet transport and military fighter designs have used carbon composite brakes because of their lighter weight. Since the very earliest jet transports, all of the braking systems are the anti-skid type.

LANDING GEAR MECHANICAL DESIGN

The detailed mechanical design of the landing gear is a major part of the aircraft design process, and the main features of the gear are usually worked out in the preliminary design phase. For small personal/utility aircraft, the most common type of main gear is the fixed, cantilever spring leaf arrangement shown in Fig. 7-8. The steel gear leg is bolted to fuselage structure at the upper end, and fitted with an axle for the main wheel at the lower end. All of the design gear loads are within the elastic deformation range of the main gear leg, so that the gear deflects under load, but springs back to its original shape when the loads are removed. The nose gear, even for these smaller aircraft, is usually of the oleo type, shown in Fig. 7-9. In an oleo type of gear. the gear leg consists of an upper strut housing, which is attached at the upper end to the aircraft structure. The lower end incorporates a hollow cylinder to which is fitted the oleo strut. At the lower end of the oleo strut there is a fork or yoke to carry the axle for the nose wheel. At the upper end of the oleo strut, where it fits inside the strut housing, there is a chamber which contains a mixture of air and hydraulic fluid. When loads are applied to the nose gear, the air is compressed, providing shock absorption and energy dissipation from the applied load. The upper strut housing and the oleo leg are connected by a scissors-type link, which allows the oleo strut to move vertically inside the upper strut housing as the air in the chamber is compressed. For all other aircraft types, the landing gear legs for both the main and nose gear are usually of the oleo type. Obviously, for aircraft with high maximum gross weights, the landing gear hardware becomes more substantial in order to handle the higher loads, and the oleo strut air/oil

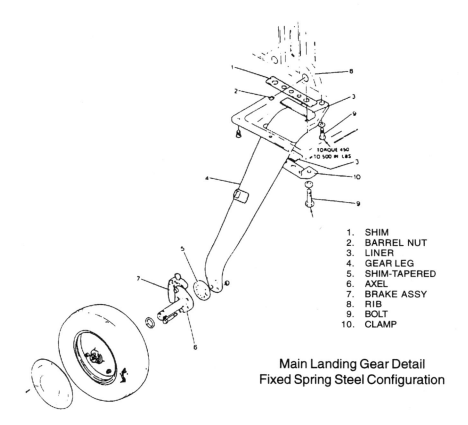

1. SHIM
2. BARREL NUT
3. LINER
4. GEAR LEG
5. SHIM-TAPERED
6. AXEL
7. BRAKE ASSY
8. RIB
9. BOLT
10. CLAMP

Main Landing Gear Detail
Fixed Spring Steel Configuration

Fig. 7-8   Fixed Main Gear Layout - Piper PA - 38

Courtesy of the New Piper Aircraft Co.

mixture is squeezed through one or more orifices to enhance the shock absorption and energy dissipation qualities of the gear. The gear design is further complicated by the requirement to retract the gear into the aircraft structure after takeoff and extend the gear prior to landing. Gear retraction and extension is usually accomplished by attaching a hydraulic actuator to the landing gear leg at a suitable point away from the gear pivot point, so that the extension and retraction of the hydraulic actuator results in the desired motion of the gear leg. Further complication is introduced by having the gear motion during retraction and extension drive the linkages that open and close the gear doors, which cover the cavity where the gear is housed in the retracted position.

The nose gear design must also include provisions for steering the nose gear during taxi operations. Typical main and nose gear arrangements for a turboprop commuter are shown in Fig. 7-10. Fig. 7-11 shows the main and nose gear configuration for a short range jet

1. BOLT
2. O-RING
3. TUBE
4. WIPER
5. O-RING
6. GREASE FITTINGS
7. O-RING
8. PLUG
9. AIR VALVE - FILLER
10. CYLINDER
11. LINK ASSY - UPPER
12. LINK ASSY - LOWER
13. FORK
14. STRUT HOUSING

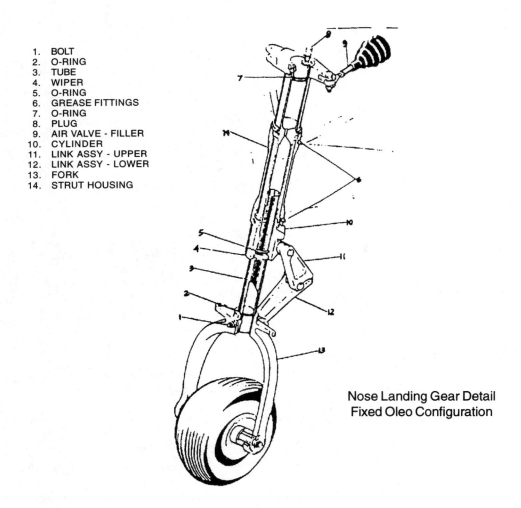

Nose Landing Gear Detail
Fixed Oleo Configuration

Fig. 7-9   Fixed Nose Gear Layout - Piper PA - 38

Courtesy of the New Piper Aircraft Co.

transport, while Figs. 7-12 and 7-13 show the main and nose gear designs for a medium range widebody jet transport. For the very heaviest aircraft, the main gear features more than two legs, to properly distribute the static loads and stay within the LCN values for existing runways. The DC-10-30 and the MD-11 have a third main landing gear leg mounted on the fuselage centerline in line with the two other main gear legs, and the 747 series all feature two main gear legs attached directly to the fuselage in addition to the two main gear legs attached to the wing. The 747 configuration is shown in Fig. 7-14.

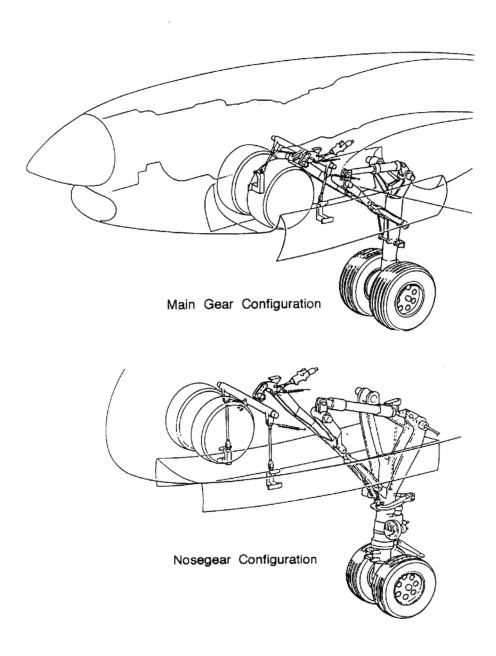

Main Gear Configuration

Nosegear Configuration

Fig. 7-10 Main Gear and Nose Gear Installation - Saab 340

Courtesy of Saab AB

171

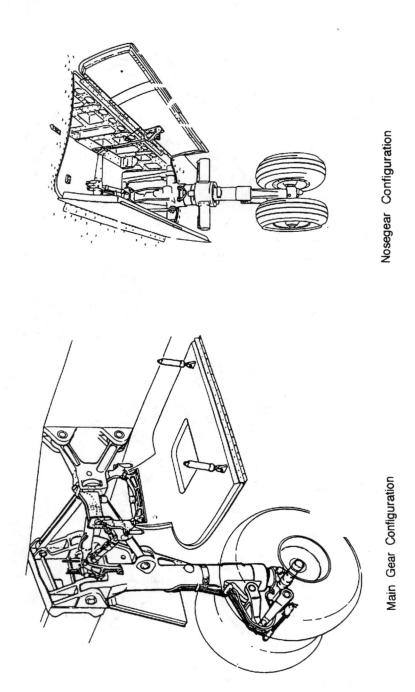

Courtesy of Fokker N.V.

Nosegear Configuration

Main Gear Configuration

Fig. 7-11 Main Gear and Nose Gear Installation - Fokker F-28

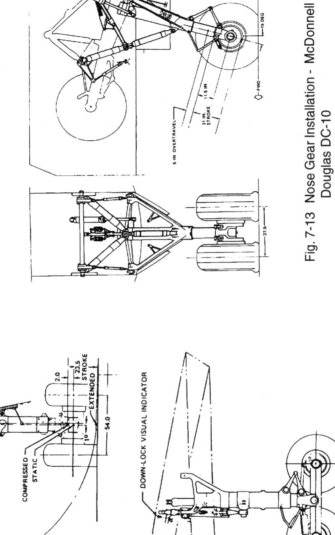

Fig. 7-13 Nose Gear Installation - McDonnell Douglas DC-10

Courtesy of McDonnell Douglas Corp., now the Boeing Co.

Fig. 7-12 Main Gear Installation - McDonnell Douglas DC-10

Courtesy of McDonnell Douglas Corp., now the Boeing Co.

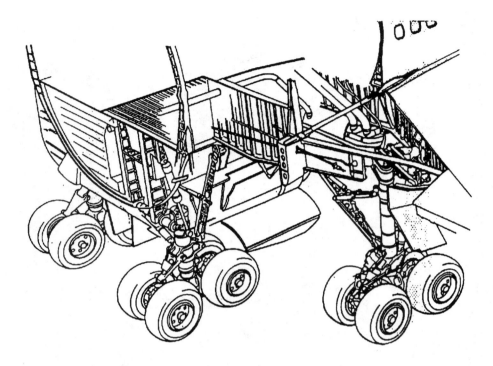

Fig. 7-14 Main Gear Installation - Boeing 747

Courtesy of the Boeing Co.

DESIGN EXERCISE

For your design project, define the landing gear geometry, wheel arrangement, tire sizes and pressures, and indicate the gear locations in both the extended and retracted positions. Make a detailed drawing of the gear in relationship to the wing and fuselage of your design.

REFERENCES

7.1   Conway, H. G., Landing Gear Design, Chapman Hall, London, England, 1958
7.2   Currey, Norman S., Aircraft Landing Gear Design. Principles and Practices, AIAA, Washington, D.C. 1988
7.3   Roskam, Jan, Airplane Design, Part IV, Layout Design of the Landing Gear and Systems, Roskam Aviation and Engineering Corporation, Ottawa, KS .1989

8

ENGINE SIZING AND ARRANGEMENT

A major step in the preliminary design process is determining the size of the engine or engines required to attain the performance requirements stated in the design mission specification. Engine sizing involves the definition of the rated takeoff horsepower for propeller driven aircraft, or the rated takeoff thrust for jet powered aircraft, as well as the geometric dimensions of the engine. Preliminary designers usually try to use available engines to meet mission requirements, since experience has shown that a new aircraft design which uses a new engine design usually has a considerably greater number of early development problems than a new aircraft which uses a proven, mature engine. For the material presented in this book, however, the engine characteristics are "generic," so that a unique engine rating may be determined that just meets the mission requirements.

NUMBER OF ENGINES

The number of engines used in the preliminary design phase is often defined in the mission specification. If not, a general rule is that the fewer number of engines used in the configuration, the simpler, lighter, and more efficient the design will be. For commuters and commercial transports certified under FAA regulations, at least two engines are required, since much of the required performance capability must be demonstrated with one engine inoperative. Sometimes the engine power or thrust requirements to perform a specific mission are so large that three or four engines of the largest types available must be used.

ENGINE RATINGS

The maximum performance output of the engine under various conditions is specified by the engine rating. In concept, the definition of the various engine ratings is virtually the same for piston engines, turbopropeller engines, and turbojet/turbofan engines. The engine ratings may be summarized as follows.

Takeoff

The takeoff rating is the maximum output that the engine is certified to supply for short periods of time, usually no longer than five minutes, to be used only for takeoff. For turbojet and turbofan engines, the takeoff rating is specified as sea level, static thrust (SLST). For these engines, there is also a maximum ambient temperature for which SLST can be maintained. At higher ambient temperatures, critical turbine parts exceed their temperature limits, so fuel flow and hence thrust must be reduced. This situation is shown in Fig. 8-1, and the engine is said to be "flat rated" to the noted ambient temperature, usually around 86° F at sea level. When describing engine "size," the takeoff rating is normally used, so that a 20,000 lb. thrust engine would have an SLST takeoff rating of 20,000 lb. For military jet engines equipped with afterburners, the takeoff rating is also known as maximum rating.

Maximum Climb

The maximum climb rating is the maximum output that the engine is certified to supply for normal climb operation. This rating is usually about 7% to 10% below the takeoff rating.

Maximum Cruise

The maximum cruise rating is the maximum output that the engine is certified to supply for normal cruise operation. This rating may be used without regard to time limitations. This is usually about 20% below the takeoff rating.

PERFORMANCE REQUIREMENTS

There are several flight performance requirements that may determine the engine size needed. For civil aircraft, these are

- The takeoff field length requirement from the mission specification, which relates directly to the takeoff rating.

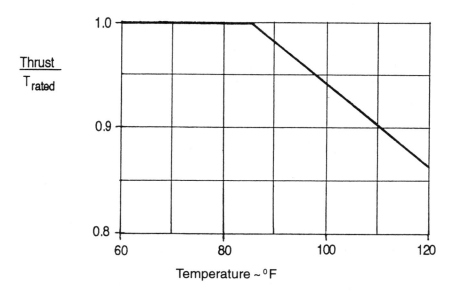

Fig. 8-1 Turbofan SLST Flat Rating Trend Data

- The minimum operational rate of climb requirement at initial cruise altitude, which is directly related to the maximum climb rating, and indirectly to the take-off rating.

- The requirement to maintain level flight at initial cruise altitude, following take-off at MTOGW which is directly related to the maximum cruise rating, and indirectly to the takeoff rating.

For military aircraft that are required to have sustained supersonic speed capability, usually with afterburner operating, it is this requirement that usually sizes the engine(s).

The approach to engine sizing will be to examine the thrust needed to meet the performance requirements at the specific conditions noted, and then determine the SLST rating of the engine from generalized engine performance charts. The performance requirement that leads to the highest takeoff rating will "size" the engine(s) for a specific design.

Engine Size for Takeoff Field Length

For civil aircraft, the takeoff field length requirement usually defines the engine size needed. It can be shown that for all conventional aircraft, the required takeoff field length is directly proportional to the takeoff wing loading, (W/S), and inversely proportional to the takeoff maximum lift coefficient, C_{LMAX} , and the takeoff power loading (P/W) for propeller driven aircraft, or takeoff thrust loading (T/W) for jet powered aircraft. Based on a substantial amount of flight test data, required takeoff field length (TOFL) has been correlated with a takeoff parameter (TOP) that incorporates the important relationships noted earlier. TOP is defined as

$$\text{for propeller driven aircraft} \qquad \text{TOP} = W^2/\sigma S P\, C_{L\,MAX_{TO}} \qquad (8\text{-}1)$$

$$\text{for jet powered aircraft} \qquad \text{TOP} = W^2/\sigma S T C_{L\,MAX_{TO}} \qquad (8\text{-}2)$$

For small, propeller driven personal/utility aircraft certified under FAR Part 23, the correlation chart of TOFL versus TOP is shown in Fig. 8-2. For propeller driven commuters and regional turboprop transports certified under FAR Part 25, where engine failure at the most critical point in the takeoff must be accounted for, the correlation chart is shown in Fig. 8-3. For business jets and jet transports certified under FAR Part 25, the correlation chart is shown in Fig. 8-4. These charts may be used to define the engine size needed to meet the takeoff field length requirement stated in the mission specification, as follows.

For the TOFL of the mission specification, determine the TOP using the appropriate correlation chart.

For propeller driven aircraft, the total installed engine horsepower may be found by solving Equation 8-1 for P.

$$P = W^2 /\sigma S(\text{TOP}) \qquad (8\text{-}3)$$

W	=	MTOGW for the design mission
σ	=	ratio of air density at takeoff to sea level standard day density
S	=	Wing area
C_{LMAX}		for takeoff may be estimated from Fig. 4-1 remembering that the higher values of C_{LMAX} are obtained with more complex high lift devices

Divide the total installed horsepower by the number of engines to obtain the engine size required. For jet powered aircraft, the thrust needed at $.7V_{TO}$ may be found by solving Equation 8-2 for T, using the same approach outlined above for propeller driven aircraft. The thrust at $.7V_{TO}$ may be related to the SLST rating through generalized

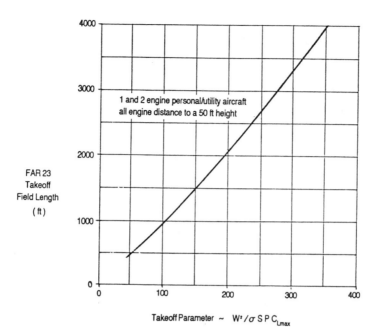

FAR 23
Takeoff
Field Length
(ft)

1 and 2 engine personal/utility aircraft
all engine distance to a 50 ft height

Takeoff Parameter ~ $W^2 / \sigma\, S\, P\, C_{Lmax}$

Fig. 8-2 FAR 23 Takeoff Field Length Trend Data

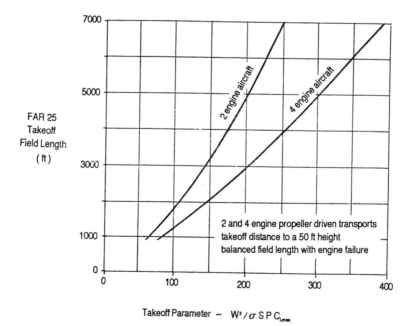

FAR 25
Takeoff
Field Length
(ft)

2 engine aircraft

4 engine aircraft

2 and 4 engine propeller driven transports
takeoff distance to a 50 ft height
balanced field length with engine failure

Takeoff Parameter ~ $W^2 / \sigma\, S\, P\, C_{Lmax}$

Fig. 8-3 FAR 25 Takeoff Field Length Trend Data ~ Props

curves of the ratio of installed takeoff thrust produced by the engine to the SLST rating as a function of takeoff speed or Mach number as shown in Fig. 8-5. Determine the installed thrust ratio at $.7V_{TO}$ for the design mission takeoff, assuming that $V_{TO} = 1.2\ V_{stall}$ for the takeoff configuration . The total sea level static thrust rquired is

$$T_{SLST} \quad = \quad \frac{T_{REQ'D} \quad @\ .7V_{TO}}{\left(\dfrac{T_{INSTALLED}}{T_{STATIC}}\right)_{@.TV_{TO}}} \qquad (8\text{-}4)$$

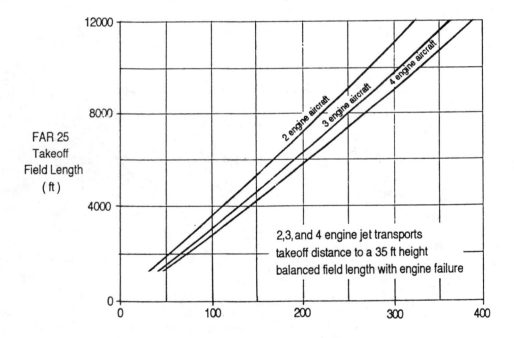

Takeoff Parameter $\sim\ W^2/\sigma\,S\,T\,C_{Lmax}$

Fig. 8-4 FAR 25 Takeoff Field Length ~ Jets

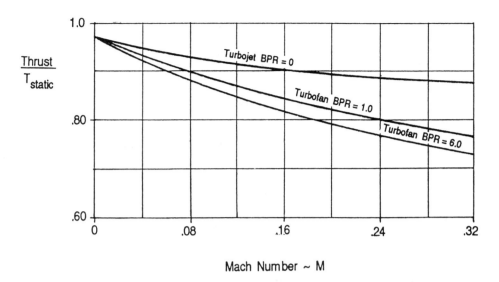

Fig. 8-5 Installed Takeoff Thrust Ratio

Adapted with permission from Ref. 8.1

Divide the quantity by the number of engines used to obtain the sea level static takeoff thrust rating for each engine.

A similar approach is used for propeller driven aircraft, except that there is no specific account taken of the installed takeoff thrust variation with Mach number, since it is similar for all propeller driven aircraft and is accounted for in the takeoff correlation charts.

Engine Size for Operational Rate of Climb

The engine size required to meet operational rate of climb requirements at initial cruise altitude may be determined using the flight performance equation for rate of climb, and generalized relationships between maximum climb thrust and sea level static takeoff thrust. The equation for rate of climb, Equation 1-22, is

$$R/C = \frac{(T - D) V}{W}$$

where V is the true climb speed. Airplanes usually climb at a speed that is easily maintained from cockpit instruments, such as constant indicated airspeed or constant Mach number. For climb at constant indicated airspeed, the true climb speed increases, as shown in Fig. 1-11, which means that some amount of (T-D) at the climb condition is being used to accelerate the aircraft along the flight path, leaving less than the entire instanta-

181

neous (T-D) to produce rate of climb. To account for this situation, the rate of climb equation for climb at other than constant true speed is modified by a "kinetic energy" correction factor.

$$\frac{R}{C} = \frac{(T - D)\ V \times K.E.\ Factor}{W} \qquad (8\text{-}4)$$

Now, (T–D)/W can be written as (T/W) – (D/W) , and for steady, unaccelerated flight,

$$\frac{D}{W} = \frac{1}{(L/D)} \qquad (8\text{-}5)$$

If the climb speed at initial cruise altitude is very close to the cruise speed, as it should be, then

$$(L/D)\ \text{at the top of climb} \doteq (L/D)\ \text{at optimum cruise}$$

The minimum operational rate of climb at initial cruise altitude for commuters, regional turboprops, business jets, and jet transports is 300 ft/min, while personal/utility aircraft may do with a lower value. The maximum climb thrust required at initial cruise altitude for a minimum operational rate of climb is

$$T_{max\ climb} = \left[\frac{(R/C)_{MIN\ REQ'D}}{V \times K.E.\ Factor} + \frac{1}{(L/D)} \right] W \qquad (8\text{-}6)$$

K.E. factors for climb at various conditions are shown in Fig. 8-6. It should be noted that for climb at constant Mach number above 36,089 ft, the K.E. factor is zero.

A realistic climb schedule from sea level to initial cruise altitude must be selected. For personal/utility aircraft, a single indicated airspeed is used to initial cruise altitude. For commuters, regional turboprops, business jets, and jet transports, the climb schedules are a bit more complicated. A typical climb schedule for a jet transport is shown in Fig. 8-7. The climb from sea level to 10,000 ft is limited to 250 knots EAS by FAA operating rules in Part 91. At 10,000 ft, the schedule calls for a constant altitude acceleration to 320 knots EAS, and then a climb at 320 knots EAS, which is very close to the best rate of climb speed. At 23,500 ft, 320 knots EAS is a Mach number of 0.74, and the climb is continued at M = 0.74 up to the initial cruise altitude of 32,000 ft where a very slight acceleration to the best long range cruise speed of M - 0.76 is indicated.

Having determined the maximum climb thrust required to meet the minimum rate of climb requirement at altitude, this thrust level must now be related back to the SLST rating for the engine. This is done using two additional generalized trend charts for turbofan engines. First, at the altitude for the operational rate of climb requirement, determine the ratio of maximum climb thrust/maximum cruise thrust from Fig. 8-8. Then, for the altitude and Mach number for the operational rate of climb requirement, determine the ratio of maximum cruise thrust/SLST for the appropriate engine bypass ratio from Fig. 8-9 through 8-11. The engine size to meet the operational rate of climb requirement is then

$$T_{SLST} = \frac{T_{max\ climb}}{(T_{max\ climb}/T_{max\ cruise})} \times \frac{1}{(T_{max\ cruise}/T_{SLST})} \qquad (8\text{-}6)$$

divided by the number of engines installed.

For turboprop and piston engined aircraft, the procedure is the same as for turbojet and turbofan powered aircraft, except that the thrust must be calculated from the relationship between thrust and brake horsepower.

$$T = \frac{BHP \times \eta}{V} \times 325 \qquad (8\text{-}7)$$

where

T	is the available thrust in lbs
BHP	is the total engine brake horsepower available at the initial cruise altitude
η	is the propeller efficiency
325	is a constant to convert ft-lbs/min to ft-n.mi/hr
V	is the true climb speed in kts.

Fig. 8-12 shows trend data for the relationship between maximum cruise power and SLS rated power for turboprop engines. For piston engined personal/utility aircraft, the approach is the same; however, some differences occur due to the nature of the engine performance. Piston engines can be supercharged to maintain sea level rated power up to a specified altitude, called the critical altitude. At higher altitudes, the power output decreases due to the lower air density, as shown in Fig. 8-13. Furthermore, modern piston engines usually allow maximum rated power for takeoff to be used for climb. For military jets with afterburners, the available thrust at various Mach numbers and altitudes may be found from Fig. 8-14.

R/C at constant V_{EAS} = R/C at constant V_{TRUE} X K E Factor

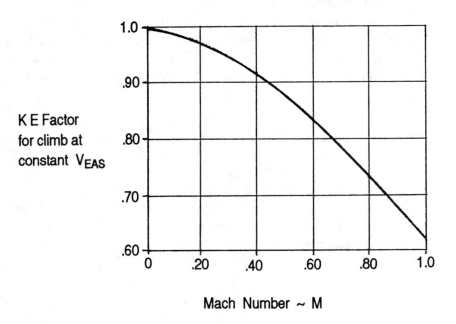

K E Factor
for climb at
constant V_{EAS}

Mach Number ~ M

R/C at constant Mach = R/C at constant V_{TRUE} X K E Factor

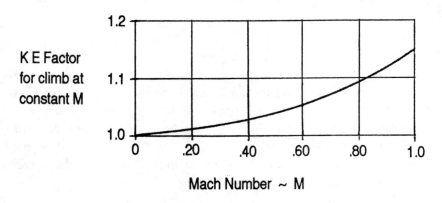

K E Factor
for climb at
constant M

Mach Number ~ M

Fig. 8-6 Kinetic Energy Correction Factors

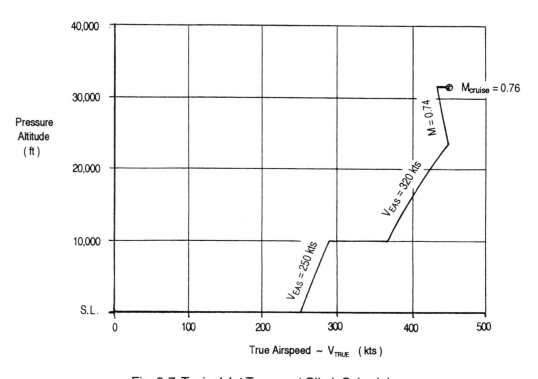

Fig. 8-7 Typical Jet Transport Climb Schedule

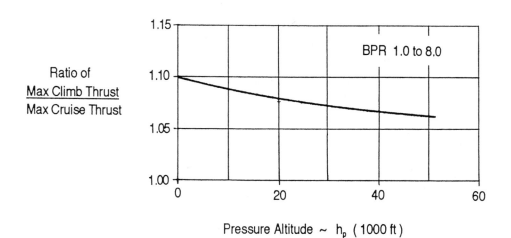

Fig. 8-8 Turbofan Engine Trend Data

Adapted with permission from Ref. 8.1

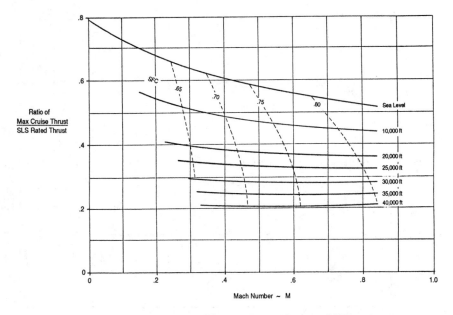

Fig. 8-9 Turbofan Engine Trend Data ~ BPR 1.0

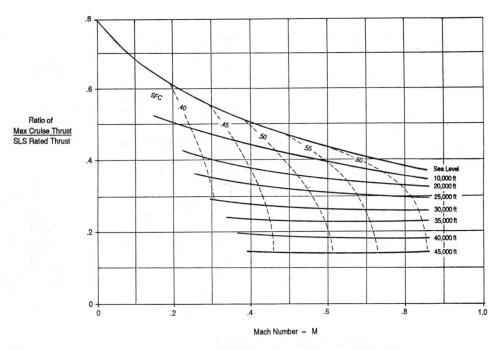

Fig. 8-10 Turbofan Engine Trend Data ~ BPR 6.0

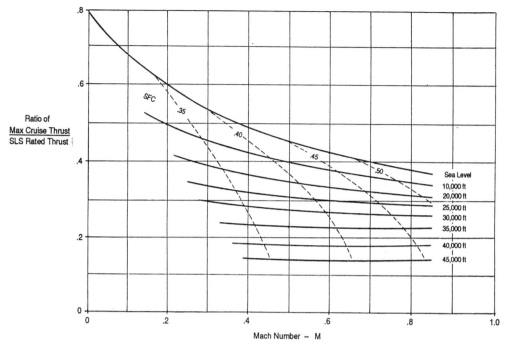

Fig. 8-11 Turbofan Engine Trend Data ~ Unducted Fan

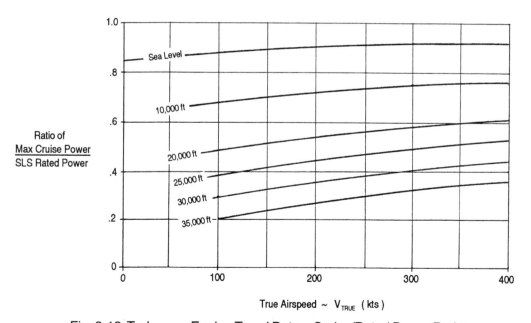

Fig. 8-12 Turboprop Engine Trend Data ~ Cruise/Rated Power Ratios

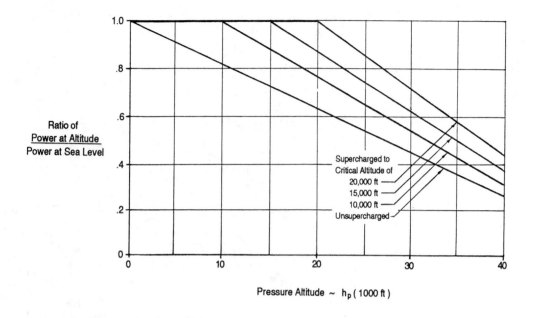

Fig. 8-13 Reciprocating Engine Trend Data ~ Altitude/Sea Level Power Ratios

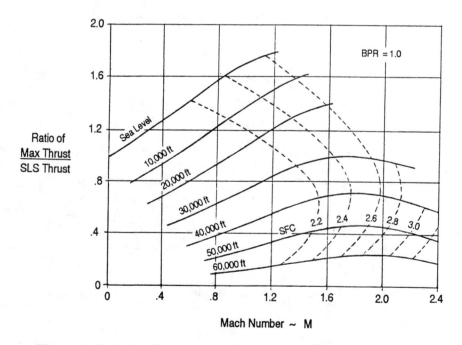

Fig. 8-14 Turbofan Engine Trend Data ~ Thrust Ratios With Afterburner

Engine Size for Initial Cruise

The engine maximum cruise thrust must be sufficient to allow operation at the initial cruise altitude at the heaviest weight for cruise. For cruise operation,

$$T = D \text{ and } L = W$$

so that

$$\frac{W}{T} = \frac{L}{D} \qquad (8\text{-}8)$$

The thrust required at start of cruise, is

$$T_{max\ cruise} = \frac{W}{(L/D)} \qquad (8\text{-}9)$$

where

> W = Initial cruise weight, conservatively taken as the maximum takeoff gross weight (MTOGW)

> (L/D) = cruise L/D at (M L/D)max

The required engine size for initial cruise may be found using Figs. 8-9 through 8-14 to determine $T_{max\ cruise}$/SLST at the initial cruise point, and the using

$$T_{SLST} = \frac{T_{max\ climb}}{(T_{max\ cruise} / T_{SLST})} \qquad (8\text{-}10)$$

For turboprop and piston engined aircraft, thrust should be calculated using Equation 8-7. T_{SLST} must be divided by the number of engines installed to obtain the SLST per engine.

ENGINE GEOMETRIC CHARACTERISTICS

Once the engine power or thrust rating has been established, the pertinent engine geometric characteristics need to be determined. Turbofan engine geometric data are presented in Fig. 8-15, while data on turbopropeller engines and propellers are shown in Fig. 8-16 and Fig. 8-17. In addition to the basic engine geometry, the engine housing or nacelle must also be defined. A typical nacelle for a turbofan engine is shown in Fig. 8-18. Generalized nacelle geometry for jet engines is listed as follows.

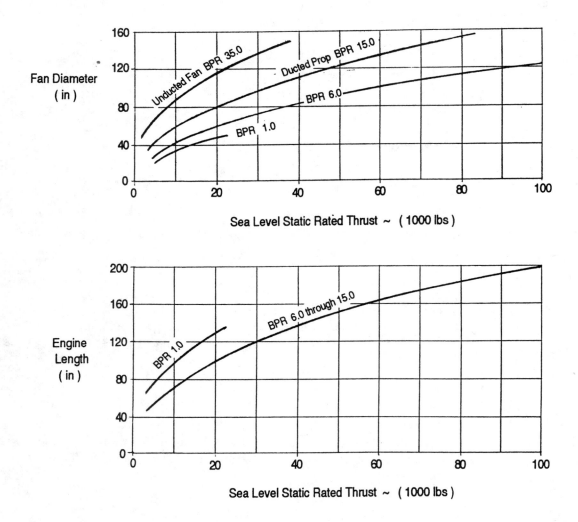

Fig. 8-15 Turbofan Engine Trend Data

190

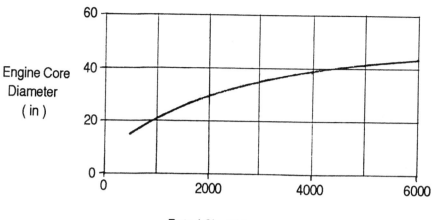

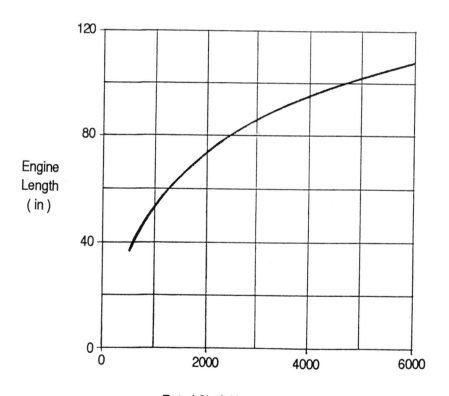

Fig. 8-16 Turboprop Engine Trend Data

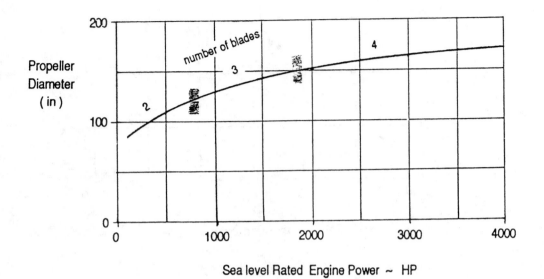

Fig. 8-17 Propeller/Engine Trend Data

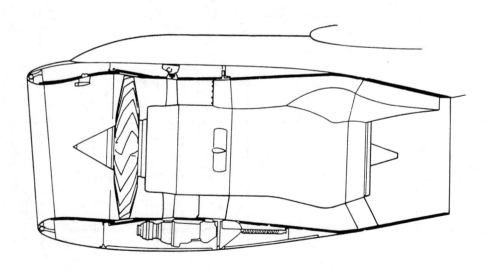

Fig. 8-18 Typical Turbofan Nacelle

Adapted with permission from Ref. 8.1

nacelle diameter	=	1.1 x fan diameter
nacelle inlet length	=	0.7 x fan diameter
nacelle total length	=	1.1 x (inlet + engine length)

ENGINE PLACEMENT

The placement of the engines is a major configuration decision on most designs, since engine location can have a significant impact on overall aerodynamic characteristics, weight and balance, stability and control, and ease of maintenance. As noted in Chapter 5, engine location for single engine personal/utility aircraft is usually at the forward end of the fuselage, while light twin engine aircraft engines are usually located on the inboard portion of the wing. Commuters and regional turboprops also favor inboard wing locations. Business jets universally locate engines on the aft fuselage, along with the "T-tail" empennage arrangement. Jet transports mostly utilize engines placed under the wing with the inlet located forward of the wing leading edge. Some transport designs have used aft fuselage mounted engines in nacelles or, on some 3-engine designs, located in or above the extreme aft end of the fuselage. Military fighter/attack aircraft usually employ one or two engines buried in the fuselage, with inlet ducts located in the forward fuselage area to provide the proper airflow to the engine.

For aft fuselage mounted engines, the engine nacelles should be above the wing wake for all normal operation, with the inlet aft of the wing trailing edge to avoid adverse effects of the inlet operation on the inboard wing aerodynamics. Care must also be taken to avoid creating a divergent channel between the engine nacelle and the aft fuselage.

For underwing mounted engines, the nacelles are usually located as close to the wing lower surface as possible, without causing undue heating of the wing by the engine exhaust. The inlet is located about two inlet diameters forward of the wing leading edge. The nacelle centerline is canted between 1 and 2 degrees off parallel, with the nose of the inlet pointed inward for alignment with the local airflow direction in cruise. The usual spanwise location for the wing mounted nacelles on a twin jet or trijet is 33% of the wing semispan, while for four engine designs, the nacelles are located at 35% and 67% of the wing semispan.

DESIGN EXERCISE

Determine the engine size required to meet the design mission specification, and make a drawing showing the engine installation and related geometric data.

REFERENCES

8.1 Shevell, Richard S., and Kroo, han, Introduction to Aircraft Design Synthesis and Analysis, Course Notes, Stanford University, Palo Alto, CA 1981

8.2 Anonymous, The Aircraft Gas Turbine Engine and its Operation, United Technologies Corporation, East Hartford, CI, 1988

8.3 Anonymous, The Jet Engine, Rolls Royce plc, Derby, England, 1986

8.4 Fraas, Arthur P., Aircraft Power Plants, McGraw- Hill, New York 1943.

9

BASELINE 3–VIEW LAYOUT DRAWING

Very early in the preliminary design process, a baseline 3-view layout drawing of the configuration is made. This layout utilizes the inputs from the various specialists in aerodynamics, propulsion, structures, and landing gear design. These inputs are integrated into a complete aircraft configuration by a very experienced preliminary design configuration specialist in the form of a 3-view layout of an aircraft that should meet the design mission specification requirements. The following notes were prepared as a guide to preparing a proper 3-view layout drawing for a turbofan powered regional transport.

GENERAL CONSIDERATIONS

The required payload from the mission specification, for this case the number of passengers plus baggage plus revenue cargo will determine the size of the fuselage. The range requirement will determine the fuel capacity and the fuel tank volume needed. The MTOGW and the MLW will affect the landing gear design and arrangement. The cruise speed and altitude will determine the wing geometry and influence the fuselage nose and afterbody shaping. The takeoff and landing runway length and the landing approach speed requirements will affect the high lift system design and the runway, taxi strip, and ramp pavement will affect the landing gear wheel and tire design. The type of terminal facilities will influence the fuselage design relative to integral stairway, cargo, and baggage compartments, galley service provisions and door locations.

PROCEDURAL STEPS FOR CONFIGURATION LAYOUT

Determination of Fuselage Cross-Section

Comfort level is a general term related to the spaciousness of the seat width between arm rest and the aisle width between armrests. The current standard for comfort level is that defined by the 747, DC-10, and the L-1011.

The passenger seat has been changing over the years as aircraft have shown capability to carry greater payloads at reduced costs, and because people in general are getting bigger.

Armrests on outer side have 2-inch width. Armrests on inner sides that share with adjoining seat vary from 3- to 8-inches depending on class; 3-inches for tourist, 8-inches first-class. Passenger seat cushion height above floor and height of seat back varies little for any class of seat.

Recent federal evacuation requirements specify 15-inch as minimum aisle width; the DC-8 has an 18-inch aisle, which is a practical minimum. The DC-9 has a 19-inch aisle width for tourist class. The DC-10 has a 20-inch aisle for tourist class, and is consistent with the B-747.

Aisle height is not critical for a 5-abreast single aisle cross-section. However, the minimum height is accepted as 78 inches, and 80 inches with overhead raft storage. In comparison, standard aisle height in the cabin for the DC-8 is 84 inches, the DC-9 is 81 inches and the DC-10 is 95 inches.

A sidewall-seat clearance allowance for shell deflection, seat width tolerances, and seat track location tolerances lead to approximately 3/4-inches as practical gap.

Fuselage frame plus stringer depth follows accepted practice as proportional to outside shell diameter. Local load path concentrations such as wing box attach and main landing gear attach bulkheads induce eccentric moments in frame cross-section. Section depth is dictated by maximum allowable deflections, and type of material employed which depends on fatigue stress level, etc.

Standard insulation design practice attained over many years and numerous transport models requires allowance of sufficient composite material to lay on frame inboard flanges, and may vary from 3/8- to 1-inch in depth. In addition, a hard surface liner is placed over the inboard surface of the insulation to function as a hard wall for the adjacent passenger; this component may be 1/8- to 1/4-inch thick.

Longitudinal routing of various systems must be considered to achieve a realistic cross-section. The largest volume is required by the air conditioning ducts. The cruise altitude requirement, the cabin seating capacity, and maximum design duct airflow dictate the duct cross-section. In addition, overhead storage racks or bins of useable size (pillows, blankets, small packages) must be placed to be accessible by a small stature attendant, and have provisions for adjustable air valves, light switches, oxygen masks, etc.

Of equal importance to the passenger cabin are the bins required for storage of baggage, cargo, and mail. Originally these items were bulk loaded, that is, piece by piece. New aircraft, however, are now expected to improve the loading - unloading time sequence by incorporating rapid handling containers. These units are configured in a modular form, with multiple shelves, to provide for storage of standard suitcases.

Also affecting the lower compartment shaping is provision for storage of the main landing gear truck. Tradeoff of belly storage versus external pod for landing gear may influence the final shaping. Additional considerations for the lower compartment are systems routing, either outboard of or beneath the modular containers.

Fuselage Shaping and Length

Definition of the fuselage is dependent upon aerodynamic, payload, and production fabrication consideration.

The mission requirements dictate a maximum cruise speed value which requires tailoring the nose and aft body shaping.

The nose shape initially is based upon a nose fitness ratio. The radome compartment for equipment storage is determined by component size and structural provisions. In turn, the crew compartment (cockpit) is defined depending upon the selection of a two versus three man cockpit. The cockpit is by nature a complex and specialized design problem, and certain basic assumptions are required for preliminary definition. Affecting the fuselage length are the pilot's rudder pedal travel, the average leg placement, and seat adjustment travel as standard for all transport-type cockpits.

The nose fairout also involves electronic shelves separating cockpit from the passenger cabin proper. The electronic components however may be placed below crew floor if in-flight servicing is not deemed necessary. Adjacent to the cockpit is the number one door, which is placed at extreme forward end of cabin for both crew use as well as permitting flexibility of cabin seating arrangements.

Aft body fairout shaping is governed by the requirement for smooth aerodynamic flow with minimum separation, while incorporating some upsweep to permit airplane rotation consistent with wing lift systems and thrust loading as defined by takeoff distance. The planform generally has a boat-tail half angle of less than 14 degrees, and a fineness ratio of about 3 to 1.

The profile is shown asymmetry with upsweep for ground rotation at takeoff, and provides sufficient depth for location of vertical tail frames.

Cross section shaping emphasizes a circular section within the pressure cabin section to the aft pressure bulkhead. The body aft of the pressure bulk-head may depart from circular shape somewhat since only tail loads are a consideration.

For configuration definition, a basic interior layout is determined. For this project, an all coach configuration is specified. Therefore starting with a specified number of passengers in a double-aisle, six abreast arrangement with a 34-inch seat row pitch, an approximate constant section length is defined.

Cabin services must be added to the passenger seating compartment. These include lavatories, closets and storage cabinets, galley cabinets, attendant seats.

Number of lavatories are based upon a ratio of number of passengers per lavatory approximately 40:1. The lavatory planform is fairly standard for contemporary transports, with a minimum floor area of 34 x 38 inches.

Closets for garments are about 3/4 inch in length per passenger as minimum. However, a first class closet provides 2-inches per passenger, and may be 1 to 1.5 inches per passenger for tourist and coach class.

Food service in a commuter operation may be thought of as minimal, but a 500 mile stage length can dictate as much as 1.5-inches galley cabinet length per passenger.

Attendant seats are required by the Federal Aviation Regulations and must be adjacent to door exits. The seat may be stowed upright but clear of exit path.

Exit doors, which may also be employed for entry, are dictated by federal evacuation safety rules. The FARs state that Type I doors (24 x 48 minimum) plus Type II doors (20 x 44 minimum) must be used for the passenger capacity of this project and there must be a 20-inch clear aisle to exit pathways. No leg room or seat backs must restrict evacuation.

It will be appreciated that several attempts are made of combined interior layouts plus nose and aft body shapes in order to arrive at an overall fuselage definition.

Additional work required to complete a preliminary design of the transport fuselage is a detailed study of shaping the nose section, specifically the pilot's enclosure and windshield area. This mission will dictate a greater field of vision than current transports due to the steeper takeoff and landing profile, lateral maneuvering, and traffic surveillance. Greater over-the-nose vision is needed, plus 270-degrees azimuth coverage. Increased vision areas are restricted by instrument display panels, and overall curvature of side shell due to wide-body design. An aerodynamically faired body must be achieved to reduce "corner post noise" in flight, as well as bad local shocks producing excessive cruise drag. So the forward body shaping is complex, and will influence the drag predictions, empty weight, and production and spare parts cost.

Wing

This major component is defined largely by aerodynamic requirements, and compromised only by weight and possibly flutter considerations. The overall geometry is specified by the Aerodynamics group; that is area, aspect ratio, taper ratio, sweep angle, thickness distribution, twist, airfoils. This airplane concept requires large flap chords, and therefore restricts the structural wing box throughout the span. Also, matching the large flaps are large chord slats along the leading edge.

Layouts of key airfoil section stations determine the slat and flap details, as well as providing a basis for wing box section area. Space provision must account for spar cap flanges, slat tracks, flap hinge brackets, spoiler supports and details, flap actuators, lateral control routing system, etc.

Wing Location on Fuselage

On a first preliminary layout, the wing and engines are located upon the fuselage based on experience from previous aircraft blended with the personal judgment of the designer. Trend data presented in Fig. 5-21 should help with positioning the wing on the fuselage. Following a preliminary weight and balance study, a more scientific placement will provide for tolerable forward and aft c.g. limits. Knowing these constraints leads to properly placing the wing spar and body attach frames in a manner consistent with frame spacing and interior seating arrangement including door locations.

Propulsion System

On this concept, the fan engines are positioned at an optimum location in order to achieve the minimum cruise drag penalty and minimum added wing weight required for flutter. Thus, the pylon and pod are tailored to the wing, and together the wing and power plant unit is assembled onto the previously defined fuselage.

The engine pod is another component which in itself requires preliminary layout definition before it can be placed upon the wing. The pod must have an efficient inlet diffuser operable at various angles of attack, and fan exit cowling containing thrust reverser, the primary air exhaust cone efficiently faired, and accessories including pumps, generators, etc., located for rapid servicing.

Landing Gear

The main landing gear is tailored to match the MTOGW, runway and ramp floatation limits, cross-wind considerations, as well as manufacturer's design practice and general system complexity. Location on airplane considers relative loading on main versus nose gear, position of main gear to aft c.g. limits and maximum rotation. Usually, if one starts with the airplane at the attitude for maximum rotation, with a line perpendicular to the ground passing through the vertical location of c.g., which can be assumed as on the quarter chord of m.a.c., and add to this a maximum of another 7.5 degrees, the wheel location will satisfy the aft c.g. limit. The maximum rotation is an aerodynamic requirement to achieve takeoff C_L, but is usually compromised by reasonable length of the main landing gear struts. This rotation angle is defined as gear fully extended, tires tangent, and either has nominal clearance to aft fuselage, or is restricted by tail bumper. Tire size and number will depend upon the type of airports specified, and whether an "unprepared field" condition is required.

From above mentioned requirement, a preliminary layout of a gear truck configuration is determined. Various concepts are sketched to illustrate possible designs. In a high wing, the manner in which the main landing gear, is mounted upon the fuselage will necessitate some form of external support and a faired landing gear pod. One may choose to keep all the main landing gear stowed externally within the pod proper, or stow the truck in an internal wheel well under the cabin floor. The tradeoff being less weight but greater drag for full external stowage or greater weight but less drag for belly stowage of the truck. Our design shows the latter case. The main landing gear strut pivot (for retraction) is dictated by the gear tread. Gear tread requires an adequate lateral spacing to avoid roll-over during cross-wind landing with high gusts. This is critical on high wing aircraft, and these types usually "push their luck" on tread design (body-mounted main landing gears).

Location of the nose gear may depend upon ground maneuvering turning radius, towing loads, braking loads, lower compartment arrangement, and fuselage structure cutouts such as entrance doors, etc. If one wants to use the lower compartment as efficiently as possible for baggage or cargo, then the nose gear may be relocated further forward to stow adjacent to the radome bulkhead.

Empennage

The high-lift system results in severe pitching and large downward angle of airflow, and large vortex shedding from the outer flap tip. Tests have emphasized that a special placement of the horizontal tail with respect to wing is mandatory. Therefore, a T-tail arrangement is required on this design. The high location of horizontal stabilizer necessitates a somewhat high aspect ratio vertical tail. A modest sweep is shown so as to place the horizontal tail at a larger tail arm ratio, l_H. The tail area is sized by an engine-out condition at minimum control speed, as is the rudder area.

The vertical tail spar box has a slight sweep and intercepts the fuselage aft of the pressure bulkhead. In the turbofan configuration, the front spar upper end serves as horizontal tail pivot for adjustable incidence trim requirements. Because of the T-tail scheme, a fairly thick airfoil is used to achieve adequate stiffness. Spar locations are dictated by airfoil structural thickness forward, and rudder chord, nose shape, and seal aft. The horizontal stabilizer is sized aerodynamically by stability and control considerations. Planform shape is based upon experience of previous T-tails. In this case the placement of spars, forward and aft, and the elevator hinge line is kept consistent with previous experience. The high aspect ratio proves very effective for the high downwash induced by the wing and high lift system.

CONCLUDING REMARKS

The foregoing description of the configuration layout has pointed out major considerations that influence the conceptual development of a transport. Some configurations do not go together easily, and must be reworked in order to satisfy either the designer's goals or those of management.

The layout, when initially released for study by engineering specialists, is in itself a first compromise. Numerous tradeoffs have been made and assumed as designer's license, and it is expected that revision will occur as more detailed analysis is made of the complete configuration and all of its component parts. It can also be stated that, frequently, the designer is unhappy with an initial design, but awaits additional inputs in order to attain a design improvement. It is of utmost importance that each configuration be established in a fair, reasonable, accurate, and consistent manner so as to permit serious comparisons of new data with previous information.

In the field of new designs, careful blending of past experience with new concepts will prove to be the key to successful configuration development. Figures 9-1 llustrates

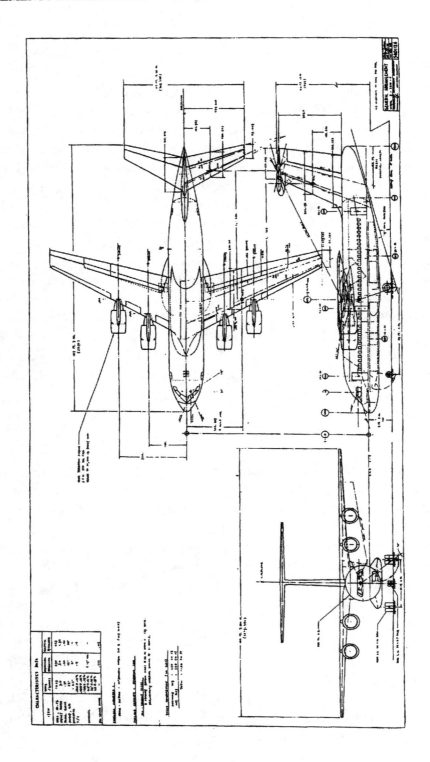

Fig. 9-1 Typical 3-View layout Drawing ~ Regional Turbofan

Courtesy of McDonnell Douglas Corp., now the Boeing Co.

the 3-view layout drawings for this regional turbofan transport. Note that the three views of the aircraft project from plan, to side, to front, in conformance with good drafting practice. In addition, the 3-view shows all the pertinent m.a.c. locations, the .25 c points, tail lengths, an angular limits in pitch and roll before the critical points on the aircraft will contact the ground. The 3-view also incorporates a small table which lists the main geometric characteristics of the wing, horizontal tail, and vertical tail.

DESIGN EXERCISE

Make a preliminary 3-view layout drawing of your design on a sheet of 11-inch by 17-inch paper. Make sure the views project. Include a table of the important geometric characteristics on the 3-view.

REFERENCES

9.1   Cathers, Richard T. Unpublished Notes, Douglas Aircraft Co., Long Beach CA, 1978

10

PRELIMINARY WEIGHT AND BALANCE CALCULATIONS

After the preliminary 3-view layout drawing is completed, the next step in the preliminary design process is to perform some preliminary weight and balance calculations. These calculations help to establish the basis for further, more detailed, studies of the aircraft weight empty and solidify the 3-view layout drawing by assuring that the wing location on the fuselage is correct.

GROUP WEIGHT STATEMENT

In order to conduct studies relating to aircraft weight empty, there is a need to establish the weight of various structural elements and systems that make up the aircraft empty weight. This process, usually conducted by aircraft weight engineers assigned to the preliminary design group, involves much reliance on empirical data from actual production aircraft, correlated with appropriate physical parameters. These individual weights are defined in a "Group Weight Statement," which is a list of weights of the major elements of the aircraft that make up the manufacturers weight empty (MWE). Examples of group weight statements for a number of commercial transport aircraft are shown in Figs. 10-1 and 10-2. The first group weight statement is formulated from trend data by weights engineers, and constitutes a set of target weights, or weight allocations, that are consistent with the W_{empty} derived in Chapter 3. Trend data for commercial jet transports is shown in Fig. 10-3. As an initial approach for a group weight statement, one may utilize the trend data of Figs. 10-3 through 10-8 at the appropriate MWE to develop a set of actual group weights. In order to establish a manufacturers empty weight, the weight of the operator's items must be subtracted from the OWE to obtain the MWE.

Weight Element	Citation	F-28	DC-9-10	BAC-111	DC-9-30	737-200	727-100	727-200
Wing Group	1,020	7,526	9,366	9,817	11,391	11,164	17,682	18,529
Tail Group	288	1,477	2,619	2,470	2,790	2,777	4,148	4,142
Body-Group	930	6,909	9,452	11,274	11,118	11,920	17,589	22,415
Landing Gear	425	2,564	3,640	4,182	4,182	4,038	7,244	7,948
Nacelle Group	241	866	1,462	1,191	1,462	1,515	2,226	2,225
Propulsion Group	340	988	1,478	1,788	2,190	1,721	3,052	3,022
Flight Controls	196	1,404	1,102	1,655	1,434	2,325	2,836	2,984
Auxiliary Power	0	320	805	719	817	855	0	849
Instruments	76	267	490	504	575	518	723	827
Hydraulic System	94	406	681	1,391	753	835	1,054	1,147
Electrical System	361	953	1,631	1,610	1,715	2,156	2,988	2,844
Avionics	321	923	1,039	1,368	1,108	1,100	1,844	1,896
Furnishings	794	3,535	6,690	7,771	8,594	9,119	11,962	14,702
Air Conditioning	188	520	1,016	1,062	1,110	1,084	1,526	1,802
Anti-Icing System	101	520	472	234	474	113	639	666
Load and Handling	2	--	19	19	57	--	15	19
Empty Weight (less dry engine)	5,377	29,178	41,962	46,328	49,770	51,240	75,528	86,017
Dry Engine	1,002	4,327	6,113	5,434	6,160	6,212	9,322	9,678
MEW	6,379	33,505	48,075	51,762	55,930	57,452	84,850	95,695
MTOGW	11,650	62,000	86,300	99,650	108,000	104,000	161,000	175,000

Fig. 10-1 Summary Weight Statements~Commercial Jets

Adapted with permission from Ref. 10.4

206

Weight Element	707-320	DC-8-55	DC-8-62	DC-10-10	L-1011-1	DC-10-30	747-100
Wing Group	28,647	34,909	36,247	48,990	47,401	57,748	88,741
Tail Group	6,004	4,952	4,930	13,657	8,570	14,454	11,958
Body Group	22,299	22,246	23,704	44,790	49,432	46,522	68,452
Landing Gear	11,216	11,682	11,449	18,581	19,923	25,085	32,220
Nacelle Group	3,176	4,644	6,648	8,493	8,916	9,328	10,830
Propulsion Group	5,306	9,410	7,840	7,673	8,279	13,503	9,605
Flight Controls	2,139	2,035	2,098	5,120	5,068	5,188	6,886
Auxiliary Power	0	0	0	1,589	1,202	1,592	1,797
Instruments	550	1,002	916	1,349	1,016	1,645	1,486
Hydraulic System	1,557	2,250	1,744	4,150	4,401	4,346	5,067
Electrical System	3,944	2,414	2,752	5,366	5,490	5,293	5,305
Avionics	1,815	1,870	2,058	2,827	2,801	3,186	4,134
Furnishings	16,875	15,884	15,340	38,072	32,829	33,114	48,007
Air Conditioning	1,602	2,388	2,296	2,386	3,344	2,527	3,634
Anti-Icing System	626	794	673	416	296	555	413
Load and Handling	--	55	54	62	--	62	228
Empty Weight (less dry engine)	105,756	116,535	118,749	203,521	198,968	224,148	297,867
Dry Engine	19,420	16,936	17,316	23,229	30,046	25,587	35,700
MEW	125,176	133,471	136,065	226,750	229,014	249,735	333,567
MTOGW	312,000	325,000	335,000	430,000	430,000	565,000	775,000

Fig. 10-2 Summary Weight Statements~Commercial Jets

Adapted with permission from Ref. 10.4

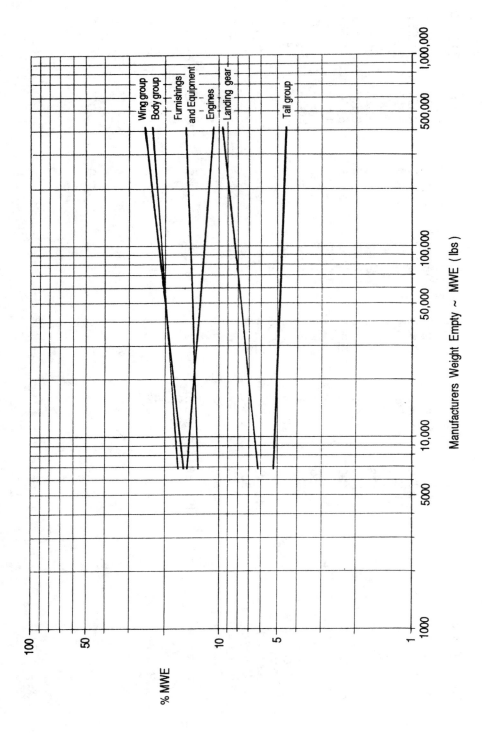

Figure 10-3 Weight Empty Trend Data

Operational Items	3,570 lb
Cockpit Crew (2 x 170 lb)	540
Cabin Crew (4 x 130 lb)	520
Crew Baggage (6 x 25 lb)	150
Flight Kits	25
Oil including Engine, Constant Speed Drive, APU and System Oil	136
Unusable Fuel	300
Food, Galley Service (12 F/C x 7.5 lb/pass + 141 E/C x 3.7 lb/pass)	612
Passenger Service Equipment (147 x 2 lb/pass)	294
Galley Inserts	750
Potable Water	196
Lavatory Fluids	69
Evacuation Slides	127
Life Vests	11

Figure 10-4 Operational Items List~Typical Short Range Jet Transport

Operational Items	21,963 lb
Cockpit Crew (2 x 170 lb)	340
Cabin Crew (20 x 130 lb)	1,300
Crew Baggage (12 x 20 lb)	260
Flight kits	50
Oil including Engine, Constant Speed Drive, APU and System Oil	300
Unusable Fuel	1,859
Potable water (5 lb x 451 pass.)	2,255
Food, Galley Service including Carts (36 F/C x 28 lb/pass + 415 E/C x 16 lb/pass)	7,640
Passenger Service Equipment (451 x 3 lb/pass)	1,353
Evacuation Slides/Slide-Rafts	1,639
Emergency Transmitters (2 x 3.5 lb/each).	7
Life Vests (451 + 15 466 x I lb/each)	466
Pallets (nine 88 x 125 x 214 lb/each)	1,926
Containers (20 LD3 x 165 lb/each)	3,300

Figure 10-5 Operational Items List~Typical Long Range Jet Transport

A list of operational items and their weights are shown in Fig. 10-4 for a short range jet transport, and in Fig. 10-5 for a long range jet transport. These operational items weights may be used to obtain specific operational item weights for any size jet transport through linear interpolation.

A typical group weight statement expressed in terms of % MWE for several types of aircraft is shown in Fig. 10-6.

Weight Element	Personal/Utility	Regional T/P	Jet Transport
Wing group	17.0	18.0	21.0
Tail group	4.0	4.0	4.5
Body group	24.0	24.0	20.0
Landing gear	8.0	8.5	8.5
Nacelle group	—	3.0	3.5
Propulsion group	4.5	4.5	4.0
Flight controls	1.5	2.0	2.5
Auxiliary power	—	—	0.5
Instruments	1.0	1.0	1.0
Hydraulic system	—	.05	1.5
Electrical system	1.0	5.0	2.5
Avionics	1.0	2.5	2.5
Furnishings	13.0	11.0	13.0
Air conditioning	0.5	1.5	1.5
Anti-icing system	—	2.0	1.5
Dry engine	24.5	12.5	12.0
	————	————	————
	100.0	100.0	100.0

Fig. 10-6 Typical Manufacturers Weight Empty Breakdown in % of MWE

CHECK ON C. G. LOCATION

The c.g. location for the preliminary 3-view layout drawing may now be determined. The basic idea is to take weight moments for the individual elements on the group weight statement about some arbitrary point, usually the fuselage nose, or station "0," in the side view of the aircraft. The sum of the moments of the individual elements of the aircraft from the group weight statement must equal the moment of the entire MWE acting at the MWE c.g. location. In equation form

$$W_{WING} \cdot \overline{X}_{WING} + W_{fus} \cdot \overline{X}_{fus} + \ldots = W_{MEW} \cdot \overline{X}_{c.g.} \qquad (10\text{-}1)$$

The c.g. location, $\overline{X}$, for each element in the group weight statement must be estimated from the geometric characteristics and location of each element. For weight items such as electrical, hydraulic, and avionics systems that are distributed throughout the aircraft, a reasonable central c.g. location may be assumed without incurring significant errors. With all of the individual moments determined, Eq. (10-1) may be solved for the $\overline{X}$ c.g. A good rule of thumb is that the MWE c.g. should be at

> 25% m.a.c. for engines located on the wing
> 35% m.a.c. for engines located on the aft fuselage

If the MWE c.g. does not fall within 1% m.a.c. of these locations, the wing location in the preliminary 3-view drawing must be shifted to bring the MWE c.g. into the correct location. For example, if the MWE c.g. is too far forward in the initial c.g. location check, then the wing must be moved forward on the 3-view drawing to bring the c.g. into the correct location. The c.g. trend with wing shift is a linear process, so only one recalcuation of c.g. relocation with wing position is required, and a linear interpolation will allow correct positioning of the wing.

BALANCE DIAGRAM AND C.G. LIMITS

The subject of aircraft weight and balance is concerned with the proper location of the aircraft center of gravity for all of the loading conditions that are possible considering

> OWE c.g. location
> Fuel loading and usage
> Passenger loading
> Cargo loading

The OWE c.g location is usually determined by an arbitrary but experienced rule of thumb as noted previously. Then the extreme excursions of the c.g. due to the most adverse loading conditions that move the c.g. forward and aft are examined by calculation to establish the c.g. range for which the airplane must be both stable and controllable. The results of these calculations are usually plotted on a chart of gross weight vs c.g. location so that appropriate c.g. limits may be established. A very simple case, the Ryan NYP airplane is analyzed in Fig. 10-7.

Starting with the OWE c.g. located at 29% m.a.c., loading the oil tank with 175 pounds of oil moves the c.g. forward to 27.6% m.a.c. Loading the wing fuel tanks with 887 pounds of fuel moves the c.g. aft to 29.6% m.a.c. Loading the fuselage nose fuel tank with 489 pounds of fuel moves the c.g. forward to 25.9% m.a.c., and loading the main fuselage fuel tank with 1224 pounds of fuel moves the c.g. aft to 28.3% m.a.c. at the MTOGW of 5130 pounds. This is the prescribed loading and useage of the fuel and oil. However, the pilot has the option to use fuel from the fuselage nose tank first, so that the c.g. moves aft to 31.6% m.a.c. if this option is selected. Then, as the main fuselage fuel tank is used, the c.g. moves forward to the 29.6% m.a.c. The extreme excursion of the airplane c.g. with prescribed and optional fuel loadings and usage are then 25.9% m.a.c.

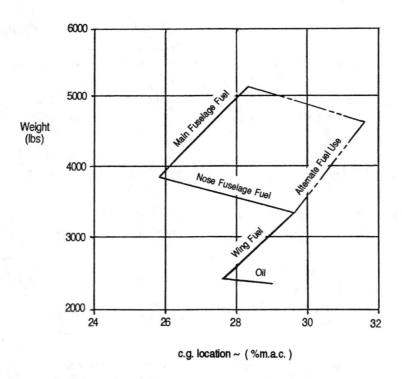

Figure 10-7 Weight and Balance Diagram~Ryan NYP

forward and 31.6% m.a.c. aft. Stability and control and structural design considerations must be met at these limits of c.g. travel.

Commercial jet transports, with large variations in passenger loading, cargo loading, and fuel loading, usually require a large c.g. range, compared to personal/utility airplanes, business jets, and military fighter/attack aircraft.

For transport aircraft, the balance diagram is constructed by starting with the c.g. location for the MWE. The effect of adding the operators items results in the OWE c.g. location. The passenger payload is accounted for next, assuming that the passenger loading may take place in either of two ways. The most forward c.g. locations with passenger loading occurs when the passengers are loaded from the front of the passenger cabin to the rear, assuming that the window seats are occupied first, then the aisle seats, and then the middle seats, for all classes. Correspondingly, the most aft c.g. locations with passenger loading occurs when the passengers are loaded from the rear of the passenger cabin to the front, again assuming that the window seats are occupied first, followed by aisle, and then middle seats. The c.g. locations for various passenger loads, generated by this process are shown in Fig. 10-8. It should be noted that the weight per passenger does not include his or her luggage weight, which is included and positioned in the appropriate cargo compartment. After all the passengers are accounted for, the effect of passenger bags and revenue cargo weight in the c.g. location is accounted for, usually by assuming a value for cargo density, of 10 lbs/cu.ft. up to the space limit payload. Finally, the effect of the most critical c.g. variation with fuel usage is accounted for. Under the above stated assumptions, a reasonable most forward c.g. and a most aft c.g. location can be determined, and the aircraft c.g. limits set accordingly. At this point, a more detailed stability and control analysis is made as a check on the selected horizontal tail geometry; that is, the area, the elevator span and chord, maximum deflection angles, and so forth in order to ensure that adequate longitudinal stability is available at the most aft c.g., and adequate longitudinal control is available at the most forward c.g. location.

A balance and loading diagram for a typical short range jet transport is shown in Fig. 10-8. Note how the established c.g. limits accomodate the extremes of "reasonably" adverse loadings.

DESIGN EXERCISE

Develop a group weight statement for your design project. Make a check on the weight empty c.g. location and, if necessary, relocate the wing on the fuselage. Finally, prepare a balance diagram for your design project and establish the c.g. limits.

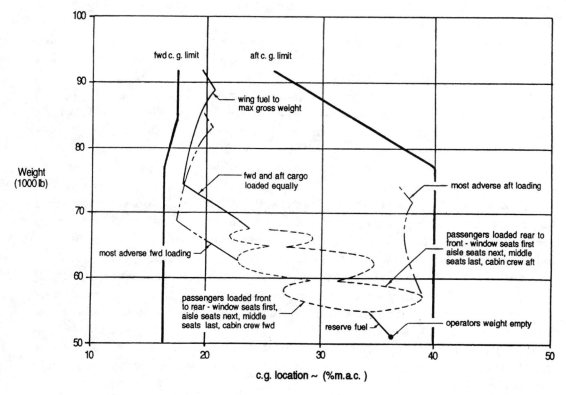

Figure 10-8 Weight and Balance Loading Diagram~Short Range Jet Transport

REFERENCES

10.1 Hiscocks, Richard D., A Case Study of the DeHavilland Family of STOL Commuter Aircraft, AIAA Professional Study Series, Washington, D.C., 1982

10.2 Corning, Gerald, Supersonic and Subsonic CTOL and VTOL Airplane Design, 4th edition, College Park, MD, 1977

10.3 Stinton, Darrol, The Design of the Aeroplane, BSP Books, London, England, 1993

10.4 Shevell, Richard S., and Kroo, Ilan, Introduction to Aircraft Design Synthesis and Analysis, Course Notes, Stanford University, Palo Alto, CA 1981

11

ESTIMATED LOW SPEED LIFT CURVES AND MAXIMUM LIFT COEFFICIENTS

In order to perform more detailed aerodynamic performance analysis on the baseline preliminary design, some basic aerodynamic characteristics of the configuration must be estimated. One of the most important set of aerodynamic characteristics are the lift curves and maximum lift coefficients for the cruise, takeoff, and landing configurations. As noted in Chapter 1, the airplane lift curve has a special relationship to airplane operation in steady, unaccelerated flight, namely that the airplane's speed is primarily a function of lift coefficient, and the lowest steady flight speed, called the stalling speed, V_{stall}, corresponds to operation at the maximum lift coefficient, C_{Lmax}. We shall see in this chapter that the cruise lift curve is the key to determining the aircraft pitch angle in cruise, and we will see in Chapter 13 that a key design airspeed depends on the C_{Lmax} for the cruise configuration. Furthermore, the C_{Lmax} in the takeoff configuration is directly involved in the determination of the FAR required takeoff field length, and the C_{Lmax} in the landing configuration is directly involved in the determination of the required FAR landing field length. .

The following paragraphs describe the background and procedure used to estimate the low speed lift curves and the maximum lift coefficients for the cruise, takeoff, and landing configurations.

CRUISE CONFIGURATION LIFT CURVE

The linear variation of lift coefficient, C_L, with airplane angle of attack α, usually written as $dC_L/d\alpha$, is related primarily to the wing planform geometry parameters, namely aspect

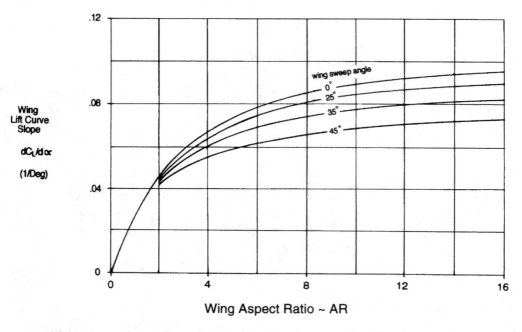

Fig.11-1 Lift Curve Slope Variation with Aspect Ratio and Sweepback

ratio, AR, and sweep angle, Λ, as shown in Fig. 11-1. Since a small amount of lift is carried on other parts of the airplane, such as the fuselage, nacelles, and horizontal tail, the value of the airplane lift curve slope is slightly higher than the wing lift curve slope. The zero lift angle, that is, the airplane angle of attack where the airplane lift coefficient is zero, called a_{OL}, depends on a number of parameters, such as the zero lift angle of the wing airfoils, the variation in the airfoil zero lift angle across the wing span or aerodynamic twist, the influence of the fuselage shape and the angle at which the entire wing is attached to the fuselage. An analysis of all of these parameters is made in the preliminary design phase of the program, with the objective of having the angle of attack of the fuselage reference plane, or floor line in the passenger cabin, between $0°$ and $+2°$ at the cruise condition.

The maximum lift coefficient in the cruise configuration is dependent on two primary parameters, the spanwise variation of local wing section lift coefficients, as the wing approaches the angle of attack for stall, and the wing airfoil section maximum lift coefficients, which are unique values for each airfoil section. For performance reasons, airfoil sections with high values of maximum lift coefficient are usually selected to achieve the highest value of airplane maximum lift coefficient. However, as shown in Fig. 11-2, the airfoil section maximum lift coefficient values are usually varied across the span, so that the wing spanwise lift distribution will reach values of the airfoil maximum lift coefficients

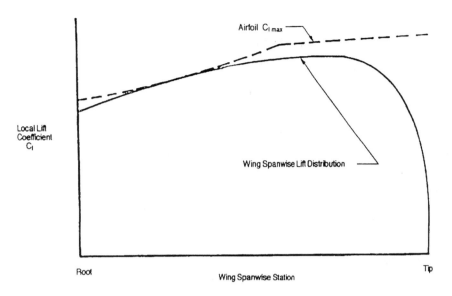

Fig.11-2 Span Loading/Airfoil $C_{L_{max}}$ Relationship for Proper Stall

over the inboard portion of the wing, producing local stalling inboard while maintaining some lift coefficient margin to stall over the outer portion of the wing. This margin in lift coefficient to stall is used to protect against initial local stalling over the outer portion of the wing, which leads to severe roll off and loss of aileron control at the stall. For this reason, the airplane maximum lift coefficient can never be as high as the airfoil maximum lift coefficients. The detailed procedure for constructing the cruise lift curve is as follows.

- Determine wing lift curve slope for your AR and sweep angle at low speed from Fig. 11-1.

- Increase this value by 8% to account for the lift contribution of the rest of the airplane, i.e., fuselage. nacelles, horizontal tail

$$C_{L\alpha_{airplane}} = 1.08\ C_{L\alpha_{wing}}$$

- On a plot of C_{L_A} vs. α_{FRP}, draw in this slope through $C_{L_A} = 0$ and $\alpha_{FRP} = 0$, as shown in Fig. 11-3.

- The next step is to set the zero lift angle for the airplane. This is a complicated process that involves data beyond the scope of this book, but the objective is to

217

have the airplane α_{FRP} between 0° and +2° at the cruise condition, $C_{L(L/D)max}$ at $(ML/D)_{max}$. So, at the desired cruise C_L, select where you want the a_{FRP} to be. Put the lift curve slope through the selected point and the zero lift angle will be determined. See Fig. 11-3 "Construction of Low Speed Lift Curves".

- Estimate the C_{Lmax} for the cruise configuration. The cruise configuration (clean airplane) C_{Lmax} is related to the outer panel airfoil C_{lmax} and the wing sweep angle, as shown in Fig. 11-4. The outer panel airfoil C_{lmax} values for supercritical airfoils are shown as a function of airfoil thickness ratio in Fig. 11-5. NACA 5 digit series airfoils have essentially the same C_{lmax} values, while the NACA 4 digit and 6 series airfoils have lower C_{lmax} values. Determine the outer panel C_{lmax} from Fig. 11-5 and obtain the airplane C_{Lmax} for the clean configuration from Fig. 11-4. On the C_{L_A} vs. α_{FRP} plot, extend the "clean airplane" lift curve until it intersects the clean C_{Lmax}. Note C_{Lmax} and α_{FRP} for C_{Lmax}.

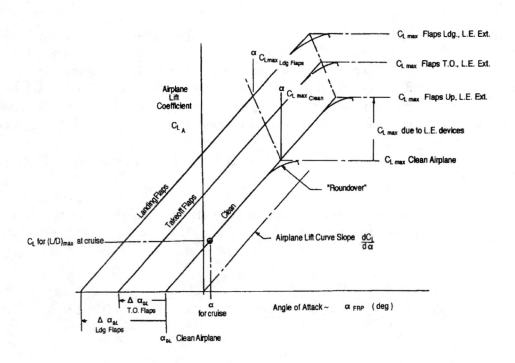

Fig. 11-3 Construction of Low Speed Lift Curves

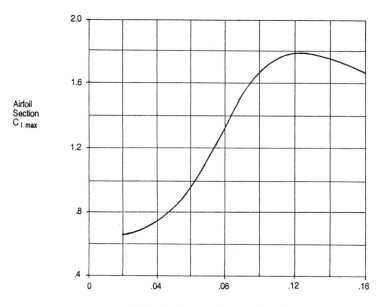

Fig. 11-4 Airfoil Section $C_{l_{max}}$ Trend with Thickness Ratio

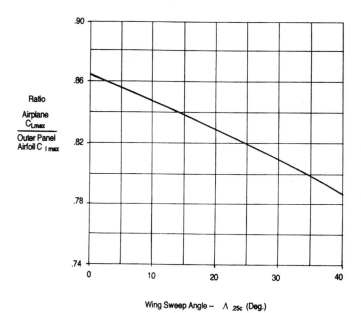

Fig. 11-5 Airplane $C_{L_{max}}$/Airfoil $C_{l_{max}}$ Ratio

Reprinted with permission from Ref. 11.2

219

TAKEOFF AND LANDING CONFIGURATIONS

The primary objective of takeoff configuration is to increase the maximum lift coefficient of the airplane to reduce the required takeoff distance, without reducing the maximum lift-to-drag ratio significantly enough to impair the climb capability. This is usually accomplished by partial extension of trailing edge flaps. The effect of the high lift devices on the cruise lift curve is as follows. Trailing edge flaps, when deflected, change the zero lift angle of the airfoils in the portion of the wing where the flaps are located. This in turn changes the zero lift angle, a_{OL}, of the airplane from the cruise configuration, but does not change the lift curve slope, $dC_L/d\alpha$. The magnitude of the change in zero lift angle depends on the ratio of flap chord to wing chord, c_f/c, the amount of flap deflection, δ_{flap} and the ratio of wing area directly affected by the deflected flap to the total wing area, S_{WF}/S_W. Leading edge slats, which must be provided over the full span of the wing to be effective in increasing C_{Lmax}, extend the lift curve in a similar manner for all trailing edge flap settings, including the flaps up configuration.

- Estimate the effect of trailing edge flaps on airplane lift curves and C_{Lmax}.

    1. First, determine the change in zero lift angle of the airplane due to trailing edge flaps. This is related to the zero lift angle change for the airfoils in the "flapped" portion of the wing, the amount of wing area affected by the trailing edge flaps, and the sweep angle

$$\Delta\alpha_{OL_{Airplane}} = \Delta\alpha_{OL_{Airfoil}} \times \frac{S_{WF}}{S_W} \times K_\Lambda \qquad (11\text{-}1)$$

The zero lift angle change for the airfoils is

$$\Delta\alpha_{OL_{Airfoil}} = \frac{d\alpha}{d\delta} \times \delta_{Flap} \qquad (11\text{-}2)$$

where $d\alpha/d\delta$ is for slotted flaps from Fig. 11-6

K_Λ is from Fig. 11-6 for the wing sweep angle

S_{WF}/S_W is estimated from the wing line diagram

δ_{Flap} is usually between 15° and 25° for takeoff, and between 40° and 50° for landing

    2. Calculate $\Delta\alpha_{OL_{Airplane}}$ for both takeoff and landing flaps.

3. On the plot of C_{L_A} vs. α_{FRP}, mark off $\Delta\,\alpha_{OL}$ due to takeoff flaps and draw the lift curve parallel to clean airplane lift curve. Repeat for landing flaps.

4. Determine α for C_{Lmax} with landing flaps

$$\alpha \text{ for } C_{Lmax_{Ldg\,Flaps}} = \alpha \text{ for } C_{Lmax_{Clean}} -3°$$

Mark off this α on the plot and extend the lift curve for landing flap until it intersects the α for $C_{L_{Max\,Ldg}}$. This determines C_{Lmax} with landing flaps.

5. Determine α for C_{Lmax} with takeoff flaps.

On the plot of C_{L_A} vs. α_{FRP}, connect with a line the C_{Lmax}, α for C_{Lmax} points for clean airplane and landing flaps. Extend the lift curve for takeoff flaps until it intersects this connecting line. This point is

$$C_{Lmax_{T.O.Flaps}} \quad \text{and } \alpha \text{ for } C_{Lmax_{T.O.Flaps}}$$

- Estimate the effect of leading edge flaps or slats

1. For full span leading edge flaps or slats,
Extend the clean airplane lift curve, to a C_{Lmax} value obtained by adding a $\Delta\,C_{Lmax}$ of 0.7 for leading edge slats and 0.5 for leading edge flaps
Repeat this process by extending the takeoff flap lift curve and the landing flap lift curve, as shown in Fig. 11-3.

2. Since airplane lift curves are not linear right up to C_{Lmax} (flow separation causes a departure from a linear C_{L_A} vs. α_{FRP}), we can approximate this as follows. On the plot of C_{L_A} vs. α_{FRP}, at the C_{Lmax} and α for C_{Lmax} points for the clean takeoff flaps (leading edge extended) and landing flaps (leading edge extended), mark off $\Delta\alpha$ of +2° at the same C_{Lmax}. Then from .9 C_{Lmax}, draw a curve to the +2° point to approximate the "round over" of the lift curves.

3. Note the C_{Lmax} values for all aircraft configurations.

DESIGN EXERCISE

Construct the low speed lift curves for your design project. Plot them on appropriate graph paper so that you may read C_{Lmax} values from them with reasonable accuracy.

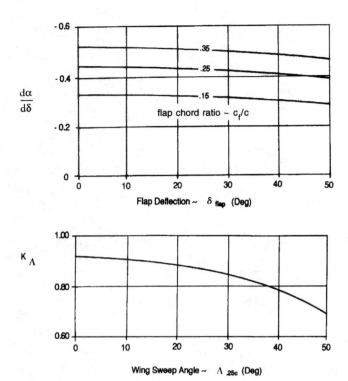

$$\frac{d\alpha}{d\delta}$$

.35

.25

.15

flap chord ratio ~ c_f/c

Flap Deflection ~ δ_{flap} (Deg)

K_Λ

Wing Sweep Angle ~ $\Lambda_{.25c}$ (Deg)

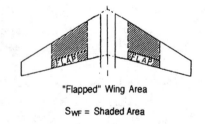

"Flapped" Wing Area

S_{WF} = Shaded Area

S_W = Total Wing Area

Fig. 11-6
Charts for Determining the Effect of
Trailing Edge Flaps on Airplane Lift
Curves

REFERENCES

11.1 USAF Stability and Control Datcom, Air Force Flight Dynamics Laboratory, Wright-Patterson Air Force Base, Dayton, Ohio, 1975

11.2 Shevell, Richard S., Fundamentals of Flight, Prentice Hall, Englewood Cliffs, NJ, 1989

11.3 Schaufele, Roger D., and Ebeling, Ann W., Aerodynamic Design of the DC-9 Wing and High Lift System, SAE Paper No. 67-0846, presented to the Aeronautics and Space Engineering Meeting, Los Angeles, CA, October, 1967

12

DETAILED DRAG BUILDUP FOR CRUISE, TAKEOFF, AND LANDING

A detailed drag buildup for every preliminary design configuration is required for more complete performance calculations. The detailed drag buildup is usually performed for three specific operating conditions:

1. Cruise configuration at the appropriate speed and altitude for cruise range calculations.
2. Takeoff configuration for takeoff field length and takeoff climb gradient calculations.
3. Landing configuration for landing field length calculations.

The following paragraphs describe the background and procedures used to estimate the complete drag characteristics for a preliminary design.

CRUISE CONFIGURATION

The cruise configuration drag buildup will vary somewhat, depending on the cruise speed of the design. Cruise drag makeup is as follows:

Cruise speed of M = 0.5 or less
    Zero lift drag   skin friction plus pressure drag
    Drag due to lift   subsonic induced drag

Cruise speed between M = 0.50 and M = 1.0
    Zero lift drag   skin friction plus pressure drag
    Drag due to lift   subsonic induced drag
    Compressibility drag   drag from local shock waves

Cruise speed greater than M = 1.0
    Zero lift drag   skin friction plus pressure drag and
                                    supersonic wave drag
    Drag due to lift   supersonic wave drag due to lift
                                      supersonic induced drag

The discussion and examples that follow are for designs with cruise Mach numbers between M = 0.50 and M = 1.0. For designs with cruise speeds lower than M = 0.50, the procedures are the same, except there is no compressibility drag element. As noted earlier, the drag coefficients for all values of lift coefficient at various Mach numbers below M = 1.0 may be estimated from three parts, the zero lift or parasite drag coefficient, C_{D_p}, the drag due to lift coefficient C_{D_i}, and the compressibility drag coefficient, ΔC_{Dc}, which is related to both Mach number and lift coefficient.

For the cruise configuration, the drag coefficient is

$$C_D = C_{D_p} + C_{D_i} + \Delta C_{Dc} \qquad (12\text{-}1)$$

Parasite Drag

The first step is to determine the parasite drag coefficient, C_{D_p}, which is made up of the skin friction drag on the external "wetted" surface of the various parts of the airplane plus a small amount of pressure drag on these parts. The skin friction drag depends on the Reynolds number at cruise, based on the appropriate characteristic length for each element of the airplane, while the pressure drag depends on a term called the "form factor" for the various elements of the airplane. The procedure is outlined as follows.

The basic approach is to determine skin friction plus pressure drag on main elements of the airplane at cruise conditions of Mach number and altitude.

$$C_D = \Sigma_i \frac{K_i \, C_{f_i} \, S_{weti}}{S_{ref}} \qquad (12\text{-}2)$$

where K_i = form factor for each element of the aircraft
             C_{f_i} = skin friction coefficient appropriate to each element
             S_{weti} = wetted area of each element
             S_{ref} = reference wing planform area

The equivalent parasite drag area, f, is defined as

$$f \, (\text{sq ft}) = C_{D_p} \, S_{ref} \qquad (12\text{-}3)$$

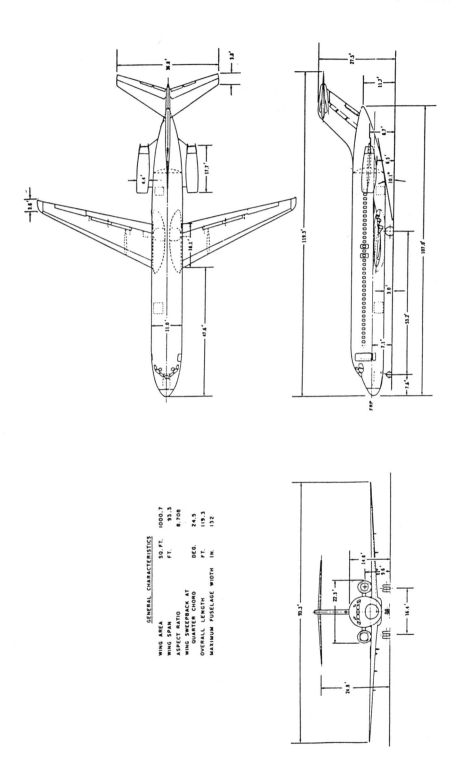

GENERAL CHARACTERISTICS		
WING AREA	SQ. FT.	1000.7
WING SPAN	FT.	93.3
ASPECT RATIO		8.708
WING SWEEPBACK AT QUARTER CHORD	DEG.	24.5
OVERALL LENGTH	FT.	119.3
MAXIMUM FUSELAGE WIDTH	IN.	132

Fig. 12-1 Aircraft for Example Problem

225

The equivalent parasite drag area, f, may also be expressed as the product of the equivalent skin friction coefficient of the complete airplane, C_F and the total wetted area, S_{wet}

$$f \text{ (sq ft)} = C_F S_{wet} \qquad (12\text{-}4)$$

An example problem has been included on the following pages to illustrate the method for estimating C_{Dp} and f for the entire airplane.

Example problem

(Adapted by permission from Ref. 12.1)

Determine the equivalent parasite drag area and the parasite drag coefficient in cruise for the airplane shown in Fig. 12-1. The cruise conditions are M = 0.78, altitude = 31,000 ft, weight = 98,000 lbs.

At 31,000 ft, from Fig. 1-9
hp = 31,000 ft
p = 601.6 psf   a = 990.5 fps   V = a   M = .78 (990.5) = 772.3 fps
Kinematic viscosity = .0003594 sq ft/sec
RN/ft = V / ν = 765.1/.0003594 = 2,203,225 or
RN = 2,203,225 L where L = characteristic length

$$q = \frac{\gamma}{2} PM^2 = .7 (601.6) (.78)^2 = 256.1 \text{ psf}$$

Wing

From Fig. 12-1 the wing chord at the side of the fuselage is 16.1 ft
The tip chord is 3.6 ft. The m.a.c. of the exposed wing is

$$\text{m.a.c.}_{exp} = 2/3 \left[(C_{SOF} + C_T) - \frac{C_{SOF}C_T}{(C_{SOF} + C_T)} \right]$$

$$= 2/3 \left[(16.1 + 3.6) - \frac{(16.1) \ (3.6)}{(16.1 + 3.6)} \right] = 11.18 \text{ ft}$$

RN = 2,203,225 L = 2,203,225(11.18) = 24,632,056
From Fig. 12-1, C_f = .00295

The average thickness ratio is $(t/c)_{avg}$ = .106   Sweep = 24.5 deg
From Fig. 12-2, K= 1.197
Wing exposed planform area = 1000.7(1.00 - .18) = 810.7 sq ft
Wing wetted area, S_{wet} = 810.7 (2) (1.02) = 1653.8 sq ft
f_{wing} = $KC_f S_{wet}$ = 1.197 (.00295) (1653.8) = 5.84 sq ft
1.197 (.00295) (1653.8) = 5.84 sq ft
ΔC_{Dp} = f_{wing} /S_{ref} = .00584

Fuselage

From Fig. 12-1, the fuselage length is 107 ft, diameter is 11 ft
The fuselage wetted area, S_{wet}, is estimated to be 3280 sq ft
The fuselage Length/Diameter is 107/11 = 9.73
From Fig. 12-4, K = 1.097
RN = 2,203,225 L = 2,203,225(107) = 2.356 x 10^8 C_f = .0020
f_{fus} = $K S_{wet} C_f$ = 1.097(3280) (.0020) = 7.20 sq ft
ΔC_{Dp} = f_{fus}/S_{ref} = 7.20/1000.7 = .0072

Horizontal Tail

S_{wet} = exposed planform area (2) (1.02) = 261(2) (1.02) = 532.4 sq ft

Root chord. C_R = 11.1 ft   Tip chord, C_T = 3.9ft

$$\text{mac.} = 2/3 \left[(C_R + C_T) - \frac{C_R C_T}{(C_R + C_T)} \right]$$

$$= 2/3 \left[(11.1 + 3.9) - \frac{(11.1)\,(3.9)}{(11.1 + 3.9)} \right] = 8.14 \text{ ft}$$

t/c = .09   Sweep = 31.5 deg   K = 1.115
RN = 2,203,225 L = 2,203,225(8.14) = 1.793x 10^7 C_f = .00305
f_{ht} = KS_{wet} C_f = 1.115(532.4) (.00305) = 1.88 sq ft
ΔC_{Dp} = f_{ht}/S_{ref} = 1.88/1000.7 = .00188

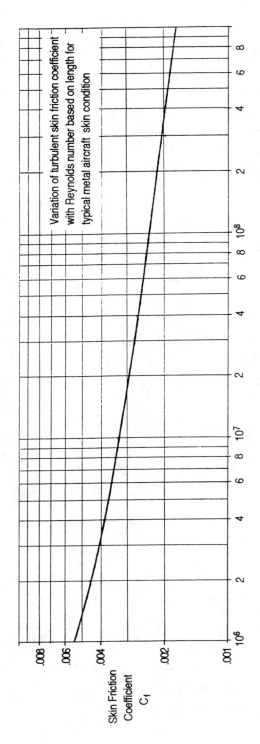

Fig. 12-2 Turbulent Skin Friction Coefficient

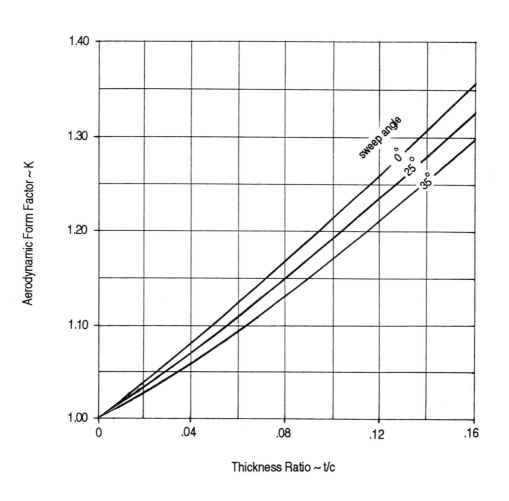

Fig. 12-3 Aerodynamic Surface Form Factors

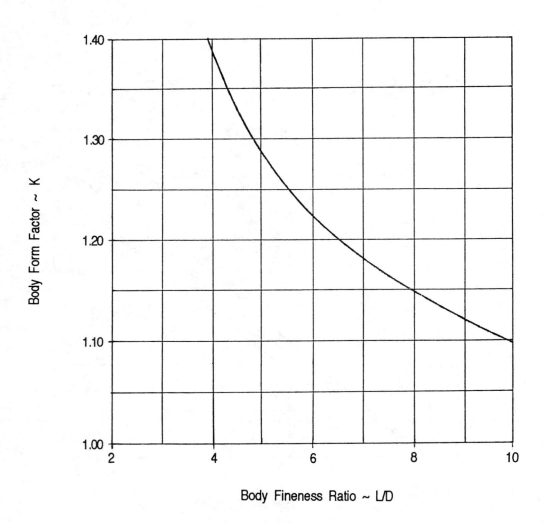

Fig. 12-4 Aerodynamic Body Form Factors

Vertical Tail

S_{wet} = exposed plantorm area (2) (1.02) = 161(2) (1.02) = 328.4 sq ft

Root chord, C_R = 15.5 ft   Tip chord = 12.4 ft

$$mac. = 2/3 \left[(C_R + C_T) - \frac{C_R C_T}{(C_R + C_T)} \right]$$

$$= 2/3 \left[(15.5 + 12.4) - \frac{(15.5)(12.4)}{(15.5 + 12.4)} \right] = 14.0 \text{ ft}$$

t/c = .09   Sweep = 43.5 deg   K = 1.127
RN = 2,203,225   L = 2,203,225 (14.0) = 3.107 x 10^7 C_f = .0027
f_{vt} = $KS_{wet} C_f$ = 1.127(328.4) (.0028) = 1.04 sq ft
ΔC_{Dp} = f_{vt}/S_{ref} = 1.04/1000.7 = .00104

Pylons

S_{wet} is estimated to be 117 sq ft   m.a.c. = 16.2 ft
RN = 2,203,225 L = 2,203,225 (16.2) = 3.569x 10^7 C_f = .0027
t/c = .06   Sweep = 0 deg   K = 1.120
f_{pylons} = $KS_{wet} C_f$ = 1.120 (117) (.0027) = .354 sqft
ΔC_{Dp} = f_{pylons}/S_{ret} = .354/1000.7 = .000354

Nacelles

S_{wet} is estimated to be 455 sq ft
Nacelle length is 17.1 ft   Diameter is 4.4 ft   L/D =3.89   K = 1.40
RN = 2,203,225 L = 2,203,225 (17.1) = 3.767x 10^7 C_f = .0027
f_{nac} = $KS_{wet} C_f$ = 1.40 (455) (.0027) = 1.72 sq ft
ΔC_{Dp} = f_{nac}/S_{ref} = 1.72/1000.7 = .00172

Flap Hinges

The equivalent parasite drag area of the flap hinges is estimated to be

$$f_{fh} = .15 \text{ sqft} \qquad \Delta C_{Dp} = .15/1000.7 = .00015$$

Airplane Parasite Drag

The complete airplane equivalent parasite drag area, f, is

$$f = (f_{wing} + f_{fus} + f_{ht} + f_{vt} + f_{pylons} + f_{nac} + f_{fh})(1.1)$$

$$f = (5.84 + 7.20 + 1.88 + 1.04 + .354 + 1.72 + .15)(1.1) = 20.0 \text{ sq ft}$$

$$C_{Dp} = = f/S_{ref} = 20.011000.7 = .0020$$

Note that when the drag coefficient increments for the various elements of the airplane are added together, the sum is increased by an arbitrary factor, usually taken as 1.1, to account for miscellaneous "dirt" items such as air conditioning inlets and vents, drain masts, antennas, control surface gaps and bellcrank fairings.

Another check on the estimated parasite drag coefficient can be made using the generalized~data on the relationship between the equivalent parasite drag area, f, and the total wetted area, S_{wet} for various types of aircraft as shown in Figs. 12-5 through 12-8. The lines of constant total airplane skin friction coefficient, C_F, are called lines of equal "cleaness" or equal values of f/S_{wet}. It should be noted that "dirt" items such as fixed landing gear, external strut bracing, etc. have an extremely adverse effect on f while adding little additional wetted area. For example on Fig. 12-5 the Cessna 172 Skyhawk is a single engine, fixed landing gear, strut braced high wing aircraft, with a total wetted area of 650 sq ft and an "f" of 5.7 sq ft, while the later, cleaner Cessna 210 Centurion is a single engine retractable landing gear, cantilever high wing aircraft with slightly higher wetted area of 700 sq ft, but with a considerably lower "f" of only 3.5 sq ft. Similar "cleaness" features contribute to the variations in C_F for airplanes with similar values of S_{wet}.

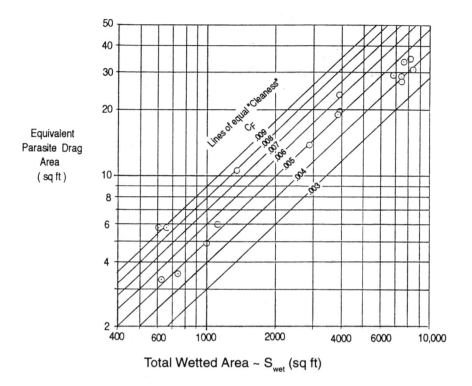

Aircraft	S_{wet} (sq ft)	f (sq ft)
Piper J-3 Cub	600	5.7
Beech V35 Bonanza	620	3.3
Cessna 172 Skyhawk	650	5.7
Cessna 210 Centurion	700	3.5
Cessna 310 Skyknight	1000	4.9
Cessna 402 Utilitwin	1100	6.0
Beech D18	1350	10.6
Saab 340	2770	14.5
Fokker F27	3850	18.4
Douglas DC-3	3880	23.7
CASAI Nusantara CN-235	3900	19.3
Douglas DC-4	6850	28.8
Douglas DC-6B	7290	27.3
Lockheed L 188 Electra	7350	29.0
Lockheed 049 Constellation	7550	34.0
Boeing 377 Stratocruiser	7950	35.0
Douglas DC-7C	8025	30.7

Fig. 12-5 Aerodynamic Cleaness Data~Prop Driven Aircraft

233

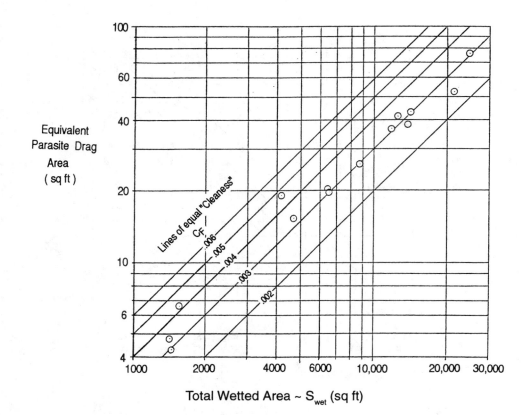

Total Wetted Area ~ S_{wet} (sq ft)

Aircraft	S_{wet} (sq ft)	f (sq ft)
Learlet 25	1415	4.8
Learlet 35	1450	4.3
Saberliner	1550	6.6
Gulfstream II	4100	19.2
Fokker F28	4650	15.5
Douglas DC-9-30	6500	20.5
Boeing 737-200	6550	19.5
Boeing 727-200	8700	26.0
Boeing 757-200	11700	37.0
Boeing 707-320	12500	41.9
Douglas DC-8-62	13600	38.2
Boeing 767-200	14000	43.5
Douglas DC-10-30	21100	52.3
Boeing 747-200	24500	77.0

Fig. 12-6 Aerodynamic Cleaness Data~Civil Jets

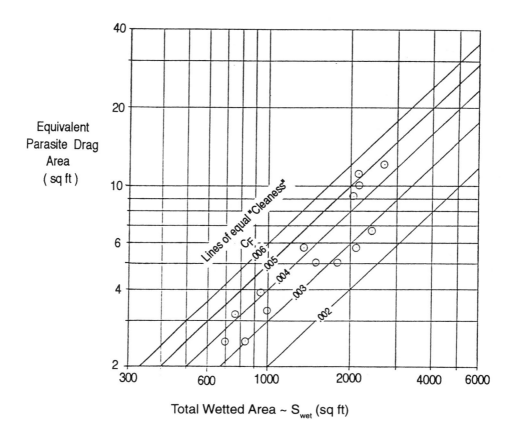

Aircraft	S_{wet} (sq ft)	f (sq ft)
Siai Marchetti S211	695	2.5
Cessna T37A	760	3.2
Northrop T 38	830	2.5
McDonnell Douglas T45A	940	3.9
Lockheed F 80	1000	3.3
LTV A7D	1350	5.7
North American F 100	1500	5.0
General Dynamics F 16	1800	5.5
McDonnell Douglas F/A 18 C/D	2050	9.1
Republic F 105	2100	5.8
McDonnell Douglas F4E	2120	11.1
Grumman A6A	2150	10.0
Convair F 102A	2400	6.7
McDonnell Douglas F15C	2630	12.0

Fig. 12-7 Aerodynamic Cleaness Data~Military Jet Trainers/Fighter/Attack Aircraft

235

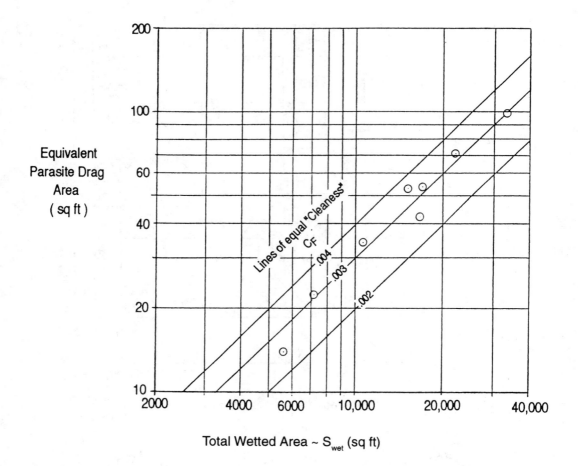

Aircraft	S_{wet} (sq ft)	f (sq ft)
Convair B58	5600	14.0
Boeing B47	7070	22.5
Boeing KCl35	10600	33.7
Lockheed Cl4lB	15200	52.5
North American B70	16700	41.0
Boeing B52G	17000	53.2
McDonnell Douglas Cl 7	22000	70.5
Lockheed C5A	33500	100.0

Fig. 12-8 Aerodynamic Cleaness Data~Military Jet Bombers/Transports

Induced Drag

The second step is to determine the drag due to lift or induced drag coefficient, C_{Di} for the various lift coefficients of interest. C_{Di} is defined as

$$C_{Di} \ = \ \frac{C_L^2}{\pi\, AR\, e} \tag{12-4}$$

AR $\quad$ = $\quad$ wing aspect ratio

e $\qquad$ = $\quad$ Airplane "efficiency" factor

The airplane efficiency factor, e, may be found from the data of Fig. 12-9.

In recent years, a number of aircraft haave been equipped with "winglets," small wing-like devices mounted at the wing tip in a vertical or near vertical orientation. These devices have been shown to reduce the total cruise drag of an aircraft by about 1-1/2 percent, by reducing the induced drag by about 3 percent. The effect of the winglet installation may be accounted for by increasing the value of "e" by 3 percent.

Compressibility Drag

The third step is to determine the compressibility drag coefficient, ΔC_{DC}, for the lift coefficients of interest for cruise. As noted earlier, the compressibility drag coefficient is the incremental drag coefficient that must be added in the high subsonic speed range to account for the drag associated with local shock waves and subsequent flow separation. This incremental drag coefficient is related to both the lift coefficient and the drag divergence Mach number, M_{DIV}, for that lift coefficient. It has been found that for the lift coefficients of interest for cruise, the shape of the compressibility drag rise curve vs Mach number may be generalized for all lift coefficients as a function of M_{DIV} as shown in Fig. 12-10. The M_{DIV} for a specific design is related to the wing average thickness ratio and the wing sweep angle for the type of airfoils being used. Charts showing the relationship between these parameters for wings using supercritical airfoils were shown in Fig. 4-8. These charts may be used to determine the M_{DIV} at various lift coefficients for a particular wing sweep and average thickness ratio. The complete cruise drag map, a plot of C_D vs Mach number at various lift coefficients as shown in the sketch of Fig. 12-11 may now be constructed. The values of C_D at the selected C_L at low Mach numbers are determined from Equation 12-1 with ΔC_{DC} set equal to zero. The compressibility drag coefficient is added at each lift coefficient in relationship to the M_{DIV} for that C_L. This must be done with a high degree of precision so that the resulting total C_D is accurate to at least four decimal places. The table shown below the chart provides more detailed data than the curve shown on Fig. 12-10.

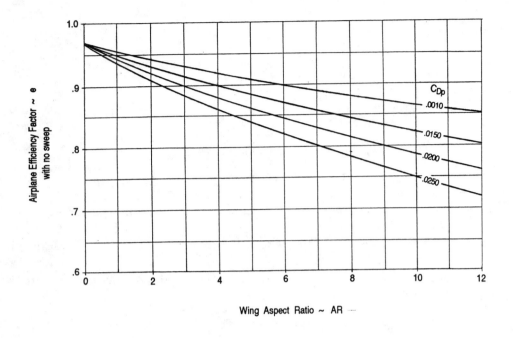

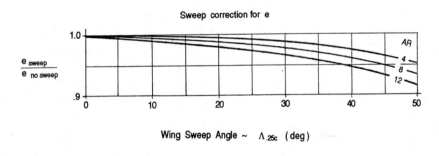

Fig. 12-9 Airplane Efficiency Factors

Adapted with permission from Ref. 12.1

L/D Curves for the Cruise Configuration

Once the complete cruise configuration drag map has been completed, curves of the lift to drag ratio L/D, vs C_L at various cruise Mach numbers, such as those shown in Fig. 12-12 may be developed. These curves show the severe impact of the compressibility drag rise on the maximum L/D in cruise as the cruise Mach number is increased. However,

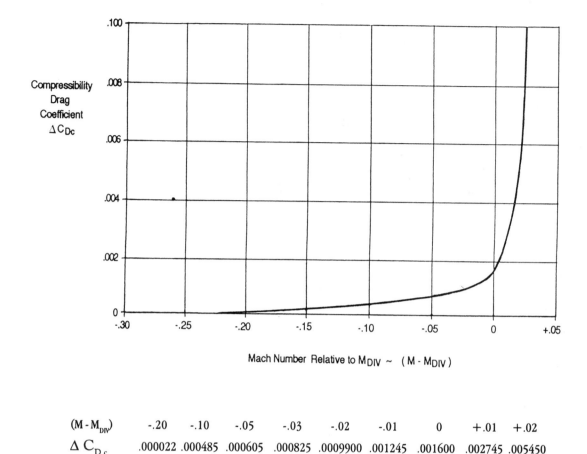

$(M - M_{DIV})$	-.20	-.10	-.05	-.03	-.02	-.01	0	+.01	+.02
$\Delta\, C_{D_c}$	.000022	.000485	.000605	.000825	.0009900	.001245	.001600	.002745	.005450

Fig. 12-10 Generalized Compressibility Drag Coefficient

from the Breguet range equation for jets, Equation 3-4, maximum range is obtained when the quantity (ML/D) is a maximum. In order to gain a better understanding of the maximum range capability for a specific design, curves of the quantity (ML/D) such as those shown in Fig. 12-13 are prepared. These curves show that even though the maximum L/D decreases significantly at Mach numbers beyond M = 0.70, the maximum value of (ML/D) continues to increase to a Mach number of at least M = 0.75. This indicates that $(ML/D)_{max}$ occurs at a Mach number where some amount of compressibility is present. A more precise picture is given by the data of Fig. 12-14, where the maximum values of (ML/D) for each Mach number are plotted, along with the lift coefficient at which

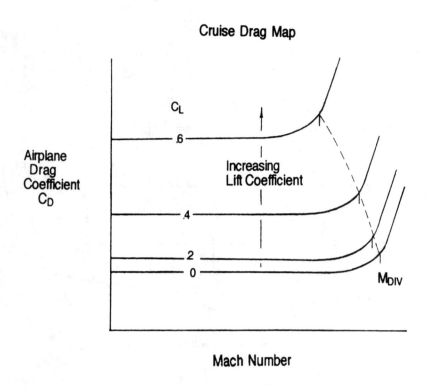

Fig. 12-11 Complete Cruise Configuration Drag Map

(ML/D) occurs. In actuality, $(ML/D)_{max}$ occurs essentially at the drag divergence Mach number, M_{DIV} for that particular design lift coefficient.

DESIGN EXERCISE

Estimate the cruise drag characteristics using the procedures described in Part 12, and construct the complete drag map for your design. Show curves of L/D versus C_L at seveal Mach numbers, including the design cruise Mach number.

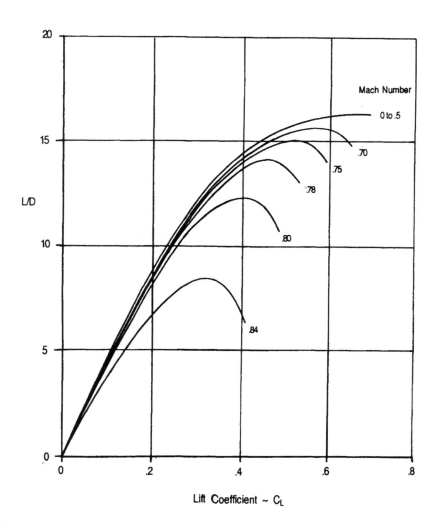

Fig. 12-12 L/D Characteristics ~ Cruise Configuration

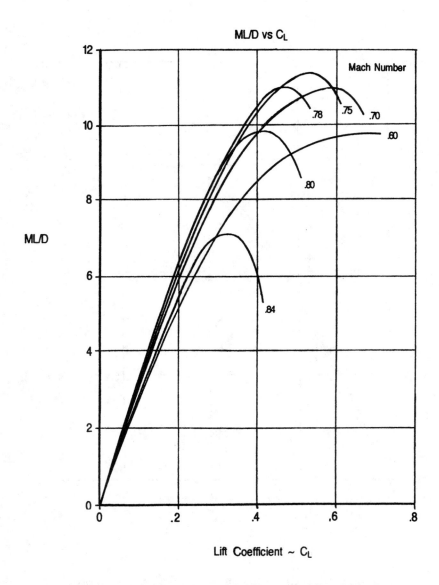

Fig. 12-13 (ML/D) Characteristics ~ Cruise Configuration

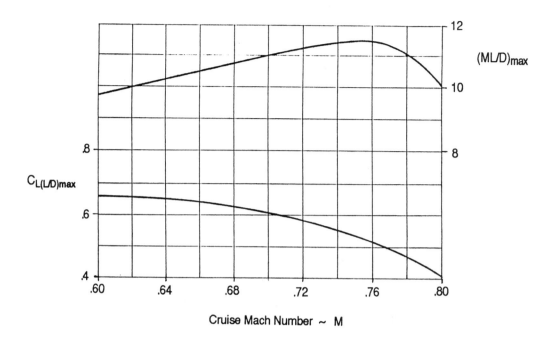

Fig. 12-14 $(ML/D)_{max}$ and $C_{L(L/D)max}$ Relationship

TAKEOFF AND LANDING CONFIGURATIONS

Takeoff configuration

The most important takeoff configuration for the conceptual design phase is the takeoff configuration for takeoff climb. This configuration is:

- Leading edge devices extended
- Trailing edge flaps set for takeoff
- Gear retracted
- Speed = 1.2 V_{Stall}

243

The total drag coefficient for this condition may be written

$$C_{D_{TO}} = C_{D_P} + \Delta C_{D_{slat}} + \Delta C_{D_{flap}} + \frac{C_L^2}{\pi \, ARe}$$

C_{D_p} = Cruise configuration parasite drag coefficient

$\Delta C_{D_{slat}}$ = Increment in parasite drag coefficient due to L.E. extension

$\Delta C_{D_{flap}}$ = Increment in parasite drag coefficient due to T.O. Flaps

$\dfrac{C_L^2}{\pi \, ARe}$ = C_{D_i} = Induced drag coefficient

The drag polar for this configuration is constructed by adding the parasite drag increments for the L.E. and T.E. high lift system components to the cruise configuration drag polar.

The increment in parasite drag coefficient due to leading edge slat extension has been evaluated for several swept wing jets and an average value is

$$\Delta C_{D_{slat}} = .006$$

The increment in parasite drag coefficient due to trailing edge flap deflection for a number of aircraft has been generalized and is shown in Fig. 12-15. The $\Delta C_{D_{flap}}$ is taken at constant C_L corresponds to 1.2 V_{Stall} with L.E. extended and flaps deflected. The construction of low speed drag polars for the takeoff and landing configurations is shown on Fig. 12-16. The steps are as follows.

- Construct the clean configuration drag polar (C_D vs C_L^2) using the cruise value of C_{D_P}, but with a low speed value for "e". Although the drag curve is close to parabolic over the entire lift coefficient range, there is some deviation between the cruise C_L region and the higher C_L region. Based on flight test data,

$$e_{low\ speed} = e_{cruise}\ (0.90)$$

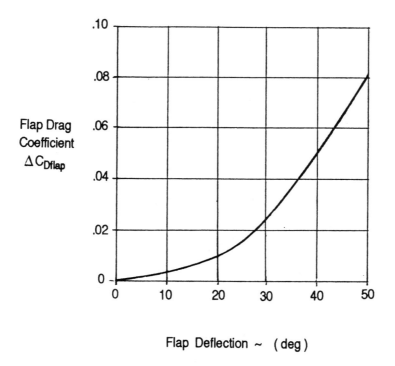

Flap Drag Coefficient $\Delta C_{D_{flap}}$

Flap Deflection ~ (deg)

Fig. 12-15 Parasite Drag Increment due to Trailing Edge Flap Deflection

Extend this low speed "clean" configuration curve to a C_L^2 of at least 1.2 V_s with flaps up and L.E. slats extended.

At this C_L^2 add the $\Delta C_{D_{slat}}$ and construct a parallel drag polar for flaps up, L.E. extended.

- Extend this curve to at least 1.2 V_s with the flaps in the takeoff setting, and the L.E. extended.

- At this C_L^2 add the $\Delta C_{D_{flap}}$ and construct a parallel drag polar for the takeoff configuration.

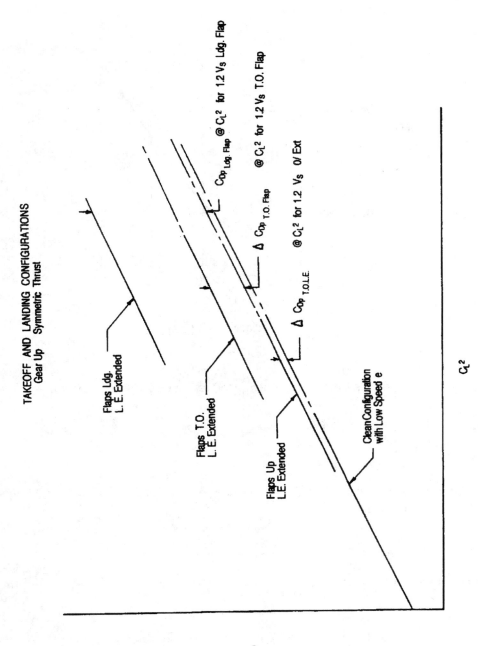

Fig. 12-16   Construction of Low Speed Drag Polars

Landing configuration

The most important landing configuration for the conceptual design phase is the landing configuration with:

- Leading edge devices extended
- Trailing edge flaps set for landing
- Gear extended
- Speed $=$ 1.3 V_{Stall}

Building on the drag polar constructed for the takeoff configuration, the drag coefficient for landing may be written

$$C_{D_{LDG}} = C_{D_p} + \Delta C_{D_{slat}} + \Delta C_{D_{flap}} + \Delta C_{D_{gear_r}} + \frac{C_L^2}{\pi \, ARe}$$

- Extend this curve to at least 1.2 V_S with the flaps in the landing configuration, and the L.E. extended.

- At this C_L^2 add the $\Delta C_{D_{gear}}$ at the landing flap setting. For takeoff and landing operations the drag of the extended landing gear is often required. Representative $\Delta C_{D_{gear}}$ values for jet transports are shown in Fig. 12-17. The decreasing $\Delta C_{D_{gear}}$ with increasing flap deflection is due to the positive pressure field (lower local velocities) in the region of the gear associated with increasing flap deflection.

It should be noted that in reality, from both wind tunnel and flight test data on many aircraft, the low speed drag polars <u>are not parallel</u>, but show increasing levels of ΔC_{D_p} due to both L.E. slats and T.E. flaps at lower C_L^2 . However, in the C_L ranges of interest, for low speed takeoff and landing operations, the "parallel" construction is reasonable for preliminary design. Fig. 12-18 shows the flight test low speed drag polars for a typical short range jet transport.

Additional low speed drag items.

- Windmilling or locked rotor engine drag - for climb calculations with one engine inoperative, the drag of a windmilling or locked rotor engine must be accounted for. A typical value is $\Delta C_{D \text{ locked rotor}} = .0020$

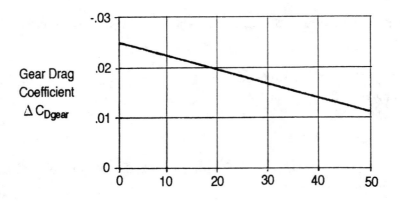

Fig. 12-17 Parasite Drag Increment due to Landing Gear Extension

- Rudder and aileron drag for asymmetric thrust climbs must also be accounted for. Wing spoiler drag during a rejected takeoff or during landing ground run stopping must be included.

- Induced drag reduction due to ground effect. When operating close to the ground, the wing downwash angle is reduced, an the induced drag is correspondingly reduced. Fig. 12-19 shows the ratio of the induced drag near the ground to the induced drag in free air.

L/D Curves for low speed configurations.

These characteristics are very important at takeoff flap settings, since they govern the takeoff climb capability with one engine inoperative. In the landing configuration they determine the amount of thrust that must be used to maintain a stabilized approach to landing. With airport noise as a sensitive issue, low L/D's in the landing configuration translate into high approach noise. Fig. 12-20 shows these characteristics for a typical short range jet transport.

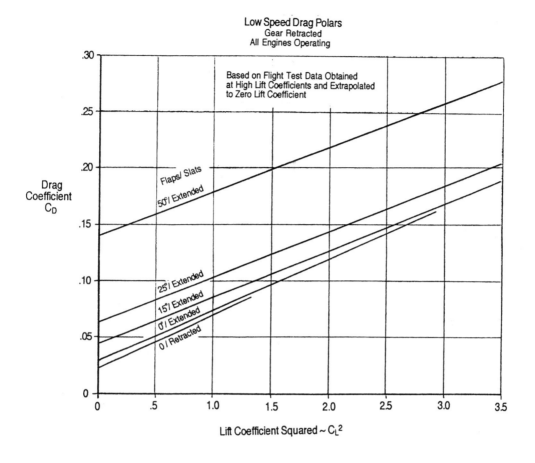

Fig. 12-18 Typical Low Speed Drag Polars

DESIGN EXERCISE

Calculate and plot on appropriate graph paper the low speed drag polars (C_D vs C_L^2) for your design for the cruise, takeoff, and landing configurations. Include the effect of landing gear extension for the landing configuration. Also plot the low speed L/D vs C_L for all configurations.

249

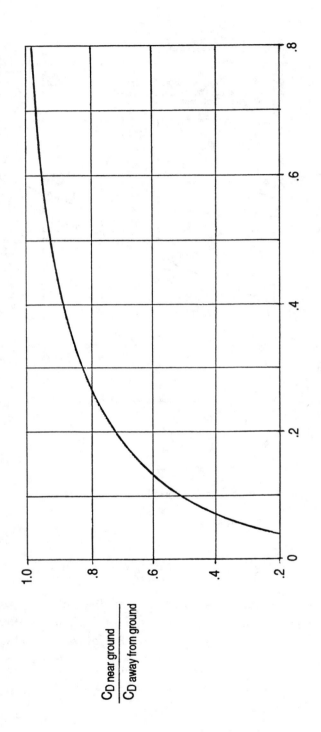

Fig. 12-19   Ground Effect Factor for Induced Drag

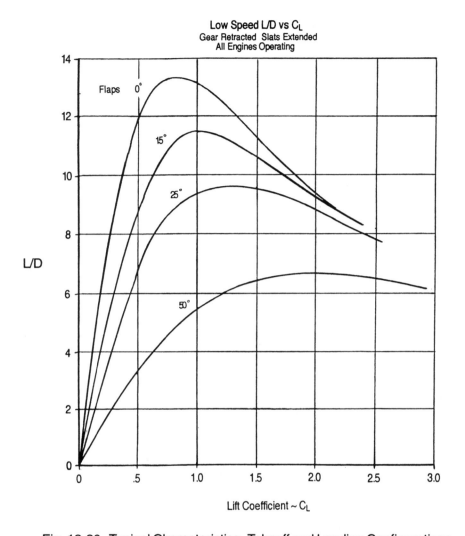

Fig. 12-20 Typical Characteristics~Takeoff and Landing Configurations

REFERENCES

12.1 Shevell, Richard S., Fundamentals of Flight, Prentice Hall, Englewood Cliffs, NJ, 1989

12.2 Anonymous, Brief Methods of Estimating Airplane Performance, Douglas Aircraft Co. Report No. SM13515, Santa Monica 1949

12.3 Anonymous, DC- 9-30 Performance Handbook, Douglas Aircraft Co. Long Beach, CA 1969

13

OPERATIONAL ENVELOPE AND ESTIMATED AIRCRAFT BUFFET BOUNDARY

OPERATIONAL ENVELOPE CONCEPT

All aircraft are constrained to operate within altitude - airspeed boundaries called the *operational envelope*. This operational envelope, described on a plot of pressure altitude versus true airspeed, is usually defined as the level flight (1 g) operational envelope, at a specific gross weight, and consists of the following boundaries:

> Minimum speed/stall speed boundary
> Minimum rate of climb/absolute ceiling boundary
> Maximum speed/thrust equals drag boundary

For low speed designs, such as personal/utility aircraft and turboprop commuters, the operational envelope is usually well defined by these boundaries, as shown in Fig. 13-1. For higher performance aircraft, such as transonic jet transports and business jets, and for supersonic military aircraft, the operational envelope boundaries can be a bit more complicated, as shown in Fig. 13-2. The stall speed boundary is the primary operational limit, but there is a minimum speed called the engine relight or restart speed, the minimum speed for which sufficient windmilling RPMs can be generated to allow an engine to be restarted following a flameout or voluntary shutdown. The minimum rate of climb/ absolute ceiling boundary and the maximum speed boundary also have two limits for supersonic military aircraft equipped with afterburners. The boundaries are defined for maximum (afterburner) thrust and military (non-afterburner) thrust. Also for most jet

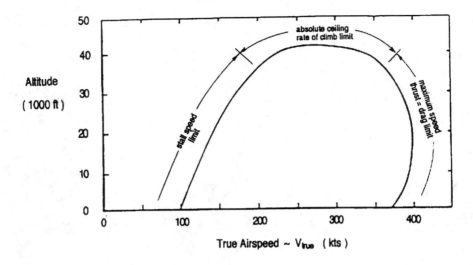

Fig. 13-1 Typical Aircraft Operational Flight Envelope ~ Subsonic Aircraft

Reprinted with permission from Ref. 13.1

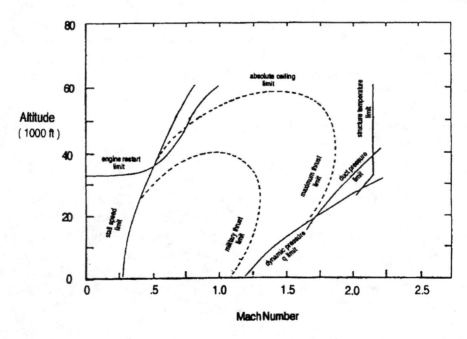

Fig. 13-2 Typical Aircraft Operational Flight Envelope ~ Supersonic Aircraft

Reprinted with permission from Ref. 13.1

aircraft, the maximum speed boundary at low altitudes is defined by an arbitrary equivalent airspeed or q limit to save on structural weight. Beyond the operational envelope, supersonic military aircraft also have limits associated with the maximum dynamic pressure that can be tolerated within the engine inlet ducts, and a structure temperature limit, a maximum Mach number beyond which the aircraft structure will overheat and lose the structural strength required to withstand the design loads.

PROCEDURE FOR ESTIMATING THE OPERATIONAL ENVELOPE

The minimum speed boundary may be estimated from Eq. 1-24, using the clean configuration C_{Lmax} and the gross weight appropriate for the operational envelope. The resulting q and corresponding V_{EAS} may be converted into a proper true airspeed at several altitudes from Eq. 1-15. The minimum rate of climb/operational ceiling boundary may be estimated from Eq. 1-22. At a few appropriate Mach numbers, derive the maximum climb thrust from the data of Figs. 8-7 through 8-13 and calculate the variation of R/C versus altitude at the selected Mach numbers. From this data, the operational envelope for any one of three definitions of operational ceiling may be found. The three definitions are:

Absolute ceiling	R/C = 0
Service ceiling	R/C = 100 ft/min
Operational ceiling	R/C = 300 ft/min

The maximum speed/thrust drag boundary may be estimated by the following. At several appropriate altitudes, calculate the aircraft drag versus speed using the idea that in level flight,

$$D = \frac{W}{(L/D)} \tag{13-1}$$

At each airspeed, the C_L may be determined and the corresponding (L/D) may be found from the (L/D) charts prepared in Chapter 12. Plot the drag versus airspeed at each altitude, and compare with the thrust at that altitude obtained from the data of Chapter 8. The intersection of the thrust required and the thrust available at each altitude will define the high speed portion of the operational envelope. The three sectors of the envelope should be joined with a smooth curve. An example problem has been included to illustrate the procedure for determining the operational envelope.

Example Problem

Determine the operational envelope for the aircraft shown in Fig. 12-1. Additional pertinent data is as follows.

> Gross Weight is 98,000 lbs.
> Engines are BPR 1.0 turbofans with a SLSTO thrust of 14,000 lbs each
> Clean configuration $C_{L_{max}} = 1.42$

Determine the stall speed boundary

The stall speed in ft/sec (EAS) is

$$Vstall = \sqrt{\frac{2(W/S)}{\rho\ C_{L_{max}}}}$$

At sea level, $\rho = .0023769$ slugs/cu ft (Fig. 1-9)

$$Vstall = \sqrt{\frac{2\ (98,000/1000.7)}{.0023769\ \times\ 1.42}} = 241 \text{ ft/sec} = 143 \text{ kts}$$

V_{stall} in true airspeed is V_{stall} (EAS) $\div \sqrt{\sigma}$

Altitude	σ	$\sqrt{\sigma}$	V_{stall}(EAS)	V_{stall}(TAS)
10,000ff	.7385	.859	143	166
20,000ff	.5328	.729	143	196
30,000ff	.3741	.612	143	234

Determine the R/C boundary

Select at least two Mach numbers to calculate R/C at two of the higher altitudes where you expect the operational envelope to be. The approach is to determine from a plot of R/C vs altitude at a specific Mach number, at what altitude does the A/C diminish to the defining value for the operational envelope. For this example, the defining value is 300 ft/min, the minimum operational R/C.

Calculate R/C at M = 0.60 and M = 0.75 at 30,000 ft and 35,000 ft.

$R/C = (\frac{T-D}{W}) \times V \times$ K.E. Factor, (T-D) / W = (T/W) - (D/W), (D/W) = 1/ (L/D)

	30,000 ft		**35,000 ft**		
q/M_2	439.9 psf		348.6 psf		Fig. 1-9
a	994.9 fps		973.1 fps		Fig. 1-9
M	0.60	0.75	0.60	0.75	
q ~ psf	158.4	247.4	125.5	196.1	
C_L	0.62	0.40	0.78	0.50	W/Sq
(L/D)	16.1	13.8	16.0	15.0	Fig. 12-12
$\frac{\text{Max Cr Thrust}}{\text{SLSTO Thrust}}$	0.29	0.29	0.24	0.24	Fig. 8-9
$\frac{\text{Max Cl Thrust}}{\text{Max Cr Thrust}}$	1.071	1.071	1.068	1.068	Fig. 8-8
$\frac{\text{Max Cl Thrust}}{\text{per engine lbs}}$	4348	4348	3588	3588	
Total Cl Thrust lbs	8696	8696	7177	7177	
(T/W)	.0887	.0887	.0732	.0732	
(D/W)	.0621	.0725	.0625	.0667	
(T/W) - (D/W)	.0266	.0162	.0107	.0065	
V ~ fps	596.9	746.1	583.8	729.8	
V ~ fpm	35,813	44,766	35.028	43,789	
K.E. Factor	1.05	1.05	1.08	1.08	Fig. 8-6
R/C ~ fpm	1000	783	394	307	

From Fig. 13-3, At M = 0.60, 300 fpm reached at 35.800 ft
At M = 0.75, 300 fpm reached at 35,000 ft
At 35,800 ft, M = 0.60 = 0.60 x a = 0.60 x 574.3 kts = 344.6 kts
At 35,000 ft, M = 0.75 = 0.75 x a = 0.75 x 576.4 kts = 432.3 kts

Determine the Thrust equals Drag boundary

At three altitudes. calculate thrust and drag vs Mach number and find graphically the point where drag in level flight equals the maximum cruise thrust.

At 30,000 ft, q/M^2 = 439.9 psf, a = 589.3 kts

M	0.70	0.80	0.84	
q ~ psf	215.6	281.6	310.0	(q/M^2) x M^2
C_L	0.454	0.348	0.316	W/Sq
(L/D)	14.8	11.9	8.4	Fig. 12-12
D-lbs	6621	8235	11,667	W/(L/D)
T-lbs	8120	8120	8120	Total SLSTO Thrust x $\frac{\text{(Max Cr Thrust)}}{\text{(SLSTO Thrust)}}$

From Fig. 13-4, thrust and drag are equal at M = 0.795, V_{TRUE} = 468.4 kts

At 20,000ft, q/M^2 = 680.8psf, a = 614.3kts

M	0.60	0.75	0.80	0.84
q ~ psf	245.0	382.9	435.7	480.4
C_L	0.400	0.256	0.225	0.204
(L/D)	14.3	10.8	9.3	6.9
D-lbs	6853	9074	10,538	14,202
T ~ lbs	10,370	10,370	10,370	10,370

Thrust and drag are equal at M - 0.795, V_{TRUE} = 488.4 kts

At sea level, q/M^2 = 1481 psf, a = 661.5 kts

M	0.60	0.70
q ~ psf	533.1	833.1
CL	0.182	0.118
(L/D)	8.2	5.7
D ~ lbs	11,951	17,192
T ~ lbs	15,680	14,840

Thrust and drag are equal at M = 0.709 V_{TRUE} = 469.0 kts

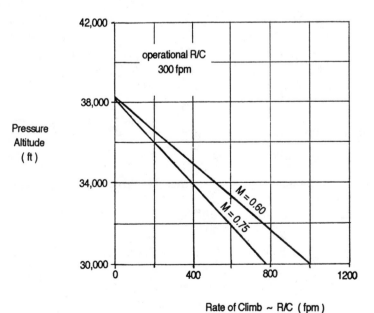

Fig. 13-3 Rate of Climb Plots ~ Example Problem

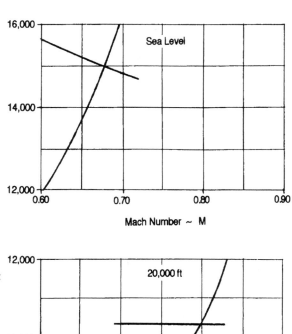

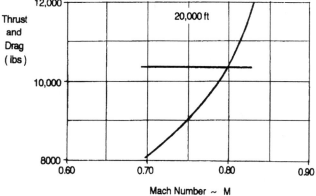

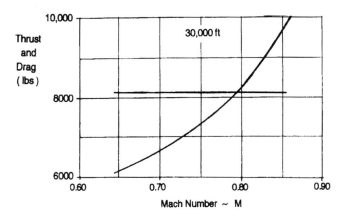

Fig. 13-4 Thrust - Drag Plots ~ Example Problem

You may now use all of the boundary points determined in the example problem to construct the operational envelope shown in Fig. 13-5.

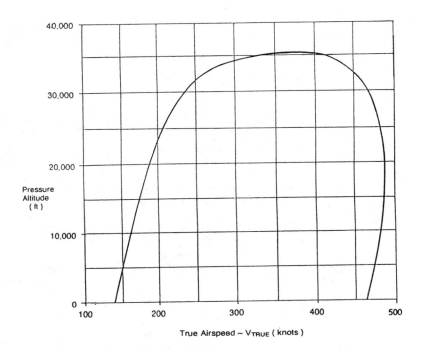

Fig. 13-5   Operational Envelope ~ Example Problem

For transonic cruise aircraft, such as jet transports and business jets, there is another operational limit called the "buffet boundary." Inside the buffet boundary, the aircraft can operate smoothly over a range of speed and altitude conditions. Outside the buffet boundary, the aircraft is subjected to significant separated flow, which results in noticeable shaking or "buffeting" of the structure and flight controls. This buffeting can be severe enough to cause minor structural damage, and can be associated with abnormal aerodynamic stability and control characteristics.

The buffet boundary is described by a single curve of airplane lift coefficient, C_L for buffet onset, or beginning of buffet versus Mach number. The curve shown in Fig. 13-6 is typical for a jet transport or business jet with moderate wing sweep (15°-35°) and moderate thickness ratio (9%-13%).

Supersonic cruise aircraft with lower wing thickness ratios (3%-5%) do not experience the near vertical boundary just short of M = 1.0 and have buffet free operation supersonically, as shown in Fig. 13-7.

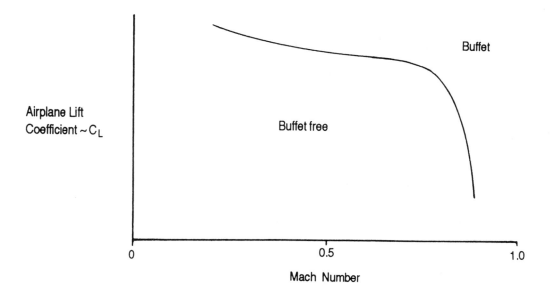

Fig. 13-6 Typical Buffet Boundary, Transonic Jet Aircraft

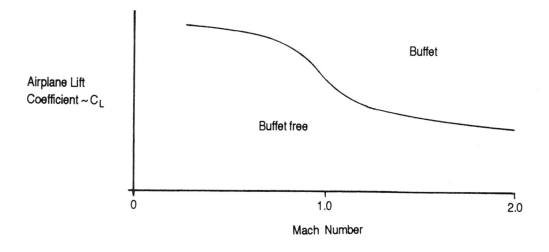

Fig. 13-7 Typical Buffet Boundary, Supersonic Aircraft.

For transonic cruise aircraft, the buffet boundary shape is related to two similar, but actually different separated airflow conditions. They are

1. Wing upper surface flow separation associated with the approach to the airplane maximum lift coeficient, C_{Lmax}

2. Wing upper surface flow separation associated with operation beyond M_{DIV}, and the unsteady flow caused by strong shock waves on the wing.

These two phenomena are quite different at the extreme ends of the buffet boundary curve, but tend to become quite similar at intermediate Mach numbers around the "knee" of the buffet boundary curve. A relatively simple procedure, based on these two flow conditions, can be used to estimate the buffet boundary for transonic cruise aircraft.

PROCEDURE FOR ESTIMATING THE BUFFET BOUNDARY

Buffet boundary related to C_{Lmax}

As noted in Fig. 1-21, the C_{Lmax} is reduced as the flight Mach number increases. Since buffet onset occurs prior to reaching C_{Lmax} a first step is to estimate the variation of airplane C_{Lmax} with Mach number. Fortunately, a trend curve which correlates the C_{Lmax} characteristics of a number of aircraff vs Mach number has been developed. The correlation is in the form of a ratio of the C_{Lmax} at high Mach number to the C_{Lmax} at low speed with no Mach number effects. This ratio is plotted vs Mach number as shown in Fig. 13-8. When the values from this curve at various Mach numbers are combined with the cruise configuration C_{Lmax} for a specific design, one can establish a curve of C_{Lmax} vs Mach number for that design. The buffet onset will occur at some C_L below C_{Lmax}. Experience indicates that the C_L for buffet occurs at about 90% of the airplane C_{Lmax}, so using this factor with the airplane C_{Lmax} vs Mach number, one may estimate the buffet boundary related to C_{Lmax}.

Buffet boundary related to M_{DIV}

At M_{DIV} compressibility drag is a already a factor in the total airplane drag buildup, due to the existence of shock waves on the wing, but the airfow is steady and there is no buffet. However, at slightly higher Mach numbers, the shock waves become stronger, which leads to separation, unsteady flow and buffet. As noted in Fig. 12-11, M_{DIV} is a function of C_L

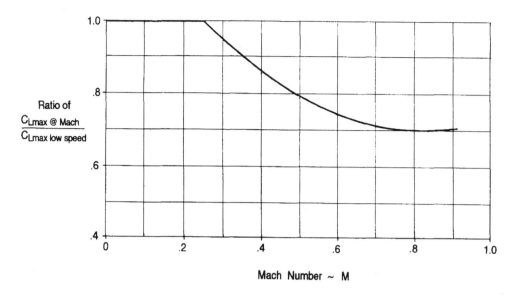

Fig. 13-8   Typical Maximum Lift Coefficient Ratios for Transonic Aircraft

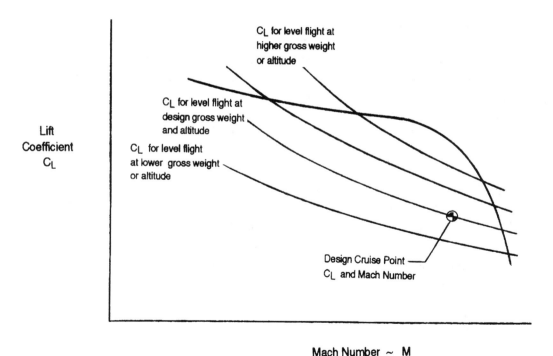

Fig. 13-9   Design Cruise Point Relative to the Buffet Boundary

263

the higher the C_L ,the lower the M_{DIV}. The variation of M_{DIV} for a specific wing sweep and thickness ratio may be determined using the applicable chart from Fig. 4-8. A good rule of thumb is that buffet occurs at a Mach number that is .03 higher than M_{DIV}. Using this information, the right hand side of the buffet boundary may be drawn.

Complete buffet boundary

With the two segments of the buffet boundary curve established, they should be joined with a smooth fair curve so that the final result looks much like Fig. 13-6.

Margin to buffet onset

For transonic cruise aircraft, there needs to be some margin between the airplane level flight 1 g operation and the buffet boundary, so that normal speed changes, gentle maneuvers, as well as gusts and other disturbances do not put the airplane into buffet Referring back to Fig. 1-16, any number of 1g operating lines may be superimposed on the buffet boundary, representing different combinations of gross weight and cruise altitude as shown in Fig. 13-9. At combinations of high gross weight an/or high altitude, the operating line moves up and to the right, resulting in a very limited Mach range between low speed and high speed buffet onset. In fact at the extreme condition, the operating line and the buffet boundary would coincide, and there would be no buffet free operation. To avoid this situation, designers select the proper wing area to allow a margin of 1.3 g to buffet onset when maneuvering, and a margin of .04 Mach for inadvertent overspeeds from the design initial cruise point. Fig.13-10 shows the buffet boundary and the normal operating conditions for a typical jet transport.

DESIGN EXERCISE

Construct the operational envelope, and if applicable, the buffet boundary for your design. On the buffet boundary, indicate the design cruise point at initial cruise altitude and gross weight, and determune the margins to buffet for both maneuvers and inadvertent overspeed.

REFERENCES

13.1 Nicolai, Leland M., Fundamentals of Aircraft Design, METS, San Jose, CA 1984

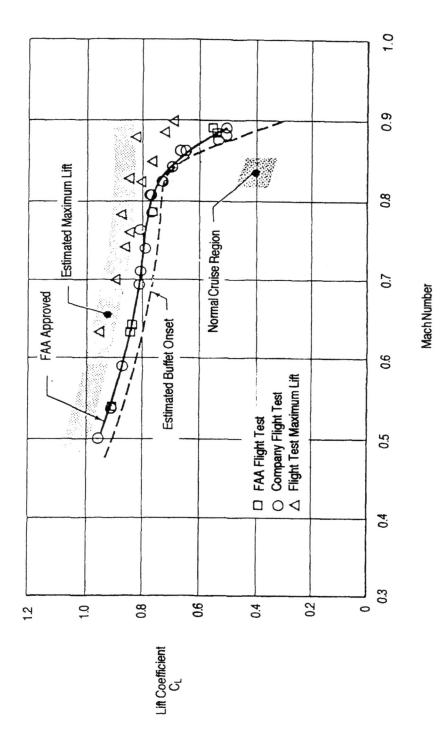

Fig. 13-10 Flight Test Buffet Boundary~Typical Jet Transport

14

DESIGN AIRLOAD REQUIREMENTS
AND DESIGN AIRSPEEDS

GENERAL CONSIDERATIONS

Aircraft structure must be designed to withstand the most serious of the infinite number of possible combinations of external forces that may act on it in flight and in landing. Experience, accumulated over many years of design, analysis, and research, has led to the formulation of a very rational set of procedures that determine the design loads and define the airspeeds for which the design loads are imposed. For civil aircraft, these requirements and procedures are described in Federal Air Regulations (FAR) Part 23 and Part 25 "Airworthiness Standards Airplanes." For military aircraft, these requirements and procedures are described in MIL-A-8660, "Airplane Strength and Rigidity, General Specification for" and MIL-A-8661, "Airplane Strength and Rigidity, Flight Loads." The requirements are, in most cases, nearly identical in both the civil and military documents. The information that follows will be based on FAR 23 and 25, with information from MIL-A-8660 and MIL-A-8661 added where significant differences exist.

- Flight conditions (FAR 25.331 through 25.459)
  - Maneuver load generated by intentional pilot application of controls.
  - Gust load generated by sudden change in angle of attack due to encountering a "gust."

FLIGHT LOAD FACTOR

An important concept in the analysis of air loads imposed under various flight conditions is the flight load factor, n, which is defined as follows:

$$n = \frac{\text{Aerodynamic Force} \perp \text{Longitudinal Axis}}{\text{Aircraft Weight}} \qquad (14\text{-}1)$$

For an aircraft in steady level flight, the aerodynamic force perpendicular to the longitudinal axis is by equation (1-24) the lift, which is equal to the weight. Since the weight is due to the force of gravity, the aircraft is said to be in 1 g flight. If the lift is four times the weight, the aircraft is said to be subjected to 4 g's. In a more simple form,

$$n = \frac{\text{Lift}}{\text{Weight}} \qquad (14\text{-}2)$$

V-n DIAGRAMS

The analysis of the critical design airloads for an aircraft employs a chart known as the V-n diagram. These charts show flight load factors that must be used for structural design as a function of equivalent airspeed and represent the maximum load factors expected in service, based on the requirements of the applicable specifications. These load factors are called "limit" load factors. The airplane structure must withstand these loads without damage. These limit loads are multiplied by a safety factor of 1.5 to define "ultimate" or failure loads. There are two types of V-n diagrams; one to define maneuver load factors, and one to define gust load factors. The following discussion is based on FAR Part 25, Airworthiness Standards: Transport Category Aircraft, the corresponding portions of FAR Part 23, Airworthiness Standards: Normal, Utility, Aerobatic, and Commuter Category Aircraft, as well as provisions of the Military Specification MIL-A-8661A: Aircraft Strength and Rigidity, Flight Loads, applicable to all military aircraft.

V-n Diagram - Maneuver Envelope

The V-n diagram showing the maximum maneuver load factors that must be used for structural design, Fig. 14-1, is an envelope defined by by various lines and points which have a specific relationship to the design load factors. A brief explanation of the key portions of the maneuvering envelope are given as follows.

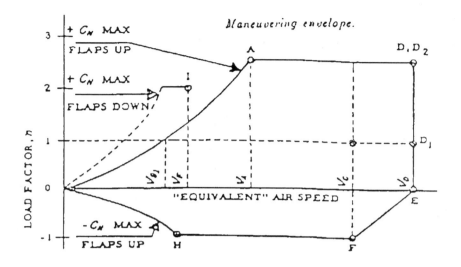

Fig. 14-1 V-n Diagram - Maneuvering Envelope

Line O-A

This line describes the load factor that results when the aircraft is maneuvered to it's maximum normal force coefficient C_{Nmax} in the clean or cruise configuration. Since this is the maximum normal force that can be generated by the aerodynamic characteristics of the configuration, it is the maximum load factor that can be generated by the pilot. The equation of this line is n= C_{Nmax} qS/W.

Point A

This is the intersection of the pull up to C_{Nmax} with the maximum positive maneuver load factor specified in the requirements for the particular type of aircraft being designed. It should be noted that Point A is not selected by the designer but determined uniquely by aircraft parameters and the maneuver limit load factor for the type.

Line A-D

This line is the maximum positive maneuver load factor for the type. The design limit load factors for various aircraft types were determined many years ago from flight tests of a number of airplanes of various types, each subjected to a number of typical maneuvers.

These tests were made with an accelerometer placed at or near the airplane center of gravity, which recorded the the imposed accelerations. Experience has indicated that these load factors resulted in highly satisfactory satisfactory designs.

Line 0-H

This line describes the load factor generated when the airplane is maneuvered to it's maximum negative C_{Nmax} value. Since wing design is focused on using airfoils that have high values of positive C_{Nmax}, the maximum values of negative C_{Nmax} are usually about 0.7 times the positive C_{Nmax} values.

Line H-F

This line describes the maximum negative maneuver load factor, again determined from flight tests as noted above. The maximum maneuver load factors vary with aircraft type. For FAR Part 23 aircraft, the maximum positive and negative maneuver load factors are

Aircraft Type	Max Positive	Max Negative
Normal	3.8	1.52
Utility	4.4	1.76
Acrobatic	6.0	3.00
Commuter	3.8	1.52

Fig. 14-2   FAR Part 23 Maximum Maneuver Load Factors

For FAR Part 25 aircraft, the maximum positive maneuver load factor varies with design gross weight. The maximum value is 3.8 up to a gross weight of 4100 lbs. At higher gross weights, the maximum value varies according to the relation

$$n_{max} = 2.1 + \left[\frac{24000}{MTOGW + 10000} \right] \qquad (14\text{-}3)$$

up to a gross weight of 50,000 lbs. where the maximum becomes a constant value of 2.5. This is shown graphically in Fig. 14-3. The maximum negative maneuver load factor for FAR Part 25 aircraft is -1.0. Corresponding maneuver load factors for military aircraft are shown in Fig. 14-4.

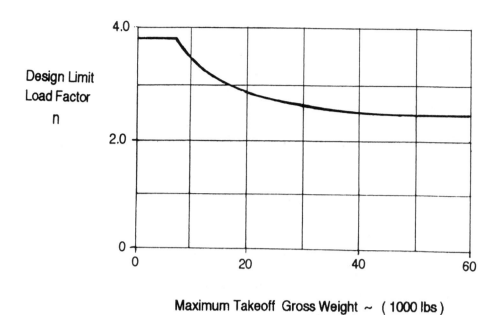

Fig. 14-3 FAR 25 Positive Limit Maneuver Load Factors

Aircraft Type	Basic Flight Design Weight		All Weights	Max Design Weight		Max Ordnance Weight	
	Max	Min@V_H	Min@V_H	Max	Min@V_H	Max	Min@V_H
Fighter/Attack (subsonic)	8.00	-3.00	-1.00	4.00	-2.00	5.50	-2.00
Fighter/Attack (supersonic)	6.50	-3.00	-1.00	4.00	-2.00	5.50	-2.00
Observation & Trainers	6.00	-3.00	-1.00	3.00	-1.00		
Utility	4.00	-2.00	0	2.50	-1.00		
Tactical Bomber	4.00	-2.00	0	2.50	-1.00		
Strategic Bomber	3.00	-1.00	0	2.00	0		
Assault Transport	3.00	-1.00	0	2.00	0		
Conventional Transport	2.50	-1.00	0	2.00	0		

Reference: MIL-A-8861A

Fig. 14-4 Military Specification Limit Maneuver Load Factors

V-n Diagram - Gust Envelope

In addition to the load factors imposed by intentional maneuvers controlled by the pilot, appreciable increases in effective angle of attack can result from entering a "gust," or current of air having a velocity component normal to the line of flight. The resulting increase in load factor depends primarily on the vertical velocity of the gust, and especially for business jets and jet transports, it may exceed the maximum due to intentional maneuvers. The load factors produced by gusts vary directly with equivalent airspeed, and are computed using the gust load factor equation given in FAR 23.341 and FAR 25.343.

The equation is

$$n = 1 + \frac{K_g \, U_{gE} \, V_E \, a}{498 \, (W/S)} \tag{14-4}$$

where

$$K_g = \frac{0.88 \, \mu g}{5.3 + \mu g} = \text{gust alleviation factor}$$

$$\mu g = \frac{2 \, (W/S)}{\rho \, \overline{C} \, ag}$$

U_{gE} = equivalent gust velocity (ft/s)
ρ = density of the air (slugs/cu ft)
W/S = wing loading (lb/sq ft)
$\overline{C}$ = mean geometric chord (ft)
g = acceleration due to gravity (ft/sec^2)
V_E = aircraft equivalent airspeed (kts)
a = slope of the airplane normal force curve <u>per radian</u>

The V-n diagram for the gust envelope is shown in Fig. 14-5.

The designer must assume a symmetrical vertical gust of
  66 fps at V_B from S.L. to 20,000 ft, decreasing to 38 fps at 50,000 ft
  50 fps at Vc from S.L. to 20,000 ft, decreasing to 25 fps at 50,000 ft
  25 fps at V_D from S.L. to 20,000 ft, decreasing to 12.5 fps at 50,000 ft

The key points of the gust envelope are as follows.

Line 0 - B'

As in the maneuver envelope, this line describes the maximum load factor that can be generated by a gust which causes the airplane to reach it's $C_{N_{max}}$.

Point B'

This point is the intersection of the load factor for $C_{N_{max}}$ and the load factor for a 66 fps gust. This point determines V_B, the design speed for maximum gust intensity.

Point C'

This point is the intersection of the load factor due to a 50 fps gust and the design cruising speed, Vc

Point D'

This point is the intersection of the load factor due to a 25 fps gust and the design dive speed, V_D

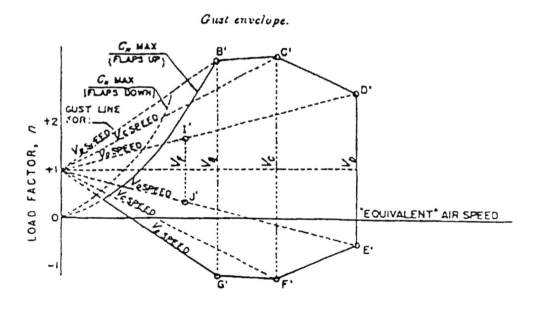

Fig. 14-5 V-n Diagram — Gust Envelope

<u>Points E',F' and G'</u>

These are the corresponding intersections for negative gusts at the designated speeds.

The manuever and gust envelopes are superimposed to determine the highest load factors for design at all speeds within the flight envelope and the entire aircraft structure analyzed for these load factors.

An example of V-n diagrams for a typical short range jet transport are shown in Figs. 14-6 and 14-7. Often the maneuver envelope and the gust envelope are both plotted on the same chart, in order to show graphically whether the design is "maneuver critical" or "gust critical" at the various design airspeeds. The higher of the two load factors must be used for structural design. An example of the relationship of the design and operating limit airspeeds and the operational envelope is shown in Fig. 14-8.

DESIGN AIRSPEEDS

The airspeeds associated with the V-n diagram except for V_A and V_B are chosen by the designer, but must meet certain definitions and criteria contained in the FARs. Fig. 14-8

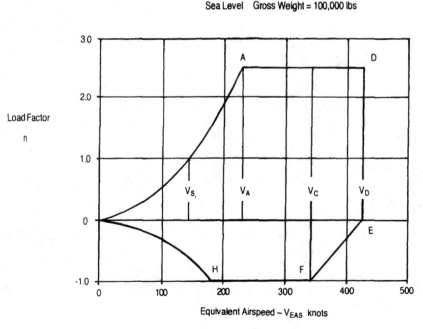

Fig. 14-6 Typical Maneuvering Envelope

is a summary of the pertinent FAR 25 airspeed definitions. The list following is a simplified summary.

Design Airspeeds - V_{EAS}

V_S	-	Stalling speed or minimum steady flight speed
V_A	-	Maneuver speed or full control deflection speed
V_B	-	Design speed for maximum gust intensity
V_{FE}	-	Design flap extended speed
V_{LE}	-	Design landing gear extended speed
V_{LO}	-	Design landing gear operating speed (if different from V_{LE})
V_C	-	Design cruising speed ($\geq V_B + 43$ KTs)
V_{MO}	-	Maximum operating limit speed ("Barber Pole" speed)
V_{FC}	-	Maximum speed at which flight characteristics requirements must be met
V_D	-	Design dive speed, $\geq V_C/0.80$, or speed reached in 7.5 degree dive for 20 sec. from V_C, followed by a 1.5 g recovery

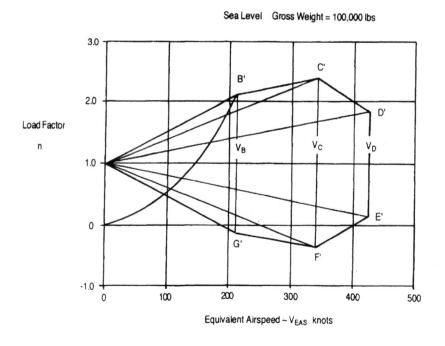

Fig. 14-7 Typical Gust Envelope

§ 25.103 Stalling speed.

(a) V_s is the calibrated stalling speed, or the minimum steady flight speed, in knots, at which the airplane is controllable with—

(1) Zero thrust at the stalling speed, or, if the resultant thrust has no appreciable effect on the stalling speed, with engines idling and throttles closed;

(2) Propeller pitch controls (if applicable) in the position necessary for compliance with paragraph (a)(1) of this section and the airplane in other respects (such as flaps and landing gear) in the condition existing in the test in which V_s is being used;

(3) The weight used when V_s is being used as a factor to determine compliance with a required performance standard; and

(4) The most unfavorable center of gravity allowable.

(b) The stalling speed V_s is the minimum speed obtained as follows:

(1) Trim the airplane for straight flight at any speed not less than 1.2 V_s or more than 1.4 V_s At a speed sufficiently above the stall speed to ensure steady conditions, apply the elevator control at a rate so that the airplane speed reduction does not exceed one knot per second.

§ 21.335 Design airspeeds.

The selected design airspeeds are equivalent airspeeds (EAS). Estimated values of Vs and V_s must be conservative.

(a) *Design cruising speed, V_C*. For V_C the following apply:

(1) The minimum value of V_C must be sufficiently greater than V_B to provide for inadvertent speed increases likely to occur as a result of severe atmospheric turbulence.

(2) In the absence of a rational investigation substantiating the use of other values, V_C may not be less than V_B+ 43 knots. However, it need not exceed the maximum speed in level flight at maximum continuous power for the corresponding altitude.

(3) At altitudes where V_D is limited by Mach number, V_C may be limited to a selected Mach number

(b) *Design dive speed, V_D*, V_D must be selected so that V_C/M_C is not greater than 0.8 V_D/M_D, or so that the minimum speed margin between V_C/M_{C_s} and V_D/M_D is the greater of the following values:

(I) From an Initial condition of stabilized flight at $V_C/M_{C'}$ the airplane is upset, flown for 20 seconds along a flight path 7.5 below the initial path, and then pulled up at a load factor of 1.5 g *(0.5 g acceleration incre-*

ment). The speed increase occurring in this or maneuver may be calculated if reliable or conservative aerodynamic data is used. Power as specified in § 25.175(b)(1)(iv) is assumed until the pull up is initiated, at which time power reduction and the use of pilot controlled drag devices may be assumed;

(2) The minimum speed margin must be enough to provide for atmospheric variations (such as horizontal gust and penetration of jet streams and cold fronts) and for instrument errors and airframe production variation. These factors may be considered on a probability basis. However, the margin at altitude where M_C is limited by compressibility effects may not be less than 0.05 M.

§ 25.253 High-speed characteristics

(b) Maximum speed for stability characteristics, V_{FC}/M_{FC}. V_{FC}/M_{FC} is the maximum speed at which the requirements §§ 25.147(e), 25.175(b)(1), 25.177, and 25.181 must be met with flaps and landing gear retracted. It may not be less than a speed midway between V_{MO}/M_{MO} and $V_{OF}/M_{OF'}$ except that, for altitudes where Mach number is the limiting factor, M_{FC} need not exceed the Mach number at which effective speed warning occurs.

§ 25.1583 Operating limitations.

(a) Airspeed Limitations. The following airspeed limitations and any other airspeed limitations necessary for safe operation must he furnished:

(1) The maximum operating limit speed V_{MO}/M_{MO} and a statement that this speed limit may not be deliberately exceeded in any regime of flight (climb, cruise, or descent) unless higher speed is authorized for flight test or pilot training.

(2) If an airspeed limitation is based upon compressibility effects, a statement to this effect and information to any symptoms, the probable behavior of the airplane, and the recommended recovery procedures.

3) The maneuvering speed V_A and a statement that full application of rudder and aileron controls, as well as maneuvers that involve angles of attack near the stall, should be confined to speeds below this value.

4) The flap extended speed V_{FE} and the pertinent flap positions and engine powers.

(5) The landing gear operating speed or speeds, and a statement explaining the speeds as defined in § 25.1515(a).

(6) The landing gear extended speed $V_{LE'}$ if greater than V_{LO} and a statement that this is the maximum speed at which the airplane can be safely flown with the landing gear extend

Fig. 14-7 FAR 25 Airspeed Definitions

The military speed definitions are basically the same although MIL-A-8660B combines V_C and V_{MO} into a maximum level flight speed, V_H, and replaces V_D with the "limit speed," V_L.

For subsonic airplanes, the design airspeeds are usually constant for the entire flight envelope. For high subsonic and supersonic airplanes, the design airspeeds are varied throughout the flight envelope, since equivalent airspeeds that are appropriate at sea level and the lower altitudes are beyond the performance capabilities of the airplane at the higher altitudes. Therefore, the design airspeeds for these types are usually defined in terms of Mach number at the higher altitudes. For example, the maximum operating limit speed is defined by a V_{MO}/M_{MO} line which is a function of altitude. As noted in Fig. 14-8, the design cruise speed (Mach number) need not be higher than the maximum speed in level flight at that altitude with maximum cruise power. This provision usually sets M_C. M_{MO} is usually set at or slightly above (.01 or 02 Mach number) M_C, providing a margin on the order of .08 Mach number between the best long range cruise Mach number and M_{MO}. The design dive Mach number is usually about .05 Mach number higher than M_{MO}. An example of the relationship between the design and operating limit airspeeds and the operational envelope is shown in Fig. 14-9.

DESIGN EXERCISE

Select the design airspeeds with appropriate rationale for your design project, and construct a V-n diagram for the maneuver envelope and a V-n diagram for the gust envelope for your design, for initial cruise altitude and gross weight conditions.

REFERENCES

14.1 U.S. Code of Federal Regulations, Title 14, Aeronautics and Space, Parts 1-199, Federal Aviation Administration, published by Office of the Federal Register, revised 1999

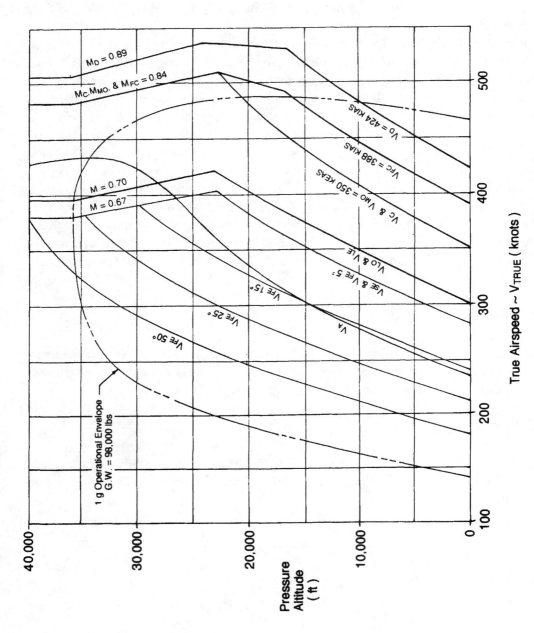

Fig. 14-9 Relationship between Design Airspeeds and Operational Envelope

15

PAYLOAD-RANGE PERFORMANCE

PAYLOAD-RANGE CURVE

The payload-range curve is one of the most important performance curves for a commercial transport or business jet aircraft. The payload-range curve establishes the envelope which shows how far the airplane can carry a given payload, or how much payload it can carry over a given range. The payload-range curve, Fig. 15-1, applies to, and is calculated for

- A specific airplane/engine combination (MWE, OWE, interior seating arrangement, fuel tank configuration, MTOGW)
- Specific flight rules (cruise Mach number, altitude, altitude steps, alternate distance)

The maximum payload is usually the volume or space limit payload (full passengers + bags and full cargo containers or pallets at some standard cargo density, i.e. 10.0 lb/cu. ft) or maximum zero fuel weight limit payload, based on the structural limit of maximum zero fuel weight.

When operating on the maximum takeoff weight limit, it is necessary to trade payload for fuel if greater range is desired. Operating on the fuel capacity limit line requires large reductions in payload to achieve small increases in range, due to modest improvements in cruise efficiency achieved by reductions in cruise weight. The key points on the payload-range curve, Figs. 15-2 and 15-3, are calculated using the Breguet range equation.

279

A330-300 range capability

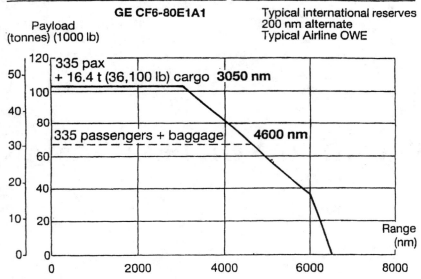

Fig. 15-1 A330-300 Typical Payload-Range Capability

Courtesy Airbus Industrie

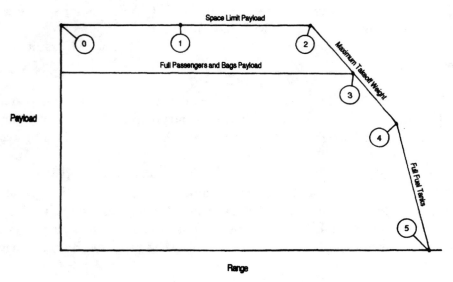

Fig. 15-2 Key points on the Payload-Range Curve

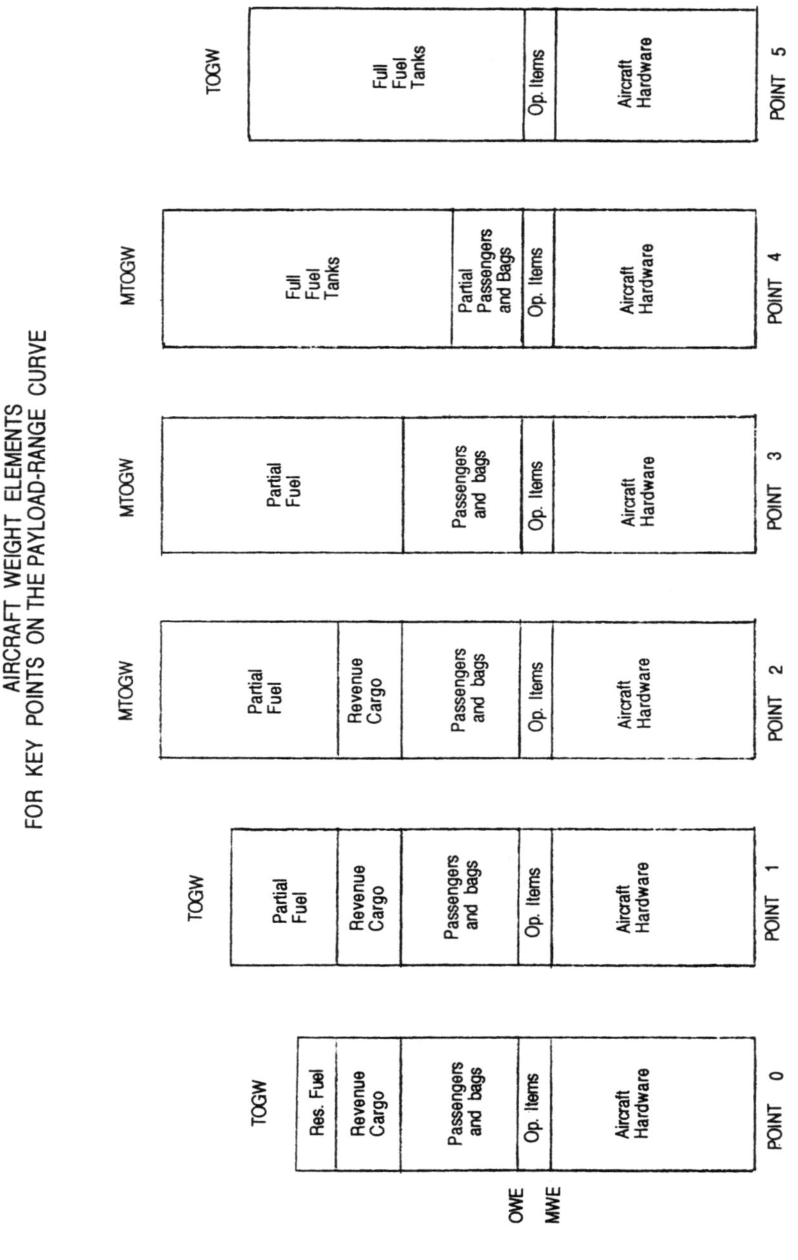

AIRCRAFT WEIGHT ELEMENTS
FOR KEY POINTS ON THE PAYLOAD-RANGE CURVE

TOGW	TOGW	MTOGW	MTOGW	MTOGW	TOGW
Res. Fuel	Partial Fuel	Partial Fuel	Partial Fuel	Full Fuel Tanks	Full Fuel Tanks
Revenue Cargo	Revenue Cargo	Revenue Cargo		Partial Passengers and Bags	
Passengers and bags	Passengers and bags	Passengers and bags	Passengers and bags	Op. Items	Op. Items
Op. Items	Op. Items	Op. Items	Op. Items	Aircraft Hardware	Aircraft Hardware
Aircraft Hardware	Aircraft Hardware	Aircraft Hardware	Aircraft Hardware		
POINT 0	POINT 1	POINT 2	POINT 3	POINT 4	POINT 5

OWE
MWE

Fig. 15-3 Aircraft Weight Elements for Key Points on the Payload-Range Curve

281

$$\text{Range} \quad (\text{N . Mi .}) = \left(\frac{V}{C}\right) \left(\frac{L}{D}\right) \ln \frac{W_{initial}}{W_{final}}$$

For a specific design, on a particular cruise operation, V, C, and L/D are usually taken as constants, $W_{initial}$ and W_{final} are derived from known weights, i.e. OWE, payload, reserve fuel, maximum takeoff weight, maximum fuel capacity.

Some key ideas about payload range curves are shown in Figs. 15-4 and 15-5

ADDITIONAL COMMENTS

- Weight limited payload = MZFW - OWE
- Space limited payload is usually slightly lower
- Passengers and bags range is usually set by MTOGW
- Greater passengers and bags range can be achieved by increasing MTOGW (allows more fuel to be carried)
- If passenger and bags range is limited by maximum fuel capacity greater range can be achieved only through increasing fuel capacity.
- For reserve fuel definitions, refer to Fig. 2-15
- To use the payload-range chart to evaluate the payload carrying capability of a specific design between two specific cities, some additional information must be developed.

  - First, the great circle distance between the specific cities must be determined.
  - Then as a first approximation, the required range may be determined as the great circle distance plus 2% for airways and 10% for worst wind conditions.
  - Historical wind data for all regions of the world has been compiled and is used for more detailed analysis of payload capabilities.
  - The equivalent still-air distance is the distance an airplane would fly in still air on a flight of the same duration as that required to fly the route with a given wind. The relationship of head winds and tail winds to the effective and actual distance flown is shown in the example. For analysis purposes, head winds are usually negative numbers, while tail winds are positive.

$$\text{ESAD} = \text{SAD} \frac{\text{True Airspeed}}{\text{True Airspeed + Windspeed}}$$

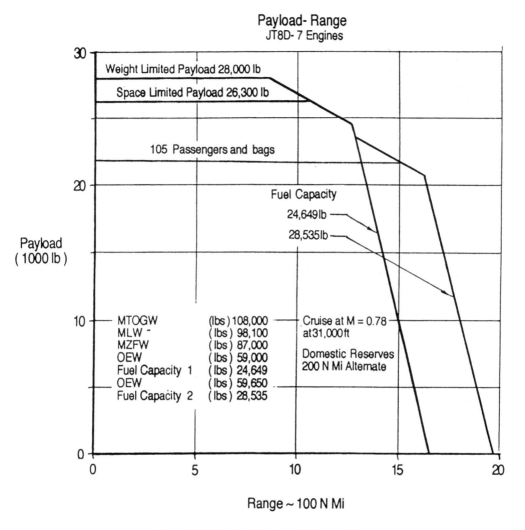

Fig. 15-4 Typical Payload-Range Curve

DESIGN EXERCISE

Construct the Payload-Range curve for your design project.

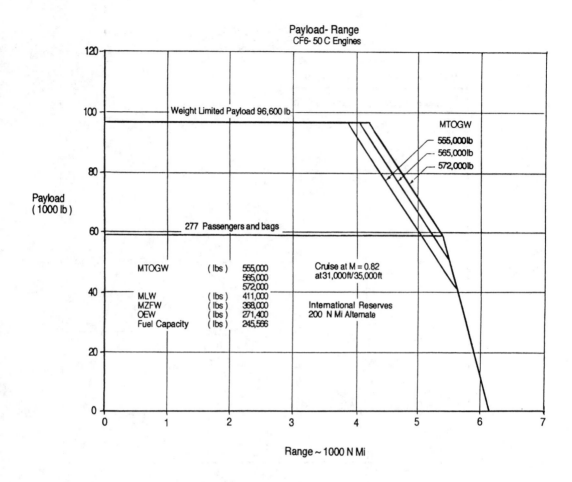

Fig. 15-5 Typical Payload ~ Range Curve

REFERENCES

15.1 Shevell, Richard S., and Kroo, Ilan, Introduction to Aircraft Design Synthesis and Analysis, Course Notes, Stanford University, Palo Alto, CA 1981

15.2 Anonymous, The DC 9 Handbook, Douglas Aircraft Co. Long Beach, CA 1991

15.3 Anonymous, The DC-10 Handbook, Douglas Aircraft Co. Long Beach, CA 1986

16

FAR REQUIRED TAKEOFF FIELD LENGTH

FAR 25 GENERAL REQUIREMENTS

The takeoff field length required by the FAR 25.113 for jet transport operation with a specified TOGW, from an airport at a specific pressure altitude and ambient temperature is the greater of
1.   The all engine takeoff distance x 1.15
2.   The takeoff distance with an engine failure at the "most critical point" in the takeoff.

For the takeoff with an engine failure, there are 3 situations:
1.   Engine failure at a point (V_{EF}) sooner than most critical point—stop on runway.
2.   Engine failure at a point (V_{EF}) later than most critical point—continue takeoff with 1 engine failed.
3.   Engine failure at the "most critical point" where the distance to stop on runway equals the distance to continue takeoff with 1 engine failed to a height of 35 ft. This is called the balanced field length concept.
These conditions are illustrated in Fig. 16-1.

"Most critical point" in a given takeoff where the "accelerated-stop" distance is equal to the "accelerated-continue-distance" is found by plotting "accelerate-stop" distance and "accelerate-continue" with 1 engine failed versus not V_{EF}, but the engine failure recognition speed, called V_1 as shown in Fig. 16-2.

For propeller driven transports the FAR balanced field length concept is the same, but

FAA REQUIRED TAKEOFF FIELD LENGTH
For a specific gross weight, altitude, and temperature

1. All engines operating takeoff

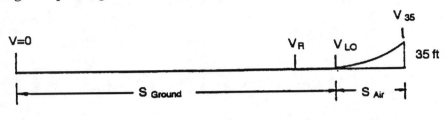

$$\text{Takeoff Distance} = (S_{Ground} + S_{Air}) \times 1.15$$

2. One engine inoperative takeoff

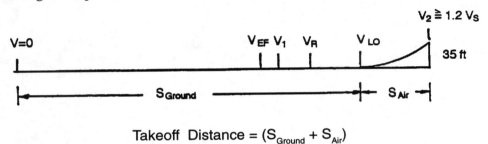

$$\text{Takeoff Distance} = (S_{Ground} + S_{Air})$$

3. One engine inoperative accelerate - stop

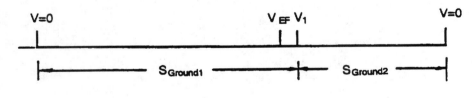

$$\text{Accelerate - Stop Distance} = (S_{Ground1} + S_{Ground2})$$

- Balanced field length requires that 2 and 3 be equal
- FAA required field length is the greater of 1 or 2

Fig. 16-1 FAA Required Takeoff Field Length

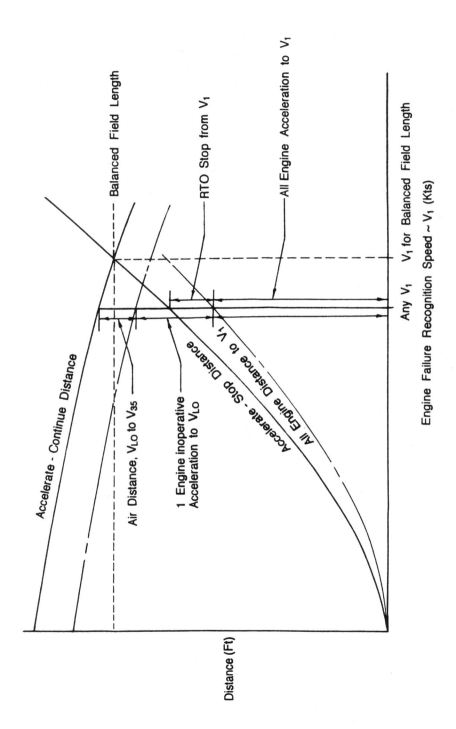

Fig. 16-2 Balanced Field Length Concept

the speed for the one-engine inoperative takeoff distance is 1.15 V_s at 35 ft for 4 or more engines, 1.2 V_S for 2 or 3 engines.

For multi-engine military aircraft the required takeoff field length is specified in MIL-C-5011B, and the balanced field length is called critical field length, and the accelerate-continue distance is to lift-off, not to 35 ft above the runway.

For single and multi-engine normal, utility, and acrobatic aircraft under 12,500 lb maximum gross weight, FAR 23 specifies only the all engine distance to a height of 50 ft at a speed equal to or greater than 1.3 Vs at 50 ft.

The balanced field length can be determined by calculating the acceleration of the airplane on the runway for the three types of operation involved.

- All engine acceleration
- One engine inoperative acceleration
- Rejected takeoff (RTO) deceleration

and adding on the takeoff air distance from liftoff to 35 ft., as shown in Fig. 16-2.

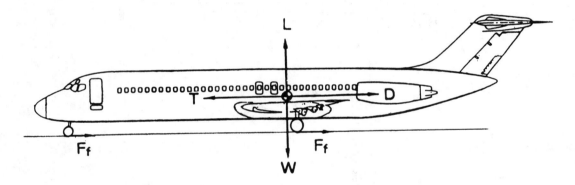

Fig. 16-3   Force Diagram During Ground Run

From the force diagram shown in the sketch above

$$a = \frac{g}{W} [T - D - F_f] = \frac{g}{W} [T - D - m(W_{TO} - L)] \qquad (16\text{-}1)$$

where μ is the rolling coefficient of friction for accelerations and the braking coefficient of friction for braked decelerations. For jet aircraft, the thrust during the takeoff run may be calculated using the data from Fig. 8-5. For turboprop and piston engined aircraft, the thrust during the takeoff run may be calculated using the methods outlined in the Appendix to Reference 16.2.

With the accelerations, a, calculated, make a plot of 1/2a versus V^2 where V is in fps. The area under the curve between any two speeds is the distance covered between those speeds for type of operation involved. By using the area under the appropriate curves for several assumed values of V_1 the all engine acceleration distance, the one engine inoperative distance to lift off and the rejected takeoff (RTO) stopping distance at the assumed V_1 may be determined. Adding the distance segments together in the proper manner will produce the data to plot the balanced field length chart. That is, the accelerate-stop distance vs V_1 and accelerate-continue distance versus V_1. This procedure is shown schematically in Fig. 16-2.

An example problem to illustrate the procedure is given as follows:

EXAMPLE PROBLEM

Construct a balanced field length chart for a short range jet transport at sea level standard day conditions, TOGW = 100,000 lbs, Flaps 15° for takeoff, JT8D-7 engines.

From given data, calculate the acceleration, a, on the runway at several speeds, from 0 to beyond V_2 for the three types of situations involved, i.e.,

- All engine acceleration
- One engine inoperative acceleration
- Rejected takeoff (RTO) deceleration

Data required for calculation of acceleration for the three conditions:

Airplane lift in takeoff attitude	C_L = .355 (given)
Airplane drag coefficient in takeoff attitude	C_D = .0585 (given)
Rolling coefficient of friction	μ_R = 0.02 (given)
Thrust/engine	from engine data
Airplane Wing Area	S = 1000 sq ft (given)
Airplane lift in RTO configuration	C_L = 0 (given)
Airplane drag in RTO configuration	C_D = 1082 (given)
Braking coefficient of friction	μ_B = 0.30 (given)
At G.W. = 100,000 lb, Flaps 15°	V_s = 110 KTS EAS

289

CALCULATION OF ACCELERATION — ALL ENGINES

V_{KTS}	0	40	80	120	140
Mach	0	.060	.120	.181	.211
T/Eng(lbs)	13,500	13,200	12,700	12,300	12,100
T_{TOTAL} (lbs)	27,000	26,400	25,400	24,600	24,100
C_D	.0585	.0585	.0585	.0585	.0585
q (psf)	0	5.3	21.3	48.5	65.9
D (lbs)	0	310	1250	2840	3860
C_L	.355	.355	.355	.355	.355
L (lbs)	0	1892	7561	17,220	23,400
W (lbs)	100,000	100,000	100,000	100,000	100,000
W-L (lbs)	100,000	98,110	92,440	82,800	76,600
F_f (lbs)	2,000	1,960	1,850	1,860	1,520
Σ Frw (lbs)	25,000	24,130	22,300	20,100	18,720
a (ft/sec²)	8.04	7.79	7.20	6.49	6.05
1/2a (ft/sec²)	.0622	.0643	.0695	.0771	.0826
V² (fps)²	0	4,480	17,960	40,800	55,450

CALCULATION OF ACCELERATION - ONE ENGINE INOPERATIVE

Since all parameters for this situation are the same as for the all engine acceleration, except for the engine thrust, the sum of the forces along the runway are reduced by the thrust of one engine.

V_{KTS}	0	40	80	120	140
ΣF_{RW} (lbs)	25,000	24,130	22,300	20,000	18,720
T/Eng (lbs)	13,500	13,200	12,700	12,300	12,100
Σ Frw (lbs) (eng. inop.)(lbs)	11,500	10,930	9,600	7,800	6,620
a (ft/sec)²	3.70	3.52	3.06	2.51	2.13
1/2a (sec²/ft)	.135	.142	.163	.199	.235
V_2 (ft/sec)²	0	4480	17,450	40,800	55,450

CALCULATION OF ACCELERATION — REJECTED TAKEOFF (RTO)

Thrust/Engine = 0 (one engine failed, one shut down)

V_{KTS}	0	40	80	120	140
q (psf)	0	5.3	21.3	48.5	65.9
C_D	.1082	.1082	.1082	.1082	.1082
D (lbs)	0	580	2305	5250	7130
W - L (lbs)	100,000	100,000	100,000	100,000	100,000
F_f (lbs)	30,000	30,000	30,000	30,000	30,000
F_{RW} (lbs)	30,000	30,580	32,300	35,250	37,130
a (ft/sec^2)	-9.65	-9.89	-10.40	-11.35	-11.95
1/2a (sec^2/ft)	-.0518	-.0510	-.0431	-.0440	-.0418
V^2 (ft/sec^2)	0	4,480	17,950	40,800	55,450

Plot 1/2a versus V^2 for the three conditions, Fig. 16-4, and obtain appropriate distances before and after assumed V_1 by integrating the area between corresponding values of V_1. This procedure yields the results shown below.

DETERMINATION OF ACCELERATE-STOP DISTANCES

(using the 1/2a curves of Fig. 16-4)

V_1 (kts)	0	40	80	120	140
Accelerate to V_1 (ft)	0	290	1150	2860	4040
Stop from V_1 (ft)	0	230	870	1950	2580
Accelerate Stop (ft)	0	520	2020	4310	6620

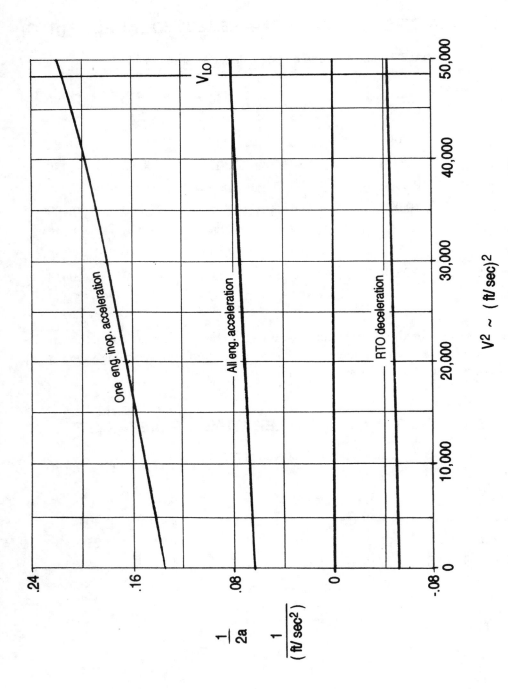

Fig. 16-4 Takeoff Acceleration ~ Deceleration Chart

Determination of accelerate-continue distances to V_2

(using the 1/2a curves + the takeoff air distance curves)

The accelerate-continue distance to V_{LO} on the runway is found from the 1/2a curves. The air distance part of the accelerate - continue distance is found from empirical correlations based on flight test data involving the time required to go from liftoff to 35 ft, and the speed increase from liftoff to 35 ft. These parameters are shown in Fig. 16-5 as S_a/V_{LO} and V_{35}/V_{LO}, as a function of free air climb gradient in the takeoff configuration.

As we shall see in Chapter 17, the minimum free air climb gradient for a twin engine transport is .024, a reasonable choice for determining the air distance in our example.

The V_{35}/V_{LO} curve is used to determining V_{LO} using the fact that $V_{35} = 1.2 V_{Stall}$ for one-engine inoperative takeoff. For our sample calculations

$$V_{35} = 1.2 V_S = 132 \text{ Kts}$$
$$\gamma = (T - D)/W = .024 \qquad S_a/V_{LO} = 6.2 \text{ sec} \qquad V_{35}/V_{LO} = 1.012$$
$$V_{LO} = 130 \text{ Kts} \qquad S_a = 130 \,(1.69)(6.2) = 1360 \text{ ft}$$

V_1 (Kts)	0	40	80	120
Accelerate to V_1 (ft)	0	290	1150	2860
Continue to V_2 (ft)	8190	7580	5700	1370
Air Distance (ft)	1360	1360	1360	1360
Accelerate Continue (ft)	10550	9230	8210	5590

The accelerate-stop and accelerate-continue curves are plotted versus assumed V_1 on Fig. 16-5. The final values from Fig. 16-5 are:
- Critical engine failure recognition speed, $V_1 = 123$ Kts
- Balanced field length = 5200 ft

FAR 23 REQUIREMENTS

For aircraft certified under FAR 23, the takeoff field length must be determined by flight test and included in the FAA flight manual. For FAR 23 commuter category aircraft, the balanced field length concept is applied and the criteria for the takeoff are basically the same as for FAR 25, except that the takeoff distance is defined to a 50 ft height instead of 35 ft, and the V_2 speed must be at least 1.3 V_S. For other FAR 23 category aircraft, the balanced field length concept is not generally applicable to single engine aircraft, and so only the takeoff field length with all engines operating must be determined and included in the aircraft flight manual.

The FAR 23 takeoff field length for preliminary design purposes may be determined with sufficient accuracy for personal/utility aircraft from the trend data of Fig. 8-2. As noted, this chart is based on a correlation of actual takeoff field length data for a number of aircraft with the generalized takeoff parameter.

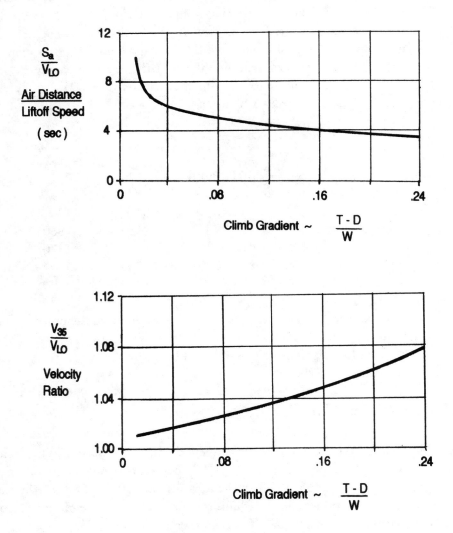

Fig. 16-5 FAR 25 Air Distance Parameters

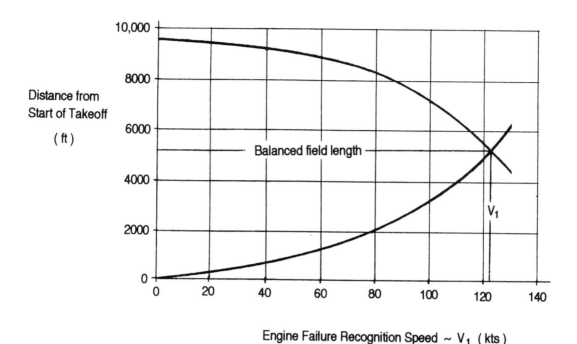

Fig. 16-6   Takeoff Acceleration-Deceleration Chart

DESIGN EXERCISE

Determine the required FAR 23, FAR 25, or MIL-C-5011B takeoff field length for your design at MTOGW, using the procedures of Part 16. Compare your result with the data on the appropriate generalized takeoff chart of Figs. 8-2 through 8-4 by plotting your calculated point on the generalized chart. Then put a faired curve similar to the generalized curve through your calculated point, and use this curve to construct a chart of takeoff distance vs takeoff weight for sea level and 2000 ft altitude standard day conditions. Also calculate the ground minimum control speed, V_{mcg}, using the method illustrated in Fig. 6-14, for sea level standard day conditions.

REFERENCES

16.1 Shevell, Richard S., Fundamentals of Flight, Prentice Hall, Englewood Cliffs, NJ, 1989

16.2 Hartman, Edwin P., and Bierman, David, The Aerodynamic Characateristics of Full Scale Propellers Having 2, 3, and 4 Blades of Clark Y and R.A.F. 6 Airfoil Sections. NACA TR 640, 1938.

17

FAR CLIMB GRADIENT REQUIREMENTS

REQUIREMENTS FOR SPECIFIC FLIGHT CONDITIONS

Another aspect of FAR 25 and MIL-Spec performance requirements is the specification of minimum climb gradients, which must be met at the maximum permissible flight weight in the appropriate condition. These requirements are as follows:

FAR 25	Flight Condition	Required Climb Gradient		
		4-engine airplanes	3-engine airplanes	2-engine airplanes
25.121a	First takeoff climb segment	0.5%	0.3%	positive
25.121b	Second takeoff climb segment	3.0%	2.7%	2.4%
25.121c	Final takeoff climb segment	1.7%	1.5%	1.2%
25.123a	Enroute climb	1.6%	1.4%	1.1%
25.121d	Approach segment	2.7%	2.4%	2.1%
25.119	Landing segment	3.2%	3.2%	3.2%

MIL-C-5011	Flight Condition	Required Climb Gradient
3.4.2.4.1 (c)	First takeoff climb segment	0.5%
3.4.2.5 (c)	Second takeoff climb segment	2.5%
3.4.2.11 (c)	Approach segment	2.5%

The flight conditions that are referred to are these:
- First takeoff climb segment is with the critical engine inoperative, takeoff thrust, from V_{LOF} until the gear is fully retracted, flaps in the takeoff position, and the weight that exists at the start of gear retraction.

- Second takeoff climb segment is with the critical engine inoperative, takeoff thrust that exists at 400 feet above the takeoff surface, gear retracted, flaps in takeoff position, takeoff speed ($V_2 = 1.20\ V_S$), and the weight that exists at the time the gear is fully retracted. It should be noted that second segment begins at gear retraction and extends to 400 feet, or higher, if necessary for terrain clearance.

- Final takeoff climb segment is with the critical engine inoperative, maximum continuous thrust that exists at the higher altitude of either 1500 feet above takeoff surface or where transition to enroute configuration is completed, gear retracted, flaps retracted, speed = $1.25\ V_S$ and weight equal to that existing at the end of the takeoff path.

- Approach climb segment is with the critical engine inoperative, takeoff thrust, gear retracted, flaps set so that $V_{S\ approach} = 1.10\ V_S$ for the related landing configuration, speed = $1.5\ V_S$, and at the landing weight.

- Landing climb segment is with all engines operating, engines at the power or thrust that is available eight seconds after initiation of movement of the power or thrust controls from the minimum flight idle to the. takeoff position, gear extended, flaps in the landing configuration, speed $\leq 1.3\ V_S$.

For commercial jet transports and business jets, the most important climb gradient requirement is the second takeoff climb segment, because it can limit the permissible takeoff weight to a value well below the maximum design takeoff gross weight, MTOGW, which impacts the payload range performance of the aircraft. The required climb gradients in other configurations do not usually limit the operational performance of the aircraft significantly.

MAXIMUM PERMISSIBLE FLIGHT WEIGHT

The relationship between required climb gradient and maximum permissible flight weight is illustrated in Fig. 17-1.

This chart represents the second takeoff climb segment gradient capability at various gross weights and altitudes for a specific airplane/engine combination in the second segment takeoff configuration. (Takeoff flaps, gear up, $V = 1.2\ V_S$).

In the expression for the gradient of climb, Equation 1-21, (T-D)/W may be written as (T/W) - (D/W), and for steady, 1g flight, (D/W) = 1/(L/D). In the second segment configuration at $1.2\ V_S$, (L/D) is constant, so that the climb gradient is related only to (T/W). Since the takeoff thrust is essentially constant at a given altitude, the second segment climb gradient at a given altitude must decrease with increasing gross weight. Looking at the sea level curve, when the second segment gradient capability decreases to the minimum required value, the gross weight is called the second segment limiting weight, SSLW. At a given gross weight, the gradient capability decreases with altitude, since the rated takeoff thrust of jet and turbofan engines decreases with altitude.

Aircraft performance reports for specific aircraft/engine combinations usually summarize the limiting weights versus altitude for all potentially critical configurations, as shown in Fig. 17-2.

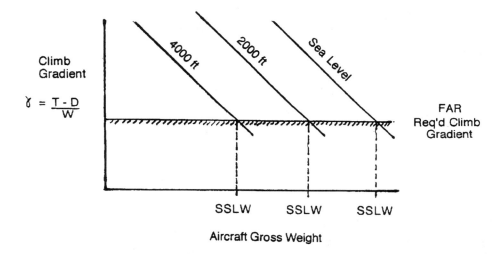

Fig. 17-1 Required Climb Gradient/Maximum Permissible Flight Weight Concept

It should also be noted that at given altitude, climb gradient performance will be reduced at temperatures beyond the engine takeoff thrust "flat rating" temperature, as shown in Fig. 17-3.

EFFECT OF SECOND SEGMENT LIMITING WEIGHTS ON PERMISSIBLE TOGW.

If one were to plot FAR required takeoff distance versus gross weight for a specific aircraft/ engine combination at sea level, standard day conditions, there would be a "cutoff" on the curve at a gross weight corresponding to the second segment limiting weight at sea level, standard day conditions, as shown in Fig. 17-4. If this gross weight were below the

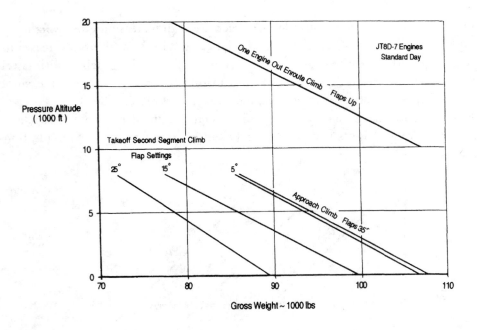

Fig. 17-2 Typical Jet Transport Limiting Weight Chart

maximum design takeoff gross weight, the second segment limiting weight would not al-low maximum payload/range performance to be achieved. Higher second segment limit-ing weights can be achieved, at some penalty in FAR required TOFL, by shifting to a lower takeoff flap setting (lower $C_{L_{max}}$), but better L/D (lower flap drag). This scheme was used in the early days of the jet transports, but invariably, some airline would have a need for operation just outside the "stair step. This situation led to the invention of "Dial-a-flap" which provides "envelope" performance as shown in Fig. 17-5, by allowing the takeoff flap setting to be selected by 1° increments.

Another way to alleviate the "stair-step" effect is to overspeed V_2 to gain improvements in second segment limiting weight. Referring back to Fig. 12-20, which shows the varia-tion in L/D with C_L for various flap settings, improved L/Ds at C_L's corresponding to speeds greater than 1.2 V_S are indicated. This procedure is called "overspeeding" V_2, and it allows higher second segment limiting weights to be achieved for a given flap setting, avoid-ing the sharp "stair-step" effect. The use of overspeeding V_2 is illustrated in Fig. 17-6, along with some other limits which affect takeoff field length performance. For example, the takeoff performance can be limited when the true speeds involved in the takeoff run exceed the maximum rated tire speed, in this case 210 mph. There also may be maximum brake energy limits, where the energy which must be absorbed by the brakes in an RTO stop exceeds the maximum energy absorption demonstrated by the 4-rotor brakes of this example.

In addition to the various ways of presenting summaries of takeoff performance already shown, the takeoff field length required with design passengers and bags payload for various mission ranges is often summarized as shown in Fig. 17-7. The variable not identified, of course, is the takeoff gross weight, which varies with the fuel weight required for the mission range.

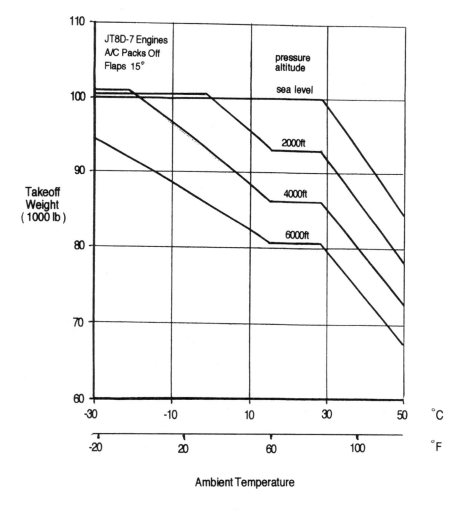

Fig. 17-3 Typical Second Segment Limiting Weight Chart

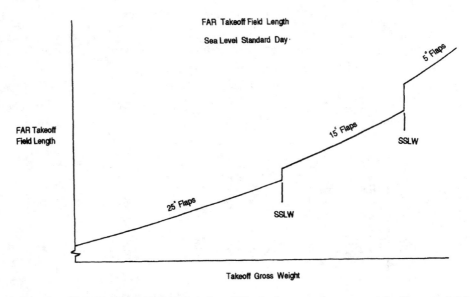

Fig. 17-4 FAR Takeoff Field Length—Effect of second segment limiting weight

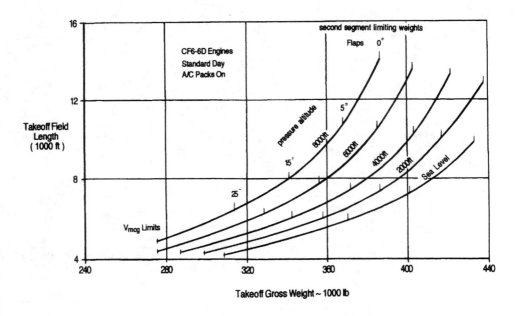

Fig. 17-5 FAR Takeoff Performance Summary

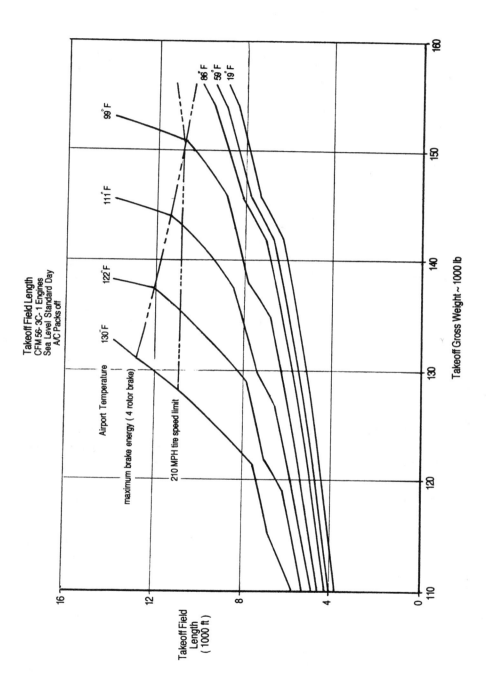

Fig. 17-6   FAR Takeoff Performance—Typical Prsentation

⬲ A330-300 take-off performance capability

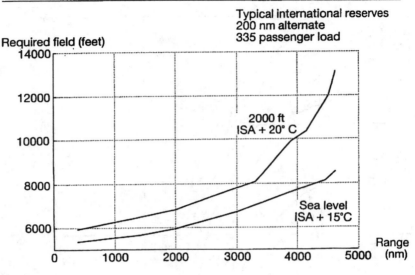

Fig. 17-7 FAR Takeoff Performance—Typical Presentation

FAR 23 CLIMB PERFORMANCE REQUIREMENTS

There are also a number of climb performance requirements for the various categories of FAR 23 aircraft defined in Fig. 2-15b. These climb performance requirements are summarized in FAR 23.65, 23.67, and 23.77.

DESIGN EXERCISE

Determine the second segment limiting weight for your design project, and show the effect of using a lower flap setting on increasing the second segment limiting weight, on the graph of TOFL versus TOGW.

REFERENCES

17.1 U.S. Code of Federal Regulations. Title 14, Aeronautics and Space. Parts 1-199, Federal Aviation Administration, published by Office of the Federal Register. revised 1999

18

FAR REQUIRED LANDING FIELD LENGTH

GENERAL CONCEPT AND DEFINITIONS

The regulations for civil aircraft, FAR 23 and FAR 25, as well as the specification for military aircraft, MIL-C-5011 B, define the actual landing distance as an air run from 50 ft above the runway to touchdown, and the ground deceleration from touchdown to a full stop on a dry, hard surface runway. A sketch of the landing distance concept and definitions is shown in Fig. 18-1.

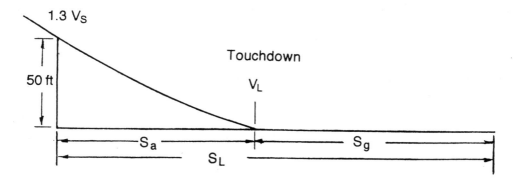

Fig. 18-1 Landing Distance Concept

The air run portion of the landing distance S_a, is not easily calculated from first principles, since the actual trajectory is influenced by the steady glide angle at the 50 ft height, the pilot technique in making the flare from 50 ft to touchdown, and the ground

305

effect on the aircraft drag. Most preliminary design estimates of landing distance are based on correlations with flight test data using the model described in the following paragraphs.

The air distance, S_a, can be approximated by a <u>steady state glide distance</u>, d_{GL}, plus an air <u>deceleration glide distance</u>, d_{decel}, at constant altitude, as shown in Fig. 18-2.

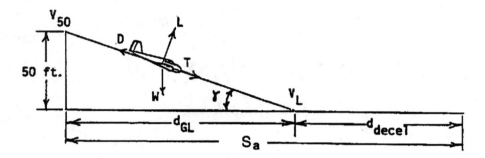

Fig. 18-2 Two Segment Approximation to the Landing Air Run

V_{SO} is the speed at the 50 ft height, specified as 1.3 Vs or higher by both the FARs and MIL-C-5011B. V_L is the landing touchdown speed, which is usually between $1.15V_S$ and $1.25V_S$ as determined from flight tests. For military aircraft, the touchdown speed is specified as $1.15V_S$ by MIL-C- 5011B.

The glide distance, d_{GL}, can be found from the climb gradient equation

$$\gamma = \frac{T - D}{W} \qquad (18\text{-}1)$$

Since the thrust in the landing air run is small compared to the drag, (T - D) may be combined into an effective $(L/D)_{eff}$

Furthermore, for small angles,

$$\gamma = \tan \gamma = \frac{50}{d_{GL}} \qquad (18\text{-}2)$$

so

$$d_{GL} = 50 \, (L/D)_{eff} \qquad (18\text{-}3)$$

The air deceleration distance, for a constant deceleration, a_{air}, is

$$d_{decel} = \frac{V_{50}^2}{2a} - \frac{V_L^2}{2a} \qquad (18\text{-}4)$$

The ground deceleration distance to a stop ($V = 0$), for a constant deceleration, is

$$S_g = \frac{V_L^2}{2a} \qquad (18\text{-}5)$$

In reality, $a_{ground} = F/m$ where F is the effective total stopping force and is equal to

$$F = \mu(W - L) + D \qquad (18\text{-}6)$$

and to a first order is constant through the stop.

We can then write

$$S_L = d_{GL} + d_{decel} + S_g \qquad (18\text{-}7)$$

and

$$= 50(L/D)_{eff} + \frac{(V_{50}^2 - V_L^2)}{2g} + \frac{V_L^2}{2a_{ground}} \qquad (18\text{-}8)$$

The $(L/D)_{eff}$ in the air run portion of the landing can be determined from flight test air runs by plotting the flight test air run distances versus $V_{50} - V_L$ as shown in Fig. 18-3.

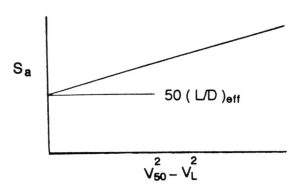

Fig. 18-3 Landing Air Run Correlation

Both the air deceleration distance, d_{decel}, and the ground stopping distance, Sg, are directly proportional to V_{50}^2 and/or V_L^2. Both V_{50} and V_L are fixed percentages above V_S. Therefore, the landing distance is linear with V^2, except for the glide distance from 50 ft which depends only on the $(L/D)_{eff}$ in the landing configuration. Based on this logic, for airplanes with similar $(L/D)_{eff}$ values and similar braking systems, the landing distances should correlate reasonably well when plotted versus V_S^2. Figs. 18-4, 18-5, and 18-6 present the results of such correlations based on flight test data for three classes of air-planes. It should be noted that these correlations are for the actual landing distances demonstrated during the FAA certification tests. The $(L/D)_{eff}$ in the air run varies signifi-cantly for the different types of aircraft. For personal/utility aircraft, the $(L/D)_{eff}$ from Fig. 18-4 is 4.0, while for regional turboprops the $(L/D)_{eff}$ is 8.0 from Fig. 18-5. For jet transports, from Fig. 18-6, the $(L/D)_{eff}$ is 18.0. These values indicate that significantly more power is carried in the landing air run, and the glide angle, γ, becomes more shallow, as the aircraft become larger and heavier.

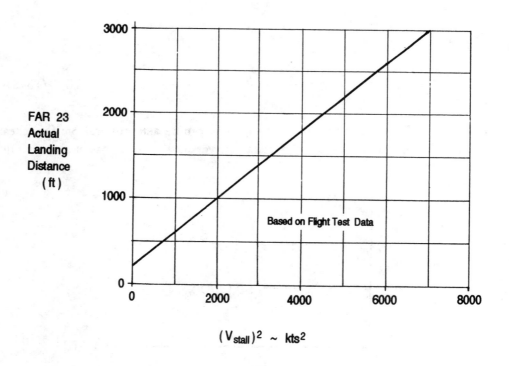

Fig. 18-4 FAR 23 Personal/Utility Aircraft

Adapted with permission from Ref. 18.2

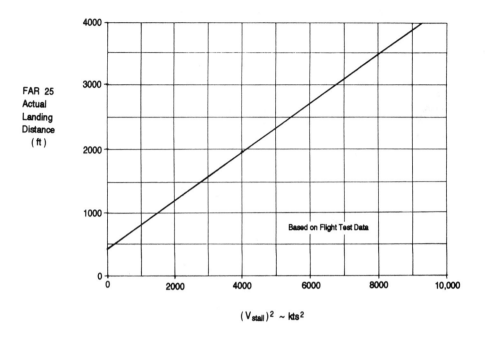

Fig. 18-5 FAR 25 Regional Turboprop Aircraft

There is a difference in the landing distance correlation between jet transport aircraft with dual tandem (4 wheel) trucks and smaller aircraft with dual (2 wheel) trucks. It appears that the effective coefficient of friction is less for wheels braking immediately behind other wheels.

The correlation is for aircraft equipped with automatic spoilers, which are operated by wheel rotation at touch down. Spoilers operated manually by the flight crew involve a time delay after touch down by FAA rules. Differences in FAR landing field length of up to 500 ft have been measured in tests of automatic and manually operated spoilers on the same aircraft.

For transport category aircraft, which are certified under FAR 25, but must operate under FAR 121 rules, the FAR required landing distance is the actual demonstrated distance, increased by a factor of 1.00/0.60. FAR landing field lengths also must be increased by 15% for wet runway operations. Note that no credit is allowed for the use of reverse thrust in FAR landing field length determination. It is considered an operational "pad" for adverse braking situations, in addition to the 1/.60 factor.

309

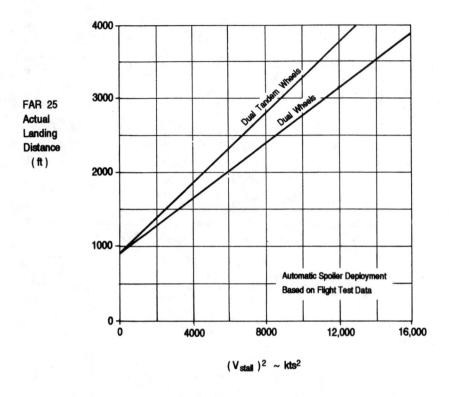

Fig. 18-6 FAR 25 Jet Transport Aircraft

DESIGN EXERCISE

Determine the landing field length required for your design at the maximum landing weight, using the appropriate correlation curves.

19

AIRCRAFT PRICING AND DIRECT OPERATING COST

AIRCRAFT PRICING

Aircraft pricing, the process of determining the price that a customer will pay for a specific aircraft, is an extremely complex task that involves many factors. Pricing is an activity that is common to all types of aircraft, but is most complicated for commercial transports, which will be the focus of this chapter. There are two types of pricing in use in the aircraft industry. They are

Cost based pricing

Wherein the price is selected by the manufacturer to cover the estimated average cost per unit over the expected number of aircraft to be sold, plus a reasonable profit margin for each unit. This type of pricing is used for small personal/utility aircraft, business jets, and in large military aircraft programs.

Market based pricing

Wherein the price is set by market factors such as payload-range performance capability, direct operating cost, passenger appeal, and the price of competing aircraft. This type of pricing is the norm for commercial transport programs. Within the concept of market based pricing, there are two types of market based prices. They are

311

Study price

Similar to the "sticker price" of an automobile. This is the price that the manufacturer would like to get for the aircraft, and is usually adequate to return an reasonable profit margin over the life of the program.

Net price

Which is equal to the study price less "concessions", discounts negotiated by the airlines and given by the manufacturer in sales situations where the airline is

- The launch customer on a new model
- Placing an order for a large quantity of aircraft
- Involved in a very competitive sales campaign
- Considered to be a "must" customer

In order to gain some insight into the magnitude of transport aircraft study prices, and the variation of study price with passenger capacity and range performance with full passengers, Fig. 19-1 has been prepared. This chart shows the study price variation from small, short range models to large, intercontinental aircraft.

DIRECT OPERATING COST

The direct operating cost (DOC) is a recognized "Figure of Merit" for evaluating competitive aircraft designs. Specifically, DOC is the direct cost of work performed by the aircraft, expressed as dollars per aircraft mile *($/Nmi)*, and cents per seat mile (¢/Seat Nmi.). A standard procedure for calculating DOC was developed many years ago by an airline industry group called the Air Transport Association (ATA) for use by all manufacturers to calculate theDOC of various aircraft. This procedure was updated periodically to account for changes inthe airline cost structure, but finally in the 1970's, each manufacturer adopted a method very similar to, but not exactly the same as the ATA procedure. Therefore one must use caution when comparing DOC's calculated by different organizations. However, DOC's are still an important preliminary design tool for estimating the effect of various design options on the operating cost of the aircraft.

Elements of DOC

The indivual elements of DOC are shown in the tabulation below.

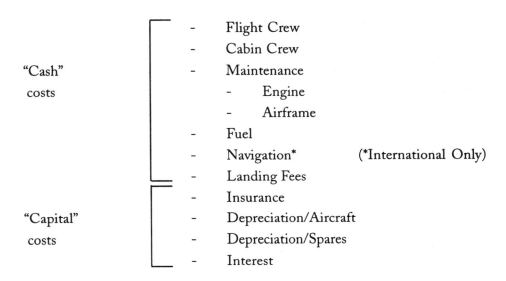

The cost elements labeled "Cash" costs are those costs that are associated with the actual operation of the aircraft in scheduled service. The costs labeled "Capital" costs are those costs that must be accounted for over the life of the aircraft, but which are allocated usually on a yearly basis to the operation of the aircraft. The basic parameter in the DOC calculation is cost per aircraft mile. In developing procedures for calculating cost per aircraft mile, account must be taken of costs associated with the time the aircraft is on the ground at the airport, going from the gate to the takeoff runway, and again from the landing back to the terminal. These considerations lead to the concept of <u>block time</u>, the entire time for an operation from start of taxi out to the end of taxi in. Correspondingly, the <u>block speed</u> is the average speed for an operation from the start of taxi out to the end of taxi in. With this background, some additional comments may be made about the individual cost elements.

Flight crew

Flight crew costs are calculated on the basis of $/block hour and are proportional to the MTOGW of the aircraft being operated.

Cabin crew

Cabin crew costs are calculated on the basis of $/block hour per seat, and are proportional to the number of seats in the aircraft.

Maintenance

Maintenance costs are calculated on the basis of estimated maintenance material cost and maintenance labor hours used per block hour of operation. The maintenance material and labor are further separated into airframe material and labor and engine material and labor, each with their own material cost and labor hours.

Labor costs are computed from the labor hours and a standard burdened labor rate per hour.

Fuel

Fuel costs are calculated on the basis of block fuel used times the fuel price.

Navigation

Navigation costs are calculated on the basis of $/Nmi. for international flights only, because outside of the U.S., there is a charge for using the Air Traffic Control (ATC) system.

Landing Fees

Landing fees are charged at all commercial airports, and are calculated on the basis of $/trip. Landing fees are proportional to the MTOGW of the aircraft.

Insurance

Annual insurance costs are calculated on the basis of a fixed percentage of the aircraft initial cost.

Manufacturer	Model	MTOGW (lbs)	No. Pass.	Range (N mi)	StudyPrice ($M)
Boeing	717-200	114,000	106	1570	36.0
Airbus	A 318	129,800	107	1500	38.4
British Aerospace	Avro RJ 100	97,500	110	2000	34.2
Boeing	737-600	144,500	110	3150	41.3
Airbus	A 319	149,900	124	3470	44.6
Boeing	737-700	154,500	126	3300	48.8
Boeing	MD-81	140,000	143	1550	45.5
Boeing	MD-83	160.000	143	2520	50.9
Airbus	A 320-200	169,800	150	2995	53.6
Boeing	MD-90	156,000	152	2400	56.0
Boeing	737-800	174,200	162	2925	57.2
Boeing	737-900	174,200	177	2400	63.8
Airbus	A 321-200	196,200	185	2690	65.5
Boeing	757-200	255,000	201	3945	66.5
Boeing	757-300	270,000	243	3470	78.4
Boeing	767-200	335,000	181	3965	82.0
Boeing	767-200 ER	395,000	181	6640	94.1
Airbus	A 310-300	361,600	185	5210	96.3
Boeing	767-300	351,000	218	4035	97.0
Boeing	767-300 ER	412,000	218	6160	108.9
Airbus	A 300-600R	378,500	222	4168	109.8
Boeing	767-400	450,000	245	5615	125.0
Airbus	A 330-300	478,400	280	4235	135.9
Airbus	A 340-200	568,800	250	6380	142.7
Airbus	A 340-300	606,300	280	6035	148.5
Boeing	MD-11	630,500	285	7000	150.5
Boeing	777-200	545,000	305	5200	153.0
Boeing	777-200 ER	656,000	305	7570	162.0
Boeing	777-300	660,000	368	5895	178.0
Boeing	747-400	875,000	416	7320	183.5

Fig. 19-1 Jet Transport Study Prices ~ Year 2000

Depreciation

Depreciation accounts for allocating the initial cost of the aircraft and the spare parts over a given period of time. The usual practice in calculating DOC's is to depreciate the aircraft initial cost over a 15 year period to 15% of its initial value.

Interest

The interest cost accounts for the interest on the money used to purchase the aircraft initially. It is calculated on the basis of a fixed annual interest rate for a period of 12 years.

Typical Presentation of DOC's

One of the first presentations of DOC characteristics for a specific transport aircraft consisted of graphs of $/Nmi and ¢/Seat Nmi vs range as shown in Fig. 19-2. At short ranges the DOC's tend to be higher because of the lower block speeds stemming from a greater percentage of the block time being spent on the ground during taxi in and taxi out. The sharp break in the ¢/Seat Nmi curve is associated with the range point where full passengers can no longer be carried due to MTOGW limits. This presentation was extended to show comparative DOC's for several sizes of aircraft as shown in Fig. 19-3. These DOC charts highlight a key aspect of transport aircraft DOC's, namely that large, high capacity transports will always have higher $/Nmi or trip costs than smaller, lower capacity models, but they will always have lower ¢/Seat Nmi or seat costs than the smaller, lower capacity models. This situation emphasizes the importance of airline fleet planning, the process of determining the proper mix of models to accommodate the number of passengers traveling on specific routes with the right size aircraft. More recent presentations of comparative DOC's have used a graph of ¢/Seat Nmi plotted vs $/Nmi at some specified range, as shown in Fig. 19-4. On this chart lines of constant numbers of seats are shown, helping to compare aircraft of different seating capacities. Currently, most DOC comparisons are in the form of relative DOC's per seat and per trip, using some specific aircraft as the baseline, as shown in Fig. 19-5.

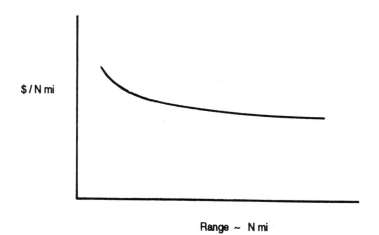

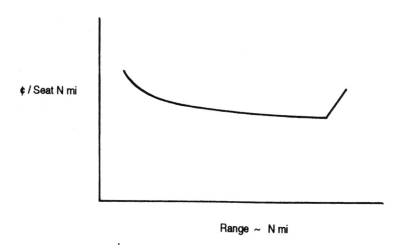

Fig. 19-2 DOC vs Range Curves

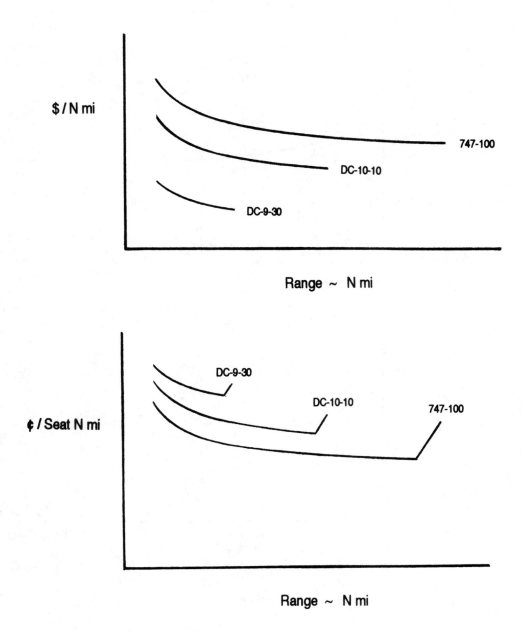

Fig. 19-3 Comparative DOC vs Range Curves

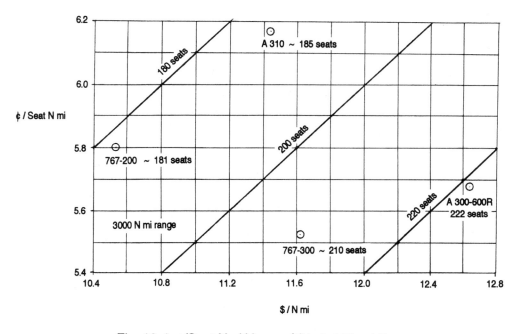

Fig. 19-4 ¢/Seat Nmi Versus $/Nmi at Fixed Range

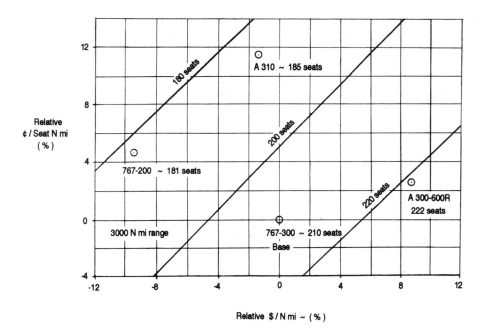

Fig. 19-5 Relative DOC Chart

Typical DOC Values

In order to provide some appreciation of the actual operating costs in dollars, the DOC's of a few transports representative of small, intermediate, and large capacities have been calculated as shown in Fig. 19-6. As noted earlier, although the 747-400 has trip costs that are more than 2.5 times the trip cost of the MD-81, the seat mile costs are 11.7% lower.

		$/Mi	¢/Seat Mi.
MD-81	at 500 N. Mi.	8.79	6.15
MD-11	at 3000 N.Mi	17.03	5.81
747-400	at 3000 N.Mi	22.58	5.43

Fig. 19-6 Typical D.O.C. Values

Relative importance of the DOC elements

It is often of interest to understand the relative importance of the individual DOC elements. Fig. 19-7 shows the cost of the indivdual elements of the total DOC, calculated on the same basis as the data of Fig. 19-6. Of interest is the fact that the fuel cost, a reflection of the cruise efficiency of the aircraft, accounts for less than 16% of the DOC. By far the largest element is the capital cost, which amounts to nearly 40% of the DOC. This suggests that to lower the DOC, technology advancements that reduce the cost of the aircraft are more important than technology advancements that improve the cruise efficiency of the aircraft.

MD-11   3000 N.Mi stage length
                           293 passengers
                           $.60/gal fuel price

MD-11 Baseline D.O.C.s

Total DOC	=	$51,085.12		
Fuel	=	$8,061.31	=	15.78%
Capital	=	$20,122.00	=	39.39%
Eng. Maint.	=	$3,465.00	=	6.78%
Airfr. Maint.	=	$4,750.00	=	9.30%
Flt. Crew	=	$5,056.00	=	9.90%
Cabin Crew	=	$6,054.00	=	11.85%
Nav. Fees	=	$1,227.00	=	2.40%
Ldg. Fees	=	$2,350.00	=	4.60%
Total DOC	=	$51,085.12	=	100.00%

Fig. 19-7 Relative Importance of DOC Elements

REFERENCES

19.1 Anonymous, Standard Method of Estimating Comparative Direct Operating Costs of Turbine Powered Transport Airplanes, Air Transport Association of America, Washington D.C., 1967

20

FAR AIRCRAFT NOISE
REQUIREMENTS

BACKGROUND

About 10 years after the introduction of the first commercial jet transport in the U.S., the FAA established airport area noise limits for commercial jet aircraft. Over the years, these regulations have been modified and broadened to include all civil aircraft, both jet and propeller driven, and have been updated to take account of improvements in noise control technology. Part 36 of the Federal Aviation Regulation (FAR 36) requires that airplane noise not exceed prescribed limits, which are based on the takeoff gross weight, the number of engines, and the category and age of the airplane. The FAR noise measuring points are shown in Fig. 20-1. The maximum allowable noise levels at these measuring points for newly certified aircraft (Stage 3) and older aircraft (Stage 2) are shown in Fig. 20-2. The regulations accomplish two things. First they allow earlier aircraft to operate under a less stringent set of limits until such time as they can be phased out with newer and quieter aircraft capable of meeting lower noise limits. Second, they ensure that the manufacturers of newer aircraft incorporate all of the noise reduction technology that is economically reasonable, technologically practical, and appropriate for the type of airplane. Consequently, the noise limits are defined in successively quieter stages (1, 2, and 3) which are applicable to progressively newer aircraft. Fortunately, much progress has been made in reducing the noise of jet aircraft, as indicated by Fig. 20-3. The aircraft manufacturer has the direct responsibility for demonstrating compliance with FAR 36. However, some part of this responsibility usually passes on to the engine manufacturer through engine guarantees and specifications.

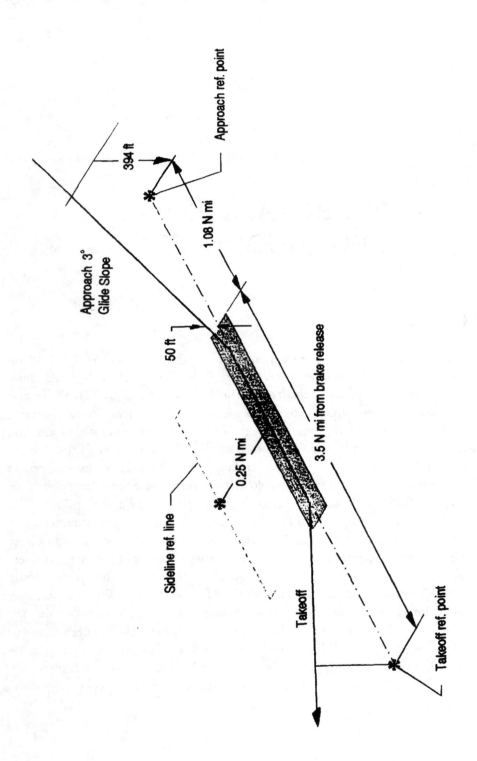

Approach ref. point

394 ft

1.08 N mi

Approach 3°
Glide Slope

50 ft

3.5 N mi from brake release

0.25 N mi

Sideline ref. line

Takeoff

Takeoff ref. point

Adapted with permission from Ref. 20.1

Fig. 20-1   FAA Noise Measuring Points

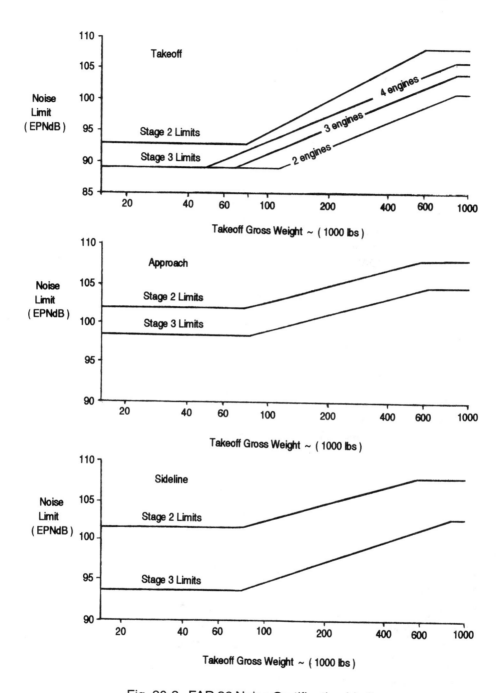

Fig. 20-2   FAR 36 Noise Certification Limits

Adapted with permission from Ref. 20.1

325

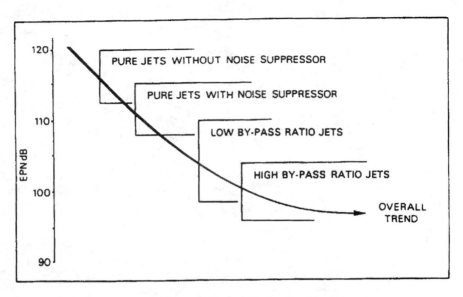

Fig. 20-3 Aircraft Noise Reduction Trends

Courtesy of Rolls Royce plc

In the preliminary design process, the FAR aircraft noise requirements must be recognized as an important performance item, and close liaison with the prospective engine manufacturer must be maintained in order to ensure that the final airplane-engine combination meets the FAR requirements.

SOUND AND NOISE FUNDAMENTALS

Sound is caused by pressure waves in a gaseous, liquid, or solid substance. The pressure waves can be initiated by many means, from human vocal chords to wind flowing around tree branches to jet exhaust. A very simple source of sound, such as a musical tuning fork, can generate a single frequency of sound which can be visualized as a sine wave pressure fluctuation. The rate at which the pressure wave fluctuates (i.e., the period of fluctuation) is called the frequency. The amplitude of pressure fluctuation is the amount that the pressure (which can actually be measured with special instruments) varies above and below the pressure of the prevailing atmosphere. These pressure waves radiate in all directions from the source of the sound, and their amplitude is attenuated, or lessened, with distance.

When sound is attenuated by distance, the frequency remains the same, but the amplitude decreases as the distance increases. Unfortunately, a jet engine is a complex source of noise which produces all of the audible frequencies, principally from the compression and combustion of air in the engine, the rotation of components through the airflow, and the turbulence of the engine exhaust stream. It should be noted that air flowing across the engine nacelle and the various parts of the aircraft also create some noise, but these sources are beyond the scope of this book.

When the fluctuations of pressure waves reach a listening device, they cause the mechanism of the listening device to vibrate. If the listening device is a person's ear, the eardrum responds to the pressure variations in the air, and transmits them to the brain by means of a complicated process. The pressure variations are sensed as sound when their frequency and amplitude fall within the hearing capability (audible range) of the human ear. Noise is any amplitude or combination of sound frequencies which the hearer finds objectionable, especially sound that is more than 120 decibels in intensity, which is the threshold of pain for the human ear.

The intensity of a sound or noise is a function of the pressure variations when they reach the ear. In sound-attenuation work, the matter of greatest concern is intensity, even though frequency, to some degree, determines whether or not some sounds are objectionable. The range of pressure variations (intensity) in the audible frequency range that the ear can detect is enormous. Between the threshold of audibility (the minimum sound that the ear can hear) and the threshold of feeling (the intensity at which sounds causes pain in the ear), the region in which the ear can distinguish gradations of intensity increases from minimum to maximum frequency in the ratio of one to 10^{12}. Such a tremendous range can be conveniently expressed only by use of the logarithmic scale.

The intensity of sound is generally described in units called the bel and the decibel (dB), which is 1/10th of a bel. The decibel is the most commonly used unit. The range from one to 12 bels, or 120 decibels, is the approximate range to which the ear responds with discrimination. Above 120 decibels, an increase in the sound pressure level (amplitude) results primarily in physical sensations in the human ear rather than a change in audibility. An increase in intensity of roughly one decibel is the smallest change in intensity that the ear can detect.

The scale most often used for aircraft noise measurement is the Perceived Noise Level (PNL) scale. The scale requires that the sound pressure level be measured in each of nine contiguous frequency ranges and combined according to a special prescription to provide a noise indication level. The units are Pndb.

ENGINE NOISE SOURCES

The major noise source of present and future high bypass engines is the fan. Three separate and distinct mechanisms contribute to fan noise. Generation of these noises may be described as follows:

Discrete tone noise is a noise of a specific frequency which produces a distinct signal or sound that can be heard above the background noises. Discrete tones at the blade passing frequency, the loudest and the most annoying noise from early turbofans, is generated by the periodic fluctuating pressure on rotor blades as they chop through the wakes of fan inlet guide-vanes. Wakes from rotor blades, sweeping past stator vanes, produce pressure fluctuations on the vane surface; fluctuating aerodynamic pressure on the surfaces of airfoils, either stationary vanes or rotating blades, produces noise. Propagation of this noise from the engine relates to the number of vanes and blades of the engine, the geometry of the duct, airflow velocity, and rotor speed.

Broadband noise is background noise of varied frequencies, such as the noise that is produced by the airflow and compression in the fan section of the engine. Because of the decreased levels of discrete tones on high bypass ratio turbofans, which have no fan inlet guide-vanes, broadband noise occurs at low power from the fan itself. Several mechanisms contribute to the generation of this noise, and, in all likelihood, it will be difficult to suppress fan noise because of the interdependence of the mechanisms which contribute to this noise and the basic aerodynamic operation of the fan.

Combination tone noise is often called "buzz saw" noise because of its distinctive sound. It is generated by the forward propagation of blade-attached shock waves when the blade tips of the rotor are operating at supersonic speeds. Small variations in blade shape, within ordinary manufacturing tolerances, cause the amplitudes of, and the spacing between, the individual blade-attached waves to become unequal. Because the shock wave pattern is projected only forward of the blades, this noise is radiated only through the inlet duct. For this reason, the noise differs from the other two major fan noise sources which radiate both upstream and downstream from the fan.

Noise from all of the low-pressure compressor stages can be identified in the far-field noise spectrum of the engine by the use of narrowband analysis techniques, although these noises are far from dominant. At low engine power, some of these discrete tones approach the levels of the fan tone even though the much smaller diameter compressor, which rotates with the fan, has a linear tip speed lower than the fan. If future engines have fans substantially quieter than those of current high-bypass engines, noise from the compressors of the gas generator will become more significant.

All the sources of discrete and broadband noise inherent in fans and compressors are potentially present in turbines. Past experience on turbojet and turbofan engines has shown that turbine noise components can be detected at idle power, but these noises become insignificant relative to the sounds generated at high engine power. Turbine noises are radiated at higher engine powers, although they are masked by fan noise. Turbine noises would contribute to the noise spectrums of an engine if fan noise could be reduced substantially.

As in a propeller, discrete noise is generated both by the direct pressure field of the rotor and by periodic fluctuations on blade and vane surfaces. Direct rotor field noise is a consequence of the spin of the blade assembly, which converts the steady, circumferentially varying pressure field around the face of the rotor into a periodic time variation. The periodic airfoil pressure fluctuations, absent when the flow is uniform, arise when rotor blades cut successively through flow-field nonuniformities of the duct, which are created by inlet guide-vanes, inlet distortion, and the presence of nearby downstream obstructions, such as stator vanes. These exit stator vanes are also affected by the wakes shed by the spinning rotor blades, creating fluctuating pressures on their surfaces. However, a ducted fan differs from a free propeller in a way that is critical from the noise standpoint. The confinement of the rotor in a duct interposes a new element - duct propagation - in the passage of noise from source to observer, introducing a powerful controlling element.

The shear turbulence generated by high velocity air being forcefully ejected from the fan air exhaust outlets and by the hot gases coming from the exhaust nozzle at the rear of the engine creates jet noise. Both of these sources create noise by creating zones of turbulence with the ambient air, as well as within the exhaust streams themselves. In the early days of commercial jet engines, the exhaust of turbojets formed the most significant noise source, but the advent of turbofans, which have slower jet exhausts, has reduced this source.

NOISE SUPPRESSION TECHNIQUES

The following steps are either being taken or can be taken to reduce the intensity of jet noise or to minimize its objectionable qualities from the stand point of the listener:

- Removal of fan inlet guide vanes - Some modern engines do not have inlet guide vanes. Their removal avoids the disturbances in the airflow created by wakes behind the vanes through which the fan blades pass.

- Vane spacing - The spacing of inlet guide vanes and/or the first-stage blades and vanes of the forward compressor or fan can be increased to reduce the amount of vane wake that is available for the compressor or fan blades to chop.

- Blade number - The optimal number of compressor or fan blades can be selected to produce a blade-vane match that will not generate noise, even if this involves some loss in performance efficiency.

- Increased bypass ratio - An increase in bypass ratio slows down the velocity of the primary exhaust stream through the jet nozzle because additional work must be done by the turbines to drive a larger fan.

- Noise attenuating materials - Noise attenuating materials lining the fan inlet and exhaust ducts as shown in Fig. 20-4 can attenuate sounds propagating from these fan ducts.

- Reducing shear in the jet exhaust - Since shear turbulence occurs outside the engine, there is very little that can be done about this source of noise except to reduce the velocity of the outgoing air and gas streams as much as possible. If one stream has a substantially higher outlet velocity than the other, mixing the two streams internally with a noise suppressor mixer, such as the one shown in Fig. 20-5, will give some reduction in noise. The application of turbofans on aircraft has substantially reduced this noise source, since turbofans move larger air masses than turbojets to produce thrust, but at lower velocity, which reduces the shear between the exhaust streams and the ambient air.

- Operational control of the engine and the aircraft flight pattern by the pilot - By keeping full takeoff thrust operation to a minimum and reducing the aircraft throttle setting as much as possible and as soon as possible after takeoff, the aircraft pilot can reduce the objectionable noise produced by the engines. Following a flight pattern that takes the aircraft over unpopulated areas during climbout will also greatly reduce the objections to jet aircraft noise by the local residents of the community. At some commercial airports located in heavily populated areas, procedures of this nature are prescribed by the airport authorities.

- Regulated land use - This represents a long-range project in most communities, which involves keeping the private homes in the vicinity of the airport at a minimum by encouraging business and manufacturing interests to locate in the area, instead. Land-use control near airports presents a very complex problem because it particularly involves municipal zoning of all land that lies within several miles of the airport.

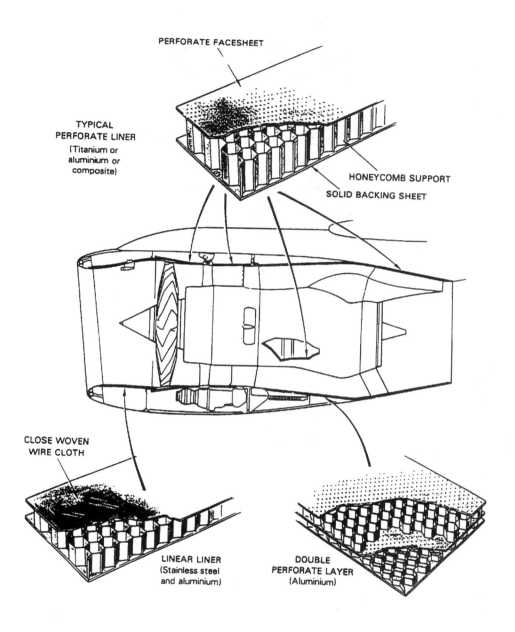

PERFORATE FACESHEET

TYPICAL
PERFORATE LINER
(Titanium or
aluminium or
composite)

HONEYCOMB SUPPORT

SOLID BACKING SHEET

CLOSE WOVEN
WIRE CLOTH

LINEAR LINER
(Stainless steel
and aluminium)

DOUBLE
PERFORATE LAYER
(Aluminium)

Fig. 20-4 Noise Absorbing Materials and Location.

Courtesy of Rolls Royce plc

Fig. 20-5 Corrugated-Perimeter Noise Suppressor (Rear View)

Courtesy of Pratt & Whitney

REFERENCES

20.1 Anonymous, Aeronautical Vestpocket Handbook, 21st edition, Pratt & Whitney Division, United Technologies, East Hartford, CT, 1990

20.2 Anonymous, The Aircraft Gas Turbine Engine and its Operation, United Technologies Corporation, East Hartford, CT, 1988

20.3 Anonymous, The Jet Engine, Rolls Royce plc, Derby, England, 1986

21

DESIGN OPTIMIZATION AND TRADE STUDIES

Up to this point, the material in the book has concentrated on developing a realistic preliminary design that meets the requirements of the stated mission specification. Many of the methods and procedures used have relied on generalized trend data from similar designs to establish the overall aircraft configuration. An obvious next step in refining the initial preliminary design is to examine variations in the configuration which may lead to a better or more optimum design.

In order to optimize an aircraft preliminary design, three elements are required.

1. A method to obtain accurate, quantitative information on how the many variables interact with each other.
2. The selection of a single measure of effectiveness, or a "Figure of Merit" related to the variables.
3. The choice of the design variables that yield the optimum desired effectiveness.

The methods associated with the first element include those used to estimate weight empty, complete lift and drag characteristics, installed engine sfc, all the flight performance equations, as well as the methods for estimating the important costs involved in the aircraft design, production, and operation.

Typical measures of effectiveness associated with the second element are minimum weight empty, minimum mission takeoff weight, minimum direct operating cost, minimum total program life cycle cost, and maximum return on investment for the manufacturer.

The design variables that are related to optimum effectiveness include wing area, sweep angle, average thickness ratio, aspect ratio, taper ratio, high lift system configuration, number and size of the engines and the types of material used for fabrication of the aircraft components.

In addition to the optimization of a preliminary design for a specific mission specification, there is often interest in determining the effect of changing some of the mission specification items on the aircraft configuration. Many "trade studies" of this nature are done early in the preliminary design process to insure that the design is achieving its greatest potential relative to the original mission requirements.

SIZING CHARTS

One of the oldest forms of optimization involves the development of a sizing chart for a preliminary design associated with a given mission. Sizing charts are usually a plot of gross weight versus wing area, with engine size, payload, range, and wing geometric characteristics held constant. An example of a typical sizing chart is shown in Fig. 21-1. Each line on the sizing chart represents a combination of takeoff weight and wing area that just meet the stated criterion under the stated assumptions. Usually the smallest wing area and the lowest takeoff weight that meet all the criteria is the optimum for the mission. As noted in Chapter 4, if the penalties are not too severe, a slightly larger wing area is often selected, especially for jet transports, to accommodate later growth versions.

TRADE STUDIES

Specific trade studies are done to determine the effect of certain variables on important "Figures of Merit" for the design. Some specific examples of trade studies that were done in the preliminary design stage of the DC-10 program will be reviewed and discussed in the following paragraphs.

As noted in Chapter 2, the original mission specification issued by American Airlines called for a twin engine aircraft that could carry a payload of 250 passengers with a range of 1850 n. mi. The stall speed in the landing configuration at normal landing weight was not to exceed 96 kts, and the cruise Mach number was set at $M = .80$. A series of trade studies were done to evaluate the impact of changes in the design requirements on the overall attractiveness and competitiveness of the airplane, using direct operating cost in cents/seat statute mile as the "Figure of Merit". Fig. 21-2 and Fig. 21-3 show the main characteristics of two airplanes that resulted from trading off the effect of having three engines instead of two in the basic configuration, while maintaining payload, range, and cruise Mach number fixed.

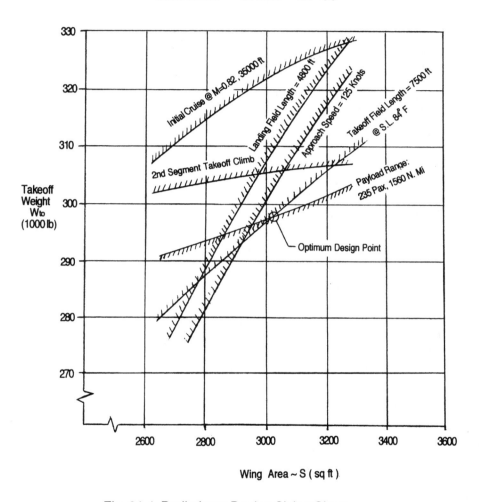

PRELIMINARY DESIGN SIZING CHART

TWIN AISLE MEDIUM RANGE JET TRANSPORT

2 GE CF6-X ENGINES

WING SWEEP ~ 30 DEG.   AR ~ 8.8

Fig. 21-1 Preliminary Design Sizing Chart

Adapted with permission from Ref. 21.1

MODEL D966
GENERAL CHARACTERISTICS
TWO ENGINE DESIGN

WING AREA	3,530 SQ FT.	TAKEOFF WEIGHT (LB)	318,000
ASPECT RATIO	8.8	O.W.E. (LB)	202,400
SWEEP	30.5°	RANGE (N.MI)	1,850
		TAKEOFF DISTANCE (FT)	9,000
		CRUISE MACH NO.	.80
		STALL SPEED (KN)	95
		ENGINE THRUST (LB/ENG)	44,000

MIXED CLASS 230 PASS. +
5,000 CARGO (51,000 LB PAYLOAD)

PASSENGER CAPACITY 250
ALL COACH @ 36 IN PITCH

Fig. 21-2 Model D966 General Characteristics

Courtesy of McDonnell Douglas Corp., now the Boeing Co.

MODEL D967
GENERAL CHARACTERISTICS
THREE ENGINE DESIGN

WING AREA	3,490 SQ FT.	TAKEOFF WEIGHT (LB)	325,000
ASPECT RATIO	7.0	O.W.E. (LB)	201,400
SWEEP	30.5°	RANGE (N.MI)	1,850
		TAKEOFF DISTANCE (FT)	5,450
		CRUISE MACH NO.	.80
		STALL SPEED (KN)	96
		ENGINE THRUST (LB/ENG)	32,000

MIXED CLASS 230 PASS. +
5,000 CARGO (51,000 LB PAYLOAD)

PASSENGER CAPACITY 250
ALL COACH @ 36 IN PITCH

Fig. 21-3 Model D967 General Characteristics

Courtesy of McDonnell Douglas Corp., now the Boeing Co.

336

One obvious result was that the individual engine size for the three engine model as reduced, although the total installed thrust was increased. The added engine made the takeoff second segment climb limitations less critical, which allowed the wing aspect ratio to be reduced saving some wing weight, and decreasing the OWE. However, the lower aspect ratio decreased the cruise (L/D), which requires more fuel to perform the mission range of 1850 n. mi., resulting in a higher takeoff weight. The higher average cruise weight and the lower cruise (L/D) require more total cruise thrust in order to meet the cruise Mach number. This increase in total installed thrust has a significant impact on the FAR takeoff field length (balanced field length with an engine failed), which was quite important to the flexibility of the design, as we shall soon see. The results of the trade study on number of engines is summarized in Fig. 21-4. The change from two large engines to three smaller ones affects the important weight numbers by only a few percent, and the DOC is increased by 5+%. However the ability to operate for longer ranges out of relatively modest runways, as shown in Fig. 21-5, was considered to be very important for the flexibility of operation of the airplane.

Similar trade studies were made to evaluate the impact of increasing the design range from 1850 n. mi. to 2500 n. mi. (Fig. 21-6), increasing the stall speed in the landing configuration from 96 kts to 100 kts (Fig. 21-7) and increasing the cruise speed from M=.80 to M=.85 (Fig. 21-8). The results of these trade studies are summarized in Fig. 21-9. The decisions that were made based on these trade studies are shown on Fig. 21-10. Additional decisions that needed to be made are also noted, and were the basis for additional trade studies.

The passenger capacity study involved an evaluation of two different length airplanes, a "standard" length and a "stretched" version, each with two different numbers of seats across in the coach section., compared to a then current type, the DC-8-61. The result of this trade study is shown on Fig. 21-11. It was decided that the standard length aircraft with 9 abreast seating was adequate to compete with the DC-8-61, and the stretch version could be developed at a later time.

The cruise speed trade study results are shown on Fig. 21-12. Based on these results, the configuration with a high speed cruise of M=.85 was selected. The fuselage cross-section trade study evaluated the impact of enlarging the fuselage diameter in order to accommodate two 8 ft x 8 ft cargo containers side by side in a freighter version of the airplane. It was decided, based on the results shown on Fig. 21-13 that the weight increases were not warranted to provide the nicety of side by side container capability on the main deck. The cockpit location trade study evaluated the effect of incorporating a high cockpit similar to the 747 as opposed to a conventional cockpit at the front end of the fuselage. The decision, based on the results shown in Fig. 21-14 was made to go with a conventional cockpit at the front end of the fuselage.

2 VS 3 ENGINE COMPARISON
CRUISE SPEED MACH .80

MODEL NO.		NUMBER OF ENGINES	
		2 vs 3	
		D966	D967
ENGINE THRUST	(LB/ENG)	44,000	32,000
TAKEOFF WT	(LB)	318,000	325,000
OPERATING WT EMPTY	(LB)	202,400	201,000
WING AREA	(SQ FT)	3,530	3,490
ASPECT RATIO		8.8	7.0
TAKEOFF FIELD LENGTH	(FT)	8,000	5,450
600 FT ALT 90°F			
TAKEOFF WT FOR LGA—ORD	(LB)	287,000	291,500
DOC 250 PASS.	(¢/SEAT ST MI)	.746	.787

Fig. 21-4 Two versus Three Engine Comparison

Courtesy of McDonnell Douglas Corp., now the Boeing Co.

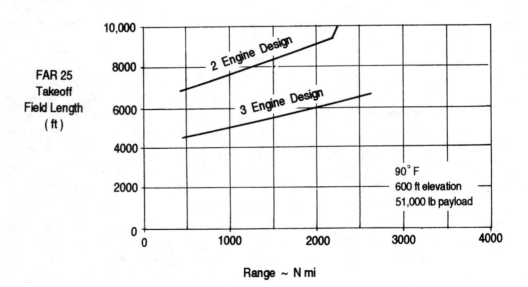

Fig. 21-5 DC-10 Type Range Increase Potential

Courtesy of McDonnell Douglas Corp., now the Boeing Co.

338

MODEL D967

DESIGN RANGE TRADE STUDY

		RANGE (N MI)	
		1850 vs	2500
CRUISE MACH NUMBER		0.85	0.83 to 0.85
TAKEOFF WT	(LB)	335,000	358,500
OPERATING WT EMPTY	(LB)	210,200	211,800
TAKEOFF FIELD LENGTH	(FT)	5,500	6,600
90°F, 600 FT ALT MAX T O G W			
TAKEOFF: FIELD LENGTH	(FT)	4,350	4,500
90°F, LGA—ORD WEIGHT	(LB)		
TAKEOFF: WT FOR LGA—ORD	(LB)	301,000	303,000
DOC (RANGE 1850 N MI).	(¢/SEAT ST MI)	.781	.784
250 PASS ALL - COACH			

CONSTANT   ASPECT RATIO 7.0
STALL SPEED 96 KNOTS
PAYLOAD 51,000 LB
ENGINE THRUST S.L.S.: 3 X 34,500 LB

Fig. 21-6 Model D967 Design Range Trade Study

Courtesy of McDonnell Douglas Corp., now the Boeing Co.

MODEL D967

STALL SPEED TRADE STUDY

		KNOTS (Vs_{1G})	
		96 vs	100
ENGINE THRUST S.L.S.	(LB)	3 X 34,500	3 X 34,000
WING AREA	(SQ FT)	3,790	3,400
TAKEOFF WT	(LB)	335,000	327,000
OPERATING WT EMPTY	(LB)	210,200	203,300
TAKEOFF FIELD LENGTH	(FT)	5,500	5,900
90°F, 600 FT ALT • MAX TOGW			
TAKEOFF: FIELD LENGTH	(FT)	4,350	4,750
90°F, LGA—ORD WEIGHT	(LB)	301,000	295,000
DOC	(¢/SEAT ST MI)	.781	.762
250 PASS - ALL COACH			

CONSTANT   CRUISE MACH .85   DESIGN RANGE 1,850 N MI
ASPECT RATIO 7.0   PAYLOAD 51,000 LB
WIND SWEEP 37.5°

Fig. 21-7 Model D967 Stall Speed Trade Study

Courtesy of McDonnell Douglas Corp., now the Boeing Co.

339

MODEL D967
CRUISE SPEED TRADE STUDY

		MACH		
		.80	vs	.85
ENGINE THRUST S.L.S.	(LB)	3 X 32,000		3 X 34,500
WING AREA	(SQ FT)	3,490		3,790
WING SWEEP	(")	30.5		37.5
TAKEOFF WT	(LB)	325,000		335,000
OPERATING WT EMPTY	(LB)	201,000		210,200
TAKEOFF FIELD LENGTH	(FT)	5,500		6,600
90°F, 600 FT ALT • MAX T O G W				
TAKEOFF: FIELD LENGTH	(FT)	4,200 FT/291,500 LB		4350 FT/301,000 LB
LOA—ORD/FIELD LENGTH				
(FIELD LENGTH - FT/T O C W - LD)				
DOC 250 PASS. ALL COACH		.787		.781
(¢/SEAT ST MI)				

CONSTANT   ASPECT RATIO 7.0
STALL SPEED 96 KNOT
DESIGN RANGE 1,050 N MI
PAYLOAD 51,000 LB
INITIAL CRUISE ALTITUDE 35,000 FT

Fig. 21-8 Model D967 Cruise Speed Trade Study

Courtesy of McDonnell Douglas Corp., now the Boeing Co.

DC-10 TYPE
TRADE STUDY SUMMARY
RANGE 1850 N MI

FLEXIBILITY OF 3 ENGINE   vs   2 ENGINE
COSTS   +7000 LB TAKEOFF GROSS WEIGHT
(SAVES 1400 LB OPERATING WEIGHT EMPTY)
.04¢/SEAT ST MILE DIRECT OPERATING COST

TRANSCONTINENTAL RANGE CAPABILITY
COSTS   2000 LB TAKEOFF WEIGHT
.01¢/SEAT ST MILE DIRECT OPERATING COST

CRUISE MACH NO. INCREASE .80 TO .85
COSTS   10,000 LB TAKEOFF WEIGHT
.NO CHANGE IN DIRECT OPERATING COST

STALL SPEED INCREASE FROM 96 TO 100 KNOTS
COSTS   8000 LB TAKEOFF WEIGHT
.02¢/SEAT ST MILE DIRECT OPERATING COST

Fig. 21-9 DC-10 Type Trade Study Summary

Courtesy of McDonnell Douglas Corp., now the Boeing Co.

DC-10
CONFIGURATION STATUS

FIRM
- 3 ENGINES
- TRANSCONTINENTAL RANGE CAPABILITY
- 8 ABREAST SEATING

UNDECIDED
- PASSENGER CAPACITY
- CRUISE SPEED
- CROSS-SECTION
- COCKPIT LOCATION

Fig. 21-10 DC-10 Configuration Status

Courtesy of McDonnell Douglas Corp., now the Boeing Co.

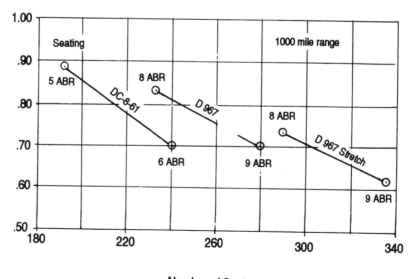

Fig. 21-11 Direct Operating Cost Comparison

Courtesy of McDonnell Douglas Corp., now the Boeing Co.

DC-10
CRUISE SPEED TRADE STUDY
D967

		MACH		
		2	vs	3
ENGINE THRUST	S.L.S. (LB)	30,200		31,000
WING AREA	(SQ FT)	3,340		3,540
WING SWEEP	(DEG)	35		37.5
MAX. TAKEOFF WT	(LB)	327,000		333,500
OPERATING WT EMPTY	(LB)	188,800		193,900
TAKEOFF FIELD LENGTH	(FT)	6,200		6,050
90°F, 600 FT ALT T.O. WT FOR 1850 N. ML				
TAKEOFF FIELD LENGTH		4800/227,000		4600/282,500
LGA—ORD (FIELD FT/T.O.G.W.)	(LB)	287,000		291,500
DOC 236 PASS. ALL COACH @ 1850 N. ML		.775		.785
(¢/SEAT ST MI)				

Fig. 21-12 DC-10 Cruise Speed Trade Study

Courtesy of McDonnell Douglas Corp., now the Boeing Co.

FUSELAGE CROSS SECTION COMPARISONS

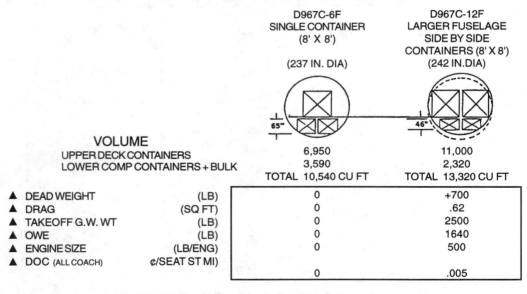

Fig. 21-13 Fuselage Cross-Section Comparisons

Courtesy of McDonnell Douglas Corp., now the Boeing Co.

DC-10
LOW vs HIGH COCKPIT

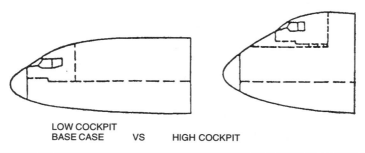

LOW COCKPIT
BASE CASE   VS   HIGH COCKPIT

		LOW COCKPIT	V S	HIGH COCKPIT
△	FUSELAGE LENGTH (FT)	0		-6
△	DEAD WEIGHT (LB)	0		-800
△	DRAG (SQ. FT.)	0		+0.68
△	TAKEOFF G.W. (LB)	0		-70
△	O.W.E. (LB)	0		-670
△	WING AREA (SQ. FT.)	0		-7
△	ENGINE S.L.S.T. (LB)	0		+280
△	DOC (ALL COACH) (¢/SEAT ST. MI.)	0		-.0005

Fig. 21-14 DC-10 Low versus High Cockpit

Courtesy of McDonnell Douglas Corp., now the Boeing Co.

    The foregoing examples show how trade studies are used to optimize a preliminary design with respect to specific criteria. In recent years, a computer-based methodology known as Multidisciplinary Design Optimization, (MDO), has been introduced to achieve the optimum design all in one operation. This procedure seems to be gaining favor in the industry, but requires a tremendously complex set of equations which may tend to obscure the reasons for the resulting configuration characteristics.

REFERENCES

21.1 Shevell, Richard S., Aerospace Systems Synthesis and Analysis, Course Notes, Stanford University, Palo Alto, CA, 1985

21.2 Cherry, H.H., and Croshere, A.B., Jr., An Approach to the Analytical Design of Aircraft, SAE Quarterly Transactions, Vol. 2, No. 1, January, 1948

21.3 De Fillipo, Ralph J., Aircraft Synthesis Using Numerical Optimization Techniques, AIAA Paper 83-2458, 1983

21.4 Sobieszczanski-Sobieski, Jaroslaw, Multidisciplinary Design Optimization: An Emerging New Engineering Discipline, NASA Technical Memorandum 107761, May, 1993

22

PROGRAM BUSINESS PLANNING

Program business planning is an integral part of the product development process. No matter how attractive the performance of a new aircraft design may be, if the program business plan does not appear attractive to the manufacturer, the program will not go ahead.

PLANNING PHASES

Program business planning involves several special and distinct phases. These are:

Overall Market Forecast

Every year, the major commercial aircraft and engine manufacturers update their projections for the total number of new aircraft required to meet the projected demand for air travel throughout the world. The demand is projected for various regions of the world based on economic factors such as Gross Domestic Product (GDP), disposable income, business growth, etc. The overall projected demand is usually carried out for 10 to 15 years in the future, roughly corresponding to the time frame for a program business plan as shown in Fig. 22-1. The projected demand, in revenue passenger kilometers (RPKs), is further divided into the demand in specific size/range sectors. An example size/range sector is "Short Range-110" or aircraft with a design range around 1200 N.Mi, and a capacity of about 110 passengers. Fig. 22-2 shows the size/range sectors as defined by one aircraft company. Other companies use similar, but not exactly the same size/range sectors in their forecasting. With the total demand for each size/range sector determined, the number of new aircraft required to satisfy the demand is estimated taking into account the

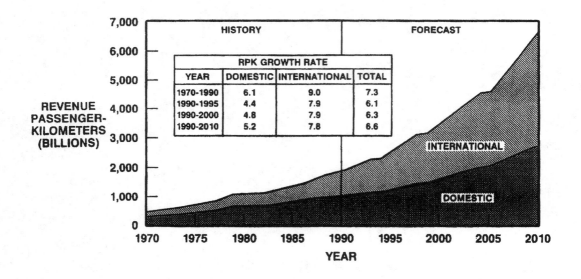

Fig. 22-1 World Passenger Traffic Growth Forecast

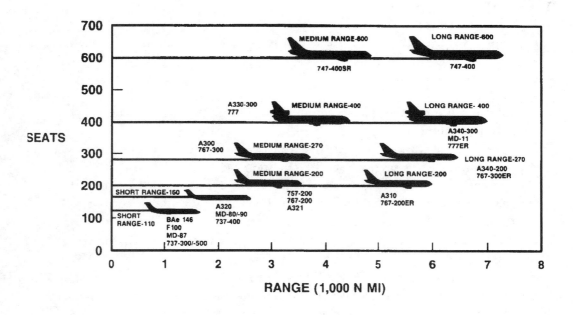

Fig. 22-2 Size/Range Classes

current number of aircraft in the sector, the forecast retirements, the variation in average seat load factor, etc. Fig. 22-3 shows the forecast total market, and the major range sector breakouts. Although not shown, the units for each individual size/range sector are forecast.

Market Share Forecast

For a proposed new entry in a given size/range sector, a market share forecast is made. That is, of the total number of new units forecast, how many will be of the proposed new model? Market share forecasts are difficult at best, but are usually based on factors such as how many competing designs, what airlines have the greatest need for aircraft in the specific size/range sector, what commonality features does the new model have with models already in service with specific airlines, etc. As a broad generality, a new model with competitive performance and economics will share equally in new sales with its competitors in a given size/range sector. The market share forecast sets the projected income or revenue for the program.

The cost side of the program is usually estimated in terms of two major categories.

Non-Recurring Costs

As the name implies, these are one-time costs associated with the design, development, and production and support of the new model. Typical non-recurring costs are engineering design, manufacturing planning, tooling design and construction, interface with major subcontractors (writing specs, negotiating contracts, providing data, etc.), flight testing, laboratory testing, preparation of complete product support publications (maintenance manuals, repair manuals, spares catalogs, flight manuals, etc.). Fig. 22-4 shows the relative size of these non-recurring costs for a modem jet transport program.

Recurring Costs

These are the costs associated with the production of a specific number of units of the new model, and include labor, raw material, engines, major systems such as the electrical system, flight guidance and control system, special equipment such as the landing gears, auxiliary power units, and subassemblies procured from major subcontractors. Fig. 22-5 shows the relative size of these costs for a modern jet transport program.

At this point, the total program costs are evaluated against the projected total program income or revenue, and a determination of return on investment (ROI) is made. A sim-

Fig. 22-3 Commercial Transport Market Forecast.

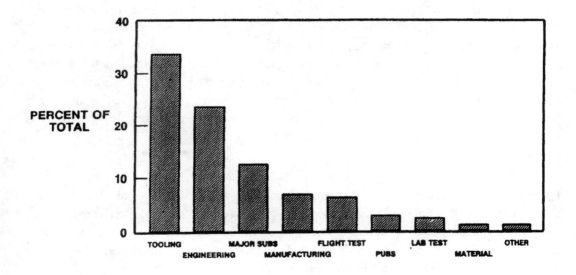

Fig. 22-4 Typical Subsonic Transport Program Non-Recurring Cost Distribution

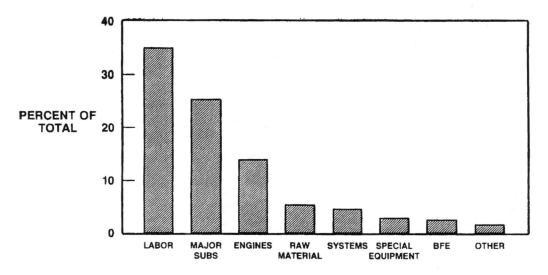

Fig. 22-5 Typical Subsonic Transport Program Recurring Cost Distribution

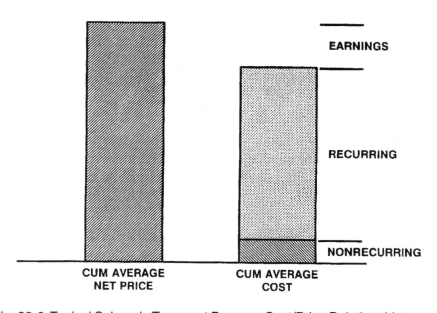

Fig. 22-6 Typical Subsonic Transport Program Cost/Price Relationships

plistic figure for ROI would be (earnings/cost) as indicated in Fig. 22-6.

If the ROI projections look favorable, say on the order of 20%, then a more detailed program cash flow analysis is made.

Program cash flow involves the variation of program costs and program income over a period of time. As noted in Fig. 22-7 in the early part of the program, there is a large amount of "negative cash flow", because of the significant non-recurring costs which are only slightly offset by "progress payment" income from airline customers. As the non-recurring costs are finishing up, the large recurring costs are incurred, but these are eventually offset by income from delivered aircraft. If the "negative cash bucket" exceeds the liquid cash assets of the manufacturer, then cash must be borrowed, further adding to the "negative cash bucket." If all goes well, the program break-even may be reached after 10 to 12 years from program start. Program "profits" then begin to accrue. While this process is reasonably well understood, there have been few truly "profitable" commercial transport programs.

REFERENCES

22.1   Anonymous, the Outlook for Commercial Aircraft 1996-2015, Douglas Aircraft Co. Long Beach, CA, 1996

22.2   Anonymous, The Competitive Status of the U.S. Civil Aviation Manufacturing Industry, the National Academy Press, Washington, D.C., 1985

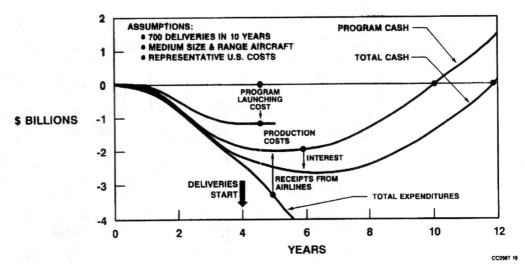

Fig. 22-7 Typical Commercial Transport Program Cash Flow

Reprinted with permission from Ref. 22.2

INDEX

AUSTIN CITY LIMITS ®

35 YEARS IN PHOTOGRAPHS

BRAD AND MICHELE MOORE ROOTS MUSIC SERIES

AUSTIN CITY LIMITS®

35 YEARS IN PHOTOGRAPHS

PHOTOGRAPHS BY
Scott Newton

EDITED BY
Terry Lickona and Scott Newton

FOREWORD BY
John Mayer

WITH ASSISTANCE FROM
MICHAEL TOLAND

UNIVERSITY OF TEXAS PRESS 🐂 AUSTIN

Requests for permission to reproduce material from this work should be sent to:
  Permissions
  University of Texas Press
  P.O. Box 7819
  Austin, TX 78713-7819
  www.utexas.edu/utpress/about/bpermission.html

♾ The paper used in this book meets the minimum requirements of ANSI/NISO Z39.48-1992
(R1997) (Permanence of Paper).

LIBRARY OF CONGRESS CATALOGING-IN-PUBLICATION DATA

Newton, Scott, 1949–
  Austin City Limits : 35 years in photographs / photographs by Scott Newton ; edited by Terry
Lickona and Scott Newton ; foreword by John Mayer. — 1st ed.
     p.   cm. — (Brad and Michele Moore roots music series)
  ISBN 978-0-292-72311-5 (cloth : alk. paper)
  1. Musicians—Pictorial works.   I. Lickona, Terry.   II. Newton, Scott, 1949.   III. *Austin City
Limits* (Television program)   IV. Title.
  ML87.N48   2010
  791.45′72—dc22
                                                                            2010007674

Contents

Foreword by **John Mayer**
Photographer's Preface by **Scott Newton**
A Note from the Executive Producer by **Terry Lickona**

THE PHOTOGRAPHS

Flipping through the television channels, you can tell within a sliver of a second that you're watching *Austin City Limits*.

Even if you don't recognize the song, or the man or woman singing it, you know that stage: that iconic foam-core cutout of Austin's skyline, one that obviously doesn't succeed in a photorealistic sense but over the last thirty-five years has become its own ethereal destination. You recognize that lighting, which by today's standards would be called "unforgiving" but, given this show's tenure, is rightfully perceived as charming and nostalgic.

You keep listening to this song you may or may not have heard before, and you keep watching this artist you might still be assessing. Then something truly rare and exciting happens: you realize that you're giving a television show your *trust*. Your brain quietly sends a signal to your artistic taste buds, as if to say, "If it's on *Austin City Limits*, there's something we're going to like about this."

The familiarity of the song, the name of the artist, or even the chronology of the performance doesn't matter. That's not what *Austin City Limits* has built a legacy on. What you connect with so instantly and so completely is the dedication of the performers you're watching. You're witnessing a group of musicians giving their best, wanting and aching and working and *trying* to be their best, knowing that they're on a stage that has already seen the greatest performances from some of the world's greatest artists. You're seeing an artist play a show they've been looking forward to not only for the days and weeks since it was booked, but for the years since the first time they felt somebody move them on an episode of *Austin City Limits*. For all the interviews and peripheral "behind the scenes" footage of artists, nothing is more revealing than an artist sharing with you his true need to make a statement that matters. When an artist performs in a way that says, "Let me entertain you," magic happens.

And that's why I care about *Austin City Limits*. Whenever

I've been asked to play on the show (twice, as of this writing), I've become something of a tactical strategist, working hard to place the date of the taping somewhere late enough in my tour to give my best but not so close to the end as to be worn out. Because whatever I do on that stage, it's going to matter. The faces in the crowd will be preserved on tape forever—wearing clothes and hairstyles that will someday date us all—and I want those faces to reflect exactly how I feel: connected to the music, proud to be in the room, and proud to be in front of that *Austin City Limits* skyline.

One lucky day, many years ago, a professor of Ancient Greek lectured my class about musicians and other performing artists during the days of yore.

He made the point that our culture's way of looking at musicians and performers is very different from the way it used to be. It was once understood that inspiration and creativity were provided by an outside spirit, or daimon, that flowed through the musician from a more ethereal place—separate from, but related to, the musician or actor or artist. In other words, it wasn't exactly the human being who was singing for us; instead it was, to a large extent, a spirit that was singing through the medium of the existing person—modified by that person, to be sure, but motivated by a purer, deeper being.

It has become my personal opinion that the ancient Greeks were on to something. Our cult of personality misses the point. It's the somehow separate, creative spirits expressing themselves through these performers that provide the deepest insights; the actual corporeal humans themselves are, to some degree, channels. That's not to denigrate the performers themselves; there's nothing wrong with becoming the channel that the most expressive spirits speak through. After all, it's quite an honor for the muses to love someone so much that they sing through him.

Often the people themselves—the performers, musicians, artists of all stripes—are truly lovely humans; just as often, they're not. It's only in our fairly modern age that we have

can see her fully in the thrall of her motivating spirit. And when we hear and see her in this state, and we like it, we can join in. We're moved by the same spirit! We've all been in a room where everyone is pulsing to the same beat, the same music, lending our bodies and beings to the stoking of the mutual larger spirit that we partake in—feeling that spirit running through us all . . .

And that's why we love music so much. It's the sound the muses make. It helps break down the smaller, separated and isolated things—ourselves—and hooks us up with the much larger thing. And it's an increasingly larger thing—if you expand enough, eventually you get to the divine, or to whatever you see as The Biggest Possible Thing.

All of that to say this: It has been my life's work, over the last thirty-one years at *ACL*, to photograph the musicians who have appeared on our stage, and to attempt to capture a sense of the invisible muses who move them. See if you can tell the difference, as you look at the photos, between when I'm shooting musicians and when I'm shooting muses. Sometimes it's both, but sometimes it's really one or the other.

And sometimes it's an ego-oriented, self-conscious person photographing these things, and sometimes it's his daimon working through him.

WHAT MADE
MIL FAMY
WALK US?
AUSTIN City Limits
Rules
AND THIS ISN'T
A Smoking AREA
PLANK
MADE
A LOSER
OUTTA
ME!
Patti Smith
you rule!
3.15.2000
THIEVERY
CORPORATION
WASHINGTON D.C.
LOVES ACL
LIVE
9/15/02
JACKMASON
Tex
profesor
Lightmaker.com
OL'97 Just Ran Me Down, Yes!
little stevie k.
listen
to Sleepy
Head
PDX
See you
on TV!
GOD
Bless
ACL
Season 29 Wrap party
10/20/03 Jonny Lang
AND NOW, THE BIG THREE-OH!
ACL
ON
Piss off the Status quo
ACL
ERIC
B-G
CAM 1 12-9-07
LIVE IN
DRESSING Rooms

A Note from the Executive Producer Terry Lickona

To most people, a photograph is little more than an instant of life, frozen in time.

Often, in fact, it seems lifeless, with little or no reference to what came before, or after, that instant. The challenge to the photographer is to capture more, to breathe life into that frame, to stir the imagination behind the eye of the beholder. The challenge is multiplied when that instant happens to be a performance—something that we would normally experience with multiple senses.

For over three decades, Scott Newton has faced that challenge thousands of times. As the principal photographer for *Austin City Limits* practically since the show's inception, he has had the opportunity—the privilege—of capturing and documenting every musical performance on what has become the longest-running music program on American television. The expression "a picture is worth a thousand words" is inadequate to convey the passion, the emotion, the muse present in each of these images. At its best, a photograph should capture *you*, the viewer, as well. Consider this book, on a basic level, to be an interactive experience; compare your own emotion with the one that jumps off the page.

The story of *Austin City Limits* has been told many times throughout its history. What started as a simple Texas music showcase on public television has become a chronicle of unique and original music from across America and beyond. Generations of music fans have been inspired and entertained by performances in every genre, as have generations of singers, songwriters, and musicians—some of whom have fulfilled their dream of walking onto that stage themselves to make their own history.

The format is as pure and simple as those moments in time. And that brings us back to the images in this book. *Austin City Limits: 35 Years in Photographs* is a collection of the best of the best: the best moments from some of the most brilliant, mesmerizing, quirky, esoteric, and unforgettable perform-

ers to appear on any stage or in front of any camera in the past thirty-five years. It has been said that *Austin City Limits* brings out the best in an artist, and if that is true, Scott's shutter always clicked at exactly the right time. You'll have to provide your own music, but enjoy the magic of these photographs, and the personal insights that accompany them—in our words and the artists' own. We hope they will leave you hungry for more!

The Photographs

Willie Nelson 1979, 1980

1979

Willie Nelson, Red Lane, Floyd Tillman (seated), Don Gant, Hank Cochran, Rock Killough, Whitey Shafer, Sonny Throckmorton. 1979

Simple equation: no Willie Nelson = no *Austin City Limits*. Thank God Willie decided to abandon Nashville in the mid-1970s and return home to Texas and settle in the hills outside of Austin. Before long he was shaking up the local music scene, and the folks at the local public television station, KLRN at the time, invited him to bring his rowdy band into the studio and record the pilot for a fledgling music show—before they even had a name for it. That was October 17, 1974. Willie has returned to that stage many times over many years, and it just keeps getting better. —T.L.

Arcade Fire 2007

"It's kind of a luxury to be in a small room with properly marked fire exits." —Win Butler

"When I was fifteen . . . I didn't really know what sadness was, or what pain was, but you live a few more years—it'll come to you. One way or another, you'll get older and you'll learn about what pain is, what sadness is, and then you'll be able to write about it. And you can't write about it without that experience."   —Seth Avett

Beck 2002

with The Flaming Lips

"I like making music in areas where I'm not really sure of myself. I like that aspect of imminent failure." —Bec

Garth Brooks, 1990

"Bad bull in ACL rodeo? If we're baseball players, this is the World Series." —Garth Broc

"I've seen some of the
greatest acts and sho[ws]
I've ever seen on *Aus[tin]*
City Limits, and to st[ep]
out there is funny—it['s a]
lot smaller than what [I]
thought. I thought, 'T[his is]
Texas, it's gonna be h[uge.']
It's little, but it's loud. [It's]
big in its own way. Bu[t it's]
a great vibe."

—Ronnie D[unn]

Wilco

My Morning Jacket

Joss Stone

Austin City Limits skyline

Andrew Bird

R.E.M.

Ibrahim Ferrer

Rubén González

Buena Vista Social Club 2001

We were fortunate to tape this band of incredible Cuban musicians, kept from our musical world for so long, before they died. In the world of music, there should be no room for politics. Ibrahim Ferrer, bandleader and vocalist, and pianist Rubén González were as heavy as Ray Charles in

"As the artist will, you try and drag the audience along into something you're interested in and [that] they may not be interested in, and some of them are willing to go with you and some of them are not. But I think that, even if they don't go with you, they respect you for doing that." —David Byrne

Neko Case's charm extended beyond her performance when she shipped homemade cookies and brownies to the *ACL* staff in appreciation. Hardly the usual thank-you note—how cool is that?   —M.T.

Johnny Cash (with June Carter Cash) 1987

He appeared on our show only once. I call this shot [on left] "Mount Rushmore," because that's where it looks like it should be, carved in stone.   —S. N.

"I love live performance because it only happens for those two hours. It's so ephemeral, and that makes it so beautiful to me—that particular audience chemistry is never gonna happen again. But I also love being in the studio, because there's none of the anxiety of the preshow stuff, worrying 'Is my voice gonna work?' and blah blah blah. Being in the studio is like painting—you can really take your time and try different things, kind of go deep into it. There's nothing that gives me more of a thrill than when I'm writing and a couplet works—I find the right rhyme, or it's just perfect."   —Rosanne Cash

Anything is possible when Chan Marshall (Cat Power) steps on stage, and that's the beauty of it. —T.L.

Manu Chao 2008

As *ACL* continues to live up to our mantra of "Great Music, No Limits," enter Manu Chao. A best-kept secret to many unfortunate Americans, he's a legend on many of the world's stages. He rejects all commercial endorsements and devotes 100 percent of his passion to the music, the message, and his multitudes of fans. Getting him here was a coup.   —T. L.

Charles 1983

Ray Charles's first appearance was a milestone for *Austin City Limits*, a sure sign that the show had grown beyond its original Texas roots. The second time was reaffirmation. As he did in every other respect, Ray paved the way.   —T.L.

Kenny Chesney 2009

Jerry Douglas (Alison Krauss & Union Station)   Rosanne Cash

John Mayer

Manu Cha

Leonard Cohen, 1988

The question everyone wants to know is what my all-time favorite *ACL* show is; the answer is this Leonard Cohen show. Deep and significant, h
almost [...]ful delivery affected me like a sacrament, and I've nev[...] seen th[...]ss[...] since [...]t[...]essing what[...] mea[...]s[...]ser do[...] S N

Coldplay 2005

"*Austin City Limits* is very important to us because it's like where we come from and what we believe in. We believe in it as an idea, and so that's why we do it. It doesn't matter how big we are. We're just very proud to be doing it."   —Chris Martin

Elvis Costello 2009

"I take what I do seriously in that I respect it. I respect what I'm doing, I respect the audience, and I respect the past as a source of information and clues to how you might solve new problems musically. But I don't live in the past. I have no nostalgia at all. I am absolutely without nostalgia about my own past or anybody else's. I don't long to be in any other time but now. I live completely in the moment with hope for the future, and that's about the best you can do."   —Elvis Costello

1997

Sheryl Crow 1997, 2004

2004

2004

Sheryl has become a mainstream success story in every respect, but she has never veered from doing things her own way. She taped her first *ACL* in 1997, then came back seven years later as a headliner at the third annual Austin City Limits Music Festival, where her show was one of the only two captured for broadcast as a special *ACL* episode.   —T.L.

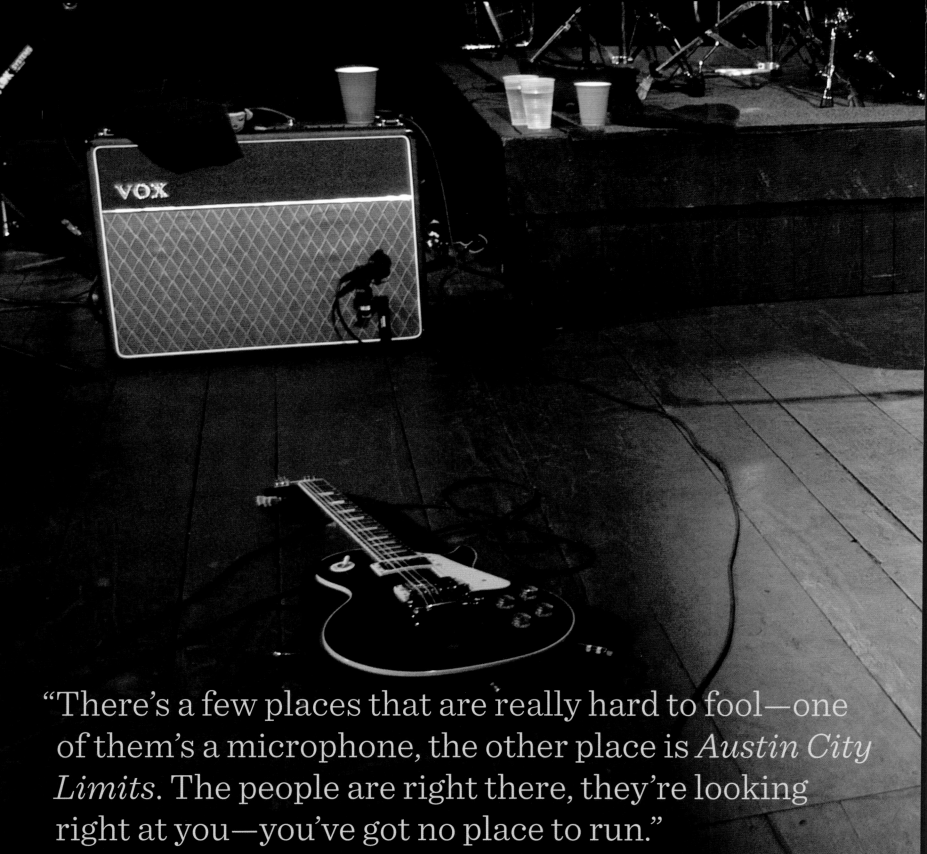

"There's a few places that are really hard to fool—one of them's a microphone, the other place is *Austin City Limits*. The people are right there, they're looking right at you—you've got no place to run."

—Merle Haggard

"Soul music is just about honesty, I think, and passion, and a sense of desperation—there's always a sense of wanting more in soul music."   —Duffy

Alejandro Escovedo 2006

"I don't know if I have any goals. I just try to play, live a good life. I just want to keep making records and writing songs—that's about it for me. I do want to be a pop star. I just want to be able to play." **Alejandro Escovedo**

The Flaming Lips 2004

"The Flaming Lips started off in 1983. I speak about it now using the band as kind of an excuse to be like what, two hundred years ago, would have been like [being] a pirate. It's just a vehicle by which you can travel around, do crazy things, see crazy things, and somehow put off becoming an adult, following this dream that looks like art and music."   —Wayne Coyne

John Fogerty 2004

"Completing something when it's a struggle and then knowing that it's good—something just kind of snaps into place. At least those times when it does, it's the greatest feeling. The times when it won't snap into place, you feel like an utter failure. Really I'm there more than in euphoria. I think I fail a lot as a songwriter. I'm darned if I know why I keep trying. I guess to get the euphoria part." —John Fogerty

Brad Paisley

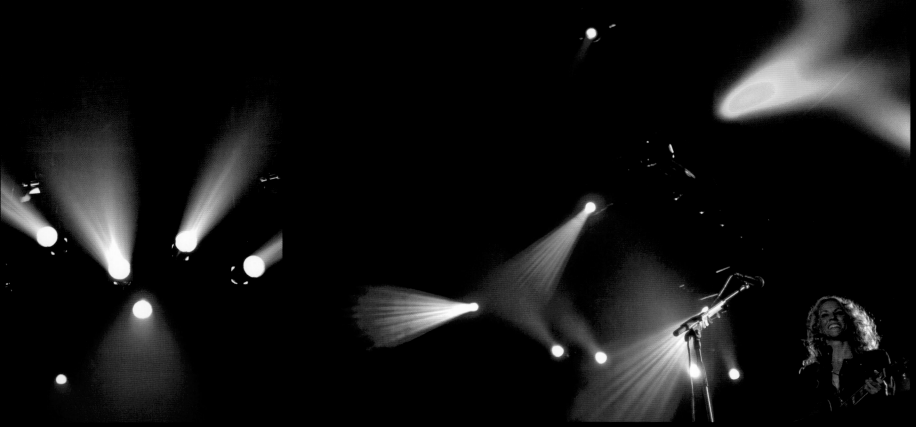

Foo Fighters 2008

"When you sit in the dressing room downstairs and look at all the pictures on the wall . . . oh my God. You can't believe you've been invited to d
this thing. Because as far as I'm concerned, we don't have to get into the Rock and Roll Hall of Fame anymore because we're fucking playing th
show tonight."   —Dave Grohl

Ghostland Observatory, 2007

"We enjoy seeing people's physical reaction to music. When we see that, it just gives us motivation to keep going and stay creative, and have fun with it." —Thomas Turner

Vince Gill 2003

"That's the one thing that is really timeless: the songs. The artistry, the popularity of the artistry—that's gonna come and go. Your talent level, as the years go by . . . you're gonna lose a little bit of what you used to be able to do—it's like an athlete. But those songs—they're really precious, and they don't know who is holdin' the pen, which I like."

Patty Griffin 2004

"My songwriting process has a lot to do with getting quiet and trying to be a listener rather than a participant. You just sit there and you wait for it to show up. Sometimes it feels like you've been annoyed for a week, and you don't have any idea why, and you can't figure out what you're annoyed about, and then bluh! A song shows up."   —Patty Griffin

Merle Haggard 1985

Whether he brought his band (considered the best in country music) or just his guitar, Merle always brought those songs and that powerful voice. He once said that his many appearances on *Austin City Limits* were like a musical scrapbook of his career. —T.L.

Etta James 2005

"I sing for myself until I hear something really soulful come out, and I know it's for me, and it's touched my heart or made a tear in the corner of my eye."   —Etta James

Norah Jones 2007

The buzz began at South by Southwest in 2002, when she played a showcase in a tiny room above an Indian restaurant, and less than a year later sh

Juanes 2006

Juanes is more than just a Latin superstar. A political and social activist back in his native Colombia, he is passionate about his music and culture. Some have dubbed him a "Colombian Bruce Springsteen," but maybe Bruce is an American Juanes?   —T.L.

Only one King has ever performed on the *Austin City Limits* stage, and no one ever would or could challenge his claim to th[e]
of the Blues made his first appearance in 1982, B.B. had done surprisingly little national TV—certainly not full-length perf[o]
ACL has showcased dozens of legendary and rising blues musicians, enough to be honored by the Blues Foundation wit[h]

Yasmin Youssef (Thievery Corporation)

Bosede Ajila, Yemi Oriyomi, Kate Onome Udi (Femi Kuti)

Aaron Kyle Behrens (Ghostland Observatory)

"Writing songs can be a chore, but if you go in there and you don't overthink it, sometimes your best stuff can come out. I think when you're in the studio recording, and you go back and the stress is over and the dust is settled, and you listen to what you've done, if after going in there and recording it and playing it two hundred times, you still get chill bumps, I think that's the best feeling of all."   —Caleb Followill

K'Naan 2009

I don't believe in the idea that everyone has to hear everyone's music. I just think it would be nice if

2002

Alison Krauss & Union Station 2002, 2005

2005

Alison and *Austin City Limits* have had a mutual love affair since the first time she appeared with her longtime band Union Station at the age of nineteen in 1992.   —T.L.

Femi Kuti 2007

"Music is making a difference worldwide. Music makes you cry, makes you think, makes you everything. It's the only profession you can't touch, but it touches you." —Femi Kuti

Created in 2002, the Austin City Limits Music Festival has become one of the premier rock festivals in the United States. Produced by C3 Presents, the annual event presents over 130 bands on eight stages—reinventing the magic of the TV show for hundreds of thousands of fans in Austin's own Zilker Park.

Ralph Stanley

Legends of Bluegrass Special 1986

WITH BILL MONROE AND RALPH STANLEY

Bill Monroe

Bill Monroe was the undisputed Father of Bluegrass (he invented the genre), but he wasn't the only bluegrass legend. Ralph Stanley was an alumnus of Bill Monroe's Bluegrass Boys, but quickly became a star on his own. So this was a historic meeting of bluegrass titans . . . one of their last appearances together onstage.   —T.L.

Jerry Lee Lewis 1983

Years later Jerry Lee turned down another invite to appear because he said he "could never do another show better than the first one." —T.I.

2002

Los Lobos 1991 2002

1991

Los Lobos is influenced by so many different musical styles that it can only be described as an *American* rock band.   —T.L.

Lyle Lovett 2004

"Writing songs is not painful. It's hard, and it's therapeutic, and it's frustrating, and it's exciting, and it's all those things at the same time."   —Lyle Lovett

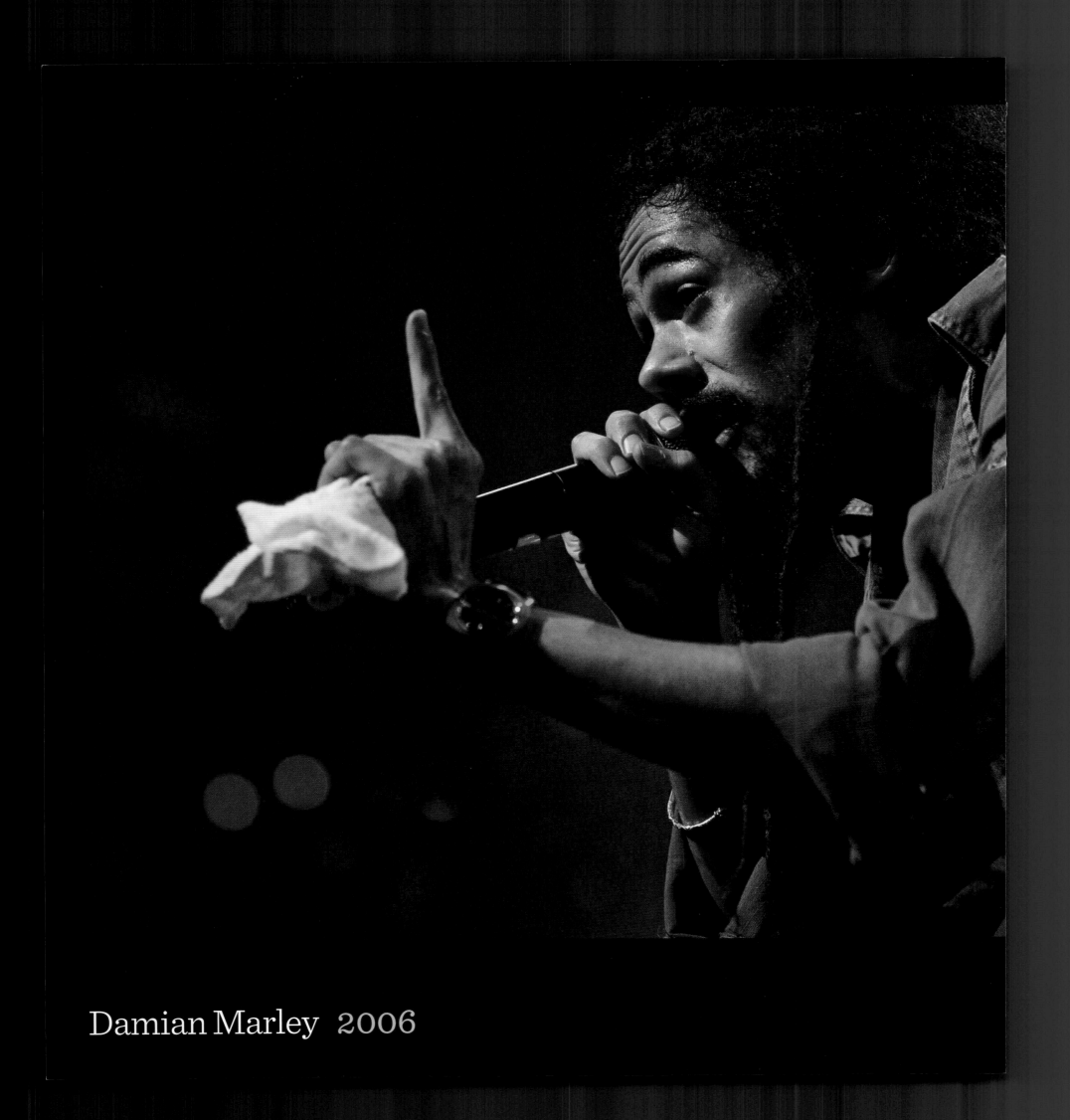

Damian Marley 2006

"When I'm making music, I don't think about, 'Oh, I'm Bob Marley's son.' It's really just, 'I'm me.' . . . To be compared to the best is a privilege. Because to me, my father is one of the best." —Damian Marley

Dixie Chicks

Manu Chao

Elvis Costello

Lucinda Williams

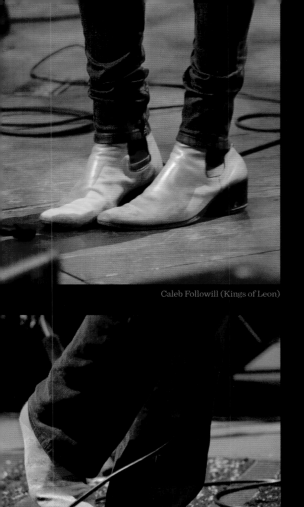

Caleb Followill (Kings of Leon)

K'Naan

Andrew Bird

Brandon Flowers (The Killers)

Duff

"When it becomes a job, or it's work, which happens occasionally, that's no fun. But when it's open and joyful, that's when it's magic for me, and then I don't care what anyone else thinks." —Dave Matthews

John Mayer 2007

"You know what *Austin City Limits* says when you walk into that room? You walk into that room and *Austin City Limits* says, 'Don't lie to me.' It's really nice to get up on a stage that says, 'Don't lie to me.' From that comes a performance that's as honest as an artist can get."   —John Mayer

The Del McCoury Band 2001

They dress and pose like they're in church, which they are; and Del is the preacher. —S.N.

Sarah McLachlan 2008

"[Songs] are little postcards of the emotional place I was in when I wrote them, a musical scrapbook of my emotional world—my maturity or imma-turity, and my growth as a musician, too." —Sarah McLachlan

Pat Metheny Group 2002

Music and joy, if not always synonymous, certainly share a lot of territory. With Pat Metheny, they appear to be two sides of the same thing.　—S.N.

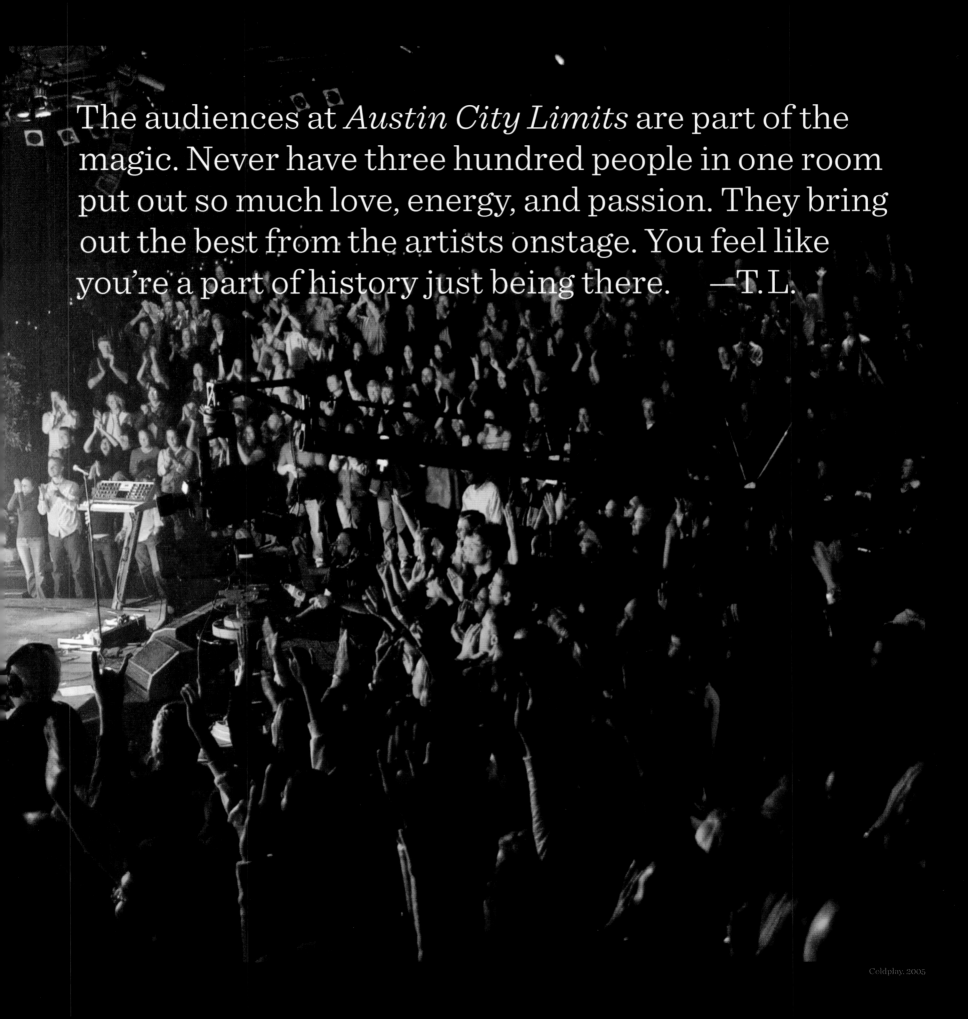

The audiences at *Austin City Limits* are part of the magic. Never have three hundred people in one room put out so much love, energy, and passion. They bring out the best from the artists onstage. You feel like you're a part of history just being there.   —T. L.

Coldplay, 2005

Mos Def 2009

The first authentic hip-hop show in *Austin City Limits* history. As Mos said, "So many artists have been on this stage . . . you want to be able to be at that level."   —T.L.

My Morning Jacket 2008

Roy's one and only appearance on *Austin City Limits* was a part of his career comeback in the early eighties. He had never done much TV, so this full-hour performance was special. He had an amazing four-octave range, and when he hit those high notes, the audience literally came out of their seats. Elvis and Bono, among many, called him the best singer ever. Sadly, he was gone six years later . . .   —T.L.

'The religious aspect of some of the music … I feel like that's one of the things that music does best, is bring you to this place where you're outside of yourself and you're part of something larger than yourself. That's something that music can do in a way that no other art form can do."

Brad Paisley 2006

Sara Watkins (Nickel Creek)   Andrew Bird

Susan Voelz (Alejandro Escovedo)

Esperanza Spalding

Dolly Parton, 2001

"I'm just a little crazy now, but I'd probably be nuts if I couldn't write."   —Dolly Parton

Pearl Jam 2009

"There's something about the history of a venue like this—it's a monument to music. And it's been built not only by you folks who've kept and main-tained it, but also by the musicians who've put the bricks in this monument. To be able to put your brick in amongst all the others . . . after eighteen years of playing as a group, there's still things out there that give us this elevated sense of experience, and this was certainly one of them."

—Eddie Vedder

"When something real happens at a concert—genuine, special, and unique—it's with you for the rest of your life, burned into your memory. Having those experiences made me want to do this, and everything we do is to try to get to a point where something special happens that's unique to that real life onstage."

—Trey Anastasio

Frank Black was an *ACL* fan as a pre-teen when he watched the show with his grandmother.
It was an electrifying night; Grandma would've been proud.

Robert Plant 2002

"In the sort of general consciousness of rock and roll, I've been typecast, because it's been considered I'm a rocker. I've got a big voice, I do wails and screams, and if I don't hit those high notes I'm not a man anymore. The kind of classic rock labels put people in certain categories. And I've never been in any one category, since 1968. It really is sailing a beautiful ship in all kinds of weather and sea, because a lot of people don't accept this. As

The Raconteurs, 2006

Jack White has *it*. That thing called, variously, charisma, stage presence, gravitas. The whole thing: riveting movement, powerful, piercing voice. Obviously his body is inhabited by an immense soul. —S.N.

Corinne Bailey Rae   2006

Some humans seem to be joy and light wrapped up in a body. She's one of them.   —S.N

Miranda Lambert

The Polyphonic Spree

Loretta Lynn

Shara Worden (Sufjan Stevens)

Monk Boudreaux (New Orleans Social Club)

Juanes

Bonnie Raitt 2002

"I wouldn't hold up any other cultural phenomenon as high as I would *Austin City Limits*."   —Bonnie Raitt

Robert Randolph & The Family Band 2002, 2004

2004   2002

"[I'm] just doin' something that, probably early on, people said I couldn't do—sayin' that steel guitar could never be in the front, it could never be played a certain way. And to be able to nix all of them from saying that, and go on just doin' what I wanted to do and accepting the love for music and

"We kinda thought, 'Well, we're a post-punk rock band,' but that didn't seem to work. And then there was 'alternative' or 'indie' or 'college.' . . . It just seemed at the time that it was bands that you would never ever hear on the radio. We were working in this part of the business that was not business-like at all—it was pretty amateurish. And then, hey, guess what? We won that revolution. Alternative is the mainstream now, whatever it's called."

—Peter Buck

Songwriters Special 2008

LYLE LOVETT, JOHN HIATT, JOE ELY, AND GUY CLARK

"There's a real tradition of storytelling in Texas. You know—bullshitters. It's always been that way."   —Guy Clark

Clement, Lyle Lovett, Rodney Crowell, Emmylou Harris, Willie Nelson, Guy Clark, John T. Van Zandt, Nanci Griffith, Steve Earle, Peter Rowan, and Mickey Raphael on harmonica

ongwriters Special 1997   A CELEBRATION OF TOWNES VAN Z

"One of my favorite Townes lines—he said there were two kinds of music: there was the blues and there was zippety-doo-dah. Even when he did a slightly upbeat, happy song, there was still the blues in it. And I guess that's what I loved about his songs, because they always spoke the truth."

—Emmylou Harris

anza Spalding 2009

"I think the music that jazz grew out of and grew into is really its own living, breathing entity. It doesn't actually have to be played in any one specific way by any one specific group of people, or be supported and patronized by any one specific group to be vibrant and alive." —Esperanza Spalding

2002   2005

"Songwriting . . . it's always different. You can work yourself into a weird place where you can't write songs. It's about your frame of mind, and it's about getting lucky. Sometimes when I was working I would sit down on my couch where I write the songs and say, 'Let's get lucky.'" —Britt Daniel

"People always ask me where it comes from, but I don't know—it's a really hard question to answer. Because I just sing. I haven't had any lessons, you know, nothing professional like that. I just make a noise. I'm lucky that it sounds good when it comes out."   —Joss Stone

"At first it's daunting that there are cameras, but then it's easy to forget, because you have really sweet people lining every wall and right at the stage. It starts to feel like a fun, really good-sounding, normal show."   —Annie Clark

The Swell Season 2008

with Conspirare Youth Choir

"Music has to be something you surrender to. It can't be something you take for granted as something that comes through you—that you're a vessel, a channel. Because the Muse is very shy—it'll only come to you when you need it."   —Glen Hansard

Alison Krauss & Union Station

Pixies

My Morning Jacket

Ruthie Foster

Taylor Hawkins (Foo Fighters)

Mos De

Josh Homme

John Paul Jones

Dave Grohl

Them Crooked Vultures 2009

"There are not many shows around the world where the music is the priority. A lot of places, you know, the camera angle is the priority. It's very refreshing." —Richard Thompson

Allen Toussaint 2009

"On *ACL*, Allen opened up as never before on film, and visited all of the magical places that make him so gifted and so special. Never to my knowledge has there been such a complete visitation to the musical universe that is Allen Toussaint . . . an invaluable chapter in New Orleans musical history."   —Quint Davis, Producer/Director, New Orleans Jazz and Heritage Festival

"So I got [Tom Waits's] *Bone Machine*, and I got *Blue* by Joni Mitchell. And it's really funny to me now, 'cause these two albums, I'm still sort of tryin to make them have sex and give birth to my brilliant love child of wonderful, beautiful femininity, and very, very lo-fi, homemade masculinity"

Keith Urban 2003

"Playing live especially is my first love, because I've been doing it so long and it's really the best outlet for every emotion. You know, the guitar's like a blank canvas every night. You get up and you just play and you don't know what's going to come out. If you're angry or if you're upset or if you're really excited or if you're confused, or if it's just *arrgh*, all that stuff comes out."   —Keith Urban

Stevie Ray Vaughan & Double Trouble   1989

It's impossible not to get emotional when writing anything about Stevie Ray Vaughan. His two *Austin City Limits* shows bookended a remarkable rocket ride through a musical space that only SRV could inhabit. As Eric Clapton observed, Stevie was channeling a higher power, and the music flowed through him like a mighty river.   —T.L.

Wilco 2007

When I introduced Wilco from the stage, I said, "When people ask what kind of music *Austin City Limits* stands for, there's one band that sums it up better than any other . . . Wilco." Need I say more?   —T.L.

nda Williams 2

"The majority of my stuff is from my point of view, and even if I'm writing about someone else [who is] inspiring the story or inspiring the song, I still have to be empathetic. I think you still have to have been through a large part of it yourself in order to be empathetic with the person you're writing about. So a lot of those songs are actually about me, too. It kind of all blends together—I'm kind of an observer and I'm kind of also writing about my own experiences." —Lucinda Williams

PLAY
WHATEVER
YOU WANT

Trey Anastasio

Arcade Fire

Ozomatli

Widespread Panic

My Morning Jacket

Thievery Corporation

Neil Young 1985

The *only* televised performance of Neil with his "country" band, the International Harvesters, during the two years they performed together in the mid-1980s.   —T.L.

Willie & The Wheel, 2009

Thirty-five years later, it all comes full circle. Willie did the original pilot episode in 1974, at the age of forty-one. Asleep at the Wheel kicked off the first episode of the first official season. In early 2009 the two came together—for the first time, believe it or not—as Willie & The Wheel. We think it's the best show either of them has ever done, but certainly not the last!   —T.L.

AUSTIN
CITY
LIMITS
EQUALS
BIG
WAVE.

The plaque reads:

AUSTIN CITY LIMITS

The longest-running music series in American television history, ACL recorded its first program with Willie Nelson in October 1974 at KLRU-TV at the University of Texas. Showcasing roots music, legends and innovative popular music from every genre, ACL has become a music icon and helped build Austin's reputation as the "Live Music Capital of the World."

Roderick P. Hart (Dean, University of Texas College of Communications), Terry Stewart (President and CEO, Rock and Roll Hall of Fame and Museum), Ray Benson, Bill Stotesbery (CEO, KLRU-TV), Terry Lickona

IN A CEREMONY ON October 1, 2009, the Rock and Roll Hall of Fame and Museum formally declared *Austin City Limits* to be a historic rock and roll landmark, commemorating the thirty-fifth anniversary of the longest-running music series in American television history.

IT'S BEEN A TRADITION for at least thirty years: after the last taping of each season we round up the cast of characters who worked the show that night (producers, crew, technicians, volunteers, interns) to pile onstage for a gang photo. Some faces change from year to year, but a remarkable number of them are still the same, which is quite a testament to the loyalty and passion these individuals feel toward *ACL*. A few are missing from this photo, but these are the folks "behind the scenes," responsible for building an incredible legacy.

Acknowledgments

WHAT STARTED AS A modest, homegrown concert show has become the longest-running music series in American television history. *Austin City Limits* wouldn't exist were it not for KLRU, the public television station in Austin, which launched the program back in 1974 (when it was KLRN). *ACL* was conceived by program executive Bill Arhos, original producer Paul Bosner, and director Bruce Scafe, but for over two decades Arhos, as executive producer, nourished, strengthened, and protected *ACL* amid the vagaries of funding, politics, and other challenges. Hundreds of individuals have contributed to the show's legacy. In two short seasons, former director Allan Muir established *ACL*'s signature look (embellished, in the over thirty years since, by current director Gary Menotti). Audio director David Hough proved from Day One that music can sound great on TV. Other notables have included video guru/editor extraordinaire Dan Martaus; the late Bob Selby, original lighting director and production manager; and the late Mike Archenhold, who as senior cameraman set the standard for capturing live music. It's a cliché, but we are all family at *ACL*, and my staff, including producer Jeff Peterson and associate producers Leslie Nichols and Emily Joyce, is a dream team. KLRU's support staff—from our award-winning marketing and promotion aces to the folks who balance the books or operate the machinery—has provided a rock-solid foundation. KLRU president and CEO Bill Stotesbery has pushed and pulled *Austin City Limits* into the twenty-first century, and we are all deeply grateful for his personal support, encouragement, and passion for *ACL*.

ACL has built some valuable partnerships over the years. Capital Sports and Entertainment, succeeded by C3 Presents, created the Austin City Limits Music Festival in 2002, and Charles Attal, Charlie Jones, and Charlie Walker have since turned it into one of the premier music festivals in America and introduced *ACL* to an even wider audience. New West Records, helmed by Cameron Strang, unlocked the *ACL* archives and released dozens of DVDs and CDs of some of the most popular shows in our history. Now, the next exciting *ACL* chapter has begun with the construction of the Moody Theater, the new home of *Austin City Limits* and a combination state-of-the-art production facility and preeminent live music venue—thanks to the generosity of Stratus Properties and CEO and President Beau Armstrong, and Canyon Johnson Urban Partners.

The process of creating this book has been a joy throughout. The University of Texas Press is the perfect medium for Scott's spectacular images, and there was never any doubt from the beginning that the UT Press staff *gets it*. Special thanks to sponsoring editor Allison Faust, manuscript editor Lynne Chapman, and assistant director/sales and marketing manager Dave Hamrick. *ACL* staffer Michael Toland helped with the paperwork, and we benefited from his creative eye throughout.

Above all, kudos to book designer Derek George, whose vision and great instincts have elevated this collection of photos to a true work of art.

Finally, thanks to the thousands of singers and musicians who created magic on our stage for the past thirty-five years; without them, the pages in this book would be blank!

Terry Lickona
Executive Producer, *Austin City Limits*

I WANT TO THANK Terry Lickona for hiring me, thirty-one years ago, and for standing by me ever since; KLRU for giving this freelancer the run of the place all these years; and Bill Stotesbery for making this project happen. Derek George at UT Press is a great designer, and it's been an honor to work with him.

I really want to thank my longtime coworkers/floor production video cameramen for letting me hang all over them without running me over or coldcocking me from behind with the boom camera. (I don't think any other stills guy in the world gets the kind of physical access I do, and it shows in the shots.) Their names are Doug Robb, Jess Doherty, Michael Emery, Robert Moorhead, Caesar Jaceldo, Dusty Sexton, Jerin Crandell, Vance Holmes, and the late great Mike Archenhold. Big thanks go to the lighting guys, Walter Olden and the late Bob Selby, who frame and enrich everything I shoot, and the whole production staff—one of the tightest and friendliest in the world.

Personal thanks go to my sons, Hawk, Orion, and Zane, and my three granddaughters, Kaia, Zadie, and Kambria. And to my Five Great Friends: Phil Zbylot, Sheri Thompson, Susan Caldwell, Danny Scales, and Katie Brooks Clayton. They are the ones who sustain and support me, year after year.

I would especially like to thank all my fellow travelers/inhabitants of the city/community of Austin. And special thanks go to the people of Texas, who, in the late sixties and most of the seventies, unwittingly expelled and casually exiled as many free-thinking, creative, freaky, weird, black-sheep sons and daughters as they could to the environs of Austin. That's where it all came from, really.

Thanks, Texas . . .

Scott Newton
Photographer, *Austin City Limits*

Neil Young

Annie Clark (St. Vincent)

Jack White (The Raconteurs)

Elvis Costello

Neko Case

Britt Daniel (Spoon)

Michael Stipe (R.E.M.)

Aaron Kyle Behrens (Ghostland Observatory)

Mos Def

Kenny Chesney

Norah Jones

Willie Nelson